CONSERVATION IN BRITAIN

an illustrated resource

W R Pickering

WILLMOT PERTWEE CONSERVATION TRUST

Published by:
Willmot Pertwee Conservation Trust
Lodge Lane
Langham
Colchester
Essex CO4 5NE

First published 1997

ISBN 0 9530028 0 2

Typeset, designed and printed by
E. C Parker Ltd, Canterbury, England

Conservation in Britain is of interest to a great many people but it is a large, complicated and often contentious subject, about which relatively few are well-informed.

This attractively-presented book will be of enormous help to students of all ages, as a guide to the main issues, ways of studying them and constructive action that can be taken to improve matters.

It is also a good guide to the many organisations involved in aspects of conservation. Some of them are especially interested in only one aspect of conservation and it is important to remember that the solution to one problem is often the cause of another.

It is therefore important that a book of this kind gives a balanced account of the whole picture, which this volume does, even if the examples used are bound to be limited.

The book should be widely read and will, I am sure, greatly stimulate interest in the subject.

Colin Spedding

Professor Sir Colin Spedding CBE
Chairman of the UK Register of Organic Food Standards (UKROFS),
the Apple and Pear Research Council (APRC) and
the Farm Animal Welfare Council (FAWC)

Acknowledgements

The author would like to thank all of those who contributed material which enabled the production of this book. Particular thanks are due to Mick Bridge, Jon Marshall and Marek Nowakowski of the Willmot Pertwee Conservation Trust, Keith Porter of English Nature, Ian Willoughby of the Forestry Commission, The Federation of Zoos, Colonel E.H. Baker of the Ministry of Defence Conservation Office, the Education Office of the Royal Society for the Protection of Birds, The Environmental Agency, The Farming and Wildlife Advisory Group, I.C.I. Industries, Gareth Huw Davies and the Telegraph, The Daily Mail, the Independent, the Times, New Scientist, H.M.S.O. and Jim Foster of Froglife. Many thanks to the many others who helped, directly or by the diffusion of ideas, and whose names I have forgotten to include.

The photographs were provided by Jon Marshall (pages 10,21, 53, 60), Marek Nowakowski (pages 13, 15, 16 17), Simon Busuttil of The Royal Society for the Protection Of Birds at Dungeness (pages from 35), the M.O.D. Conservation Office/Mike Birkhead (pages 105 and 108), Oxford Scientific Films (page 140) and the author.

The extract from Biodiversity: the UK Steering Group Report Vol 1 (ISBN 0117532185) an advisory report to the Government.

Finally I would like to personally thank Barry Sharp of Willmot Pertwee for his invaluable support and encouragement at every stage in the production of this book.

About the author :
Ron Pickering is Head of Biology at the King's School, Canterbury. He admits to an enthusiasm for Everton Football Club and the A.C. Cobra Owners' Club as well as a long-standing interest in wildlife and its conservation. He is married, and lives in Canterbury with his wife and two sons.

Other books by Ron Pickering currently available are

Introducing Biochemistry (with E.J.Wood) John Murray ISBN 0-7195-3897-1

Advanced Biology Revision Handbook Oxford University Press
ISBN 0-19-914583-0

Revise Through Diagrams - Biology Oxford University Press ISBN 0-19-914301-3

Life Chemistry and Molecular Biology (with E.J.Wood and C.Smith)
Portland Press ISBN 1-85578-064-X

Contents

Section Three : POLITICS AND CONSERVATION

Conclusion

What is Nature Conservation?

To be aware of our natural environment is possibly the single most important lesson that we can learn - to understand what nature conservation is about we must first recognise that Man is part of nature. Man's actions have a powerful effect upon other living things, either directly or indirectly, and once we understand the possible consequences of these actions then we are better placed to make decisions that prevent damage to our environment. Nature conservation involves assessment of risks to the environment and the development of management strategies which might minimise these risks.

WHY IS NATURE CONSERVATION IMPORTANT?

Today we are often conditioned to judge success by economic wealth, and progress is measured by Man's increasing control over the environment. The most powerful nations are those which are 'developed', those which have the most sophisticated industrial and agricultural systems. This 'success' has been costly - in recent decades concerned scientists have documented the loss of species, the destruction of natural forests and damage to our air, water and soils. The **benefits**, such as increased cereal production by removal of East Anglian hedgerows, are often **short-term** but the **environmental effects**, wind erosion and loss of habitat are too often **long-term.**

What can we do? The most simple answer is to raise the awareness of society of our dependence on the natural environment. We live in a world dominated by our own actions - the food we eat, the air we breathe, the houses we live in are products of our skill at using natural resources, our crops and farm animals are all derived from 'wild' species. Our tools and building materials are made from natural raw materials, and we must learn that many of them will run out one day unless we use them more sensibly.

Who does it involve? All of us, but we are each capable of making different contributions. The decision makers, who include politicians and managers, have to balance the pressures of current demand against the longer-term good. They seek information from knowledgeable advisors but they are influenced by public opinion. To make our opinions more valuable in helping the decision makers arrive at sensible conclusions **we** need to be more informed. This places a great responsibility on all of us to learn more about our natural environment and to represent this in public opinion.

We are all **stewards of the environment**, looking after the inheritance of future generations. Whether we are farmers or politicians, teachers or factory workers, scientists or industrial developers we all have a responsibility to maintain the variety of species and natural resources of today's world. This is why nature conservation is important, and why the topics covered in this book are central to students of all ages.

Government involvement in conservation includes management of National Nature Reserves - here near Loch Maree in Scotland

Changing Landscapes

The term "natural environment" is misleading in Great Britain as virtually all of our landscape has been influenced by humans to some extent. The native climax vegetation of woodland has been cleared, cultivated or managed in such a way as to change the natural pattern of distribution of plants and animals, and even the mountain tops have been modified by the fall of acid rain and other airborne pollutants. In recognition of this influence the conservation bodies use the phrase "semi-natural" which accepts that although not entirely "natural" some parts of Great Britain are closer to the natural condition than others.

There have always been changes in the landscape. From the first temporary clearance of primaeval woodland to the modern changes in farming practice the land has been subject to human pressures -the pressures of population growth and the need for shelter, food and fuel. There have been changes in demand as disease, famine or wars took their toll, and pressures have continued as our expectation of what constitutes an acceptable 'standard of living' has changed. Woods have been felled and have regrown, fields have been cultivated and then abandoned to woodland and in more recent times our ability to manipulate and exploit our environment has produced more permanent dramatic changes in our landscape.

Thus humans have become important competitors for environmental resources with other species. Human exploitation of the environment has often caused a reduction in available habitats for other organisms which share this country - farming has affected hedgerow and wetland communities, water extraction has reduced populations of aquatic organisms and industrial activities have eliminated species through pollution, for example. Table 1, overleaf, lists some of those species which have become extinct in Britain in the past century largely through human activity.

Moral and aesthetic

- We should conserve species and habitats because they enrich our lives.
- We should hand on to the next generation an environment no less rich than the one we ourselves inherited.
- The culture of a nation is closely allied to its landscapes and wildlife. Poets, painters, writers and composers have been inspired by the nature around them.
- A culture which encourages respect for wildlife and landscapes is preferable to one that does not.

Stewardship

- Human beings exercise a determinative power over other creatures: with this dominion comes responsibility.
- Species which have evolved over many thousands of years may be lost very quickly and cannot be recreated. Biodiversity cannot be regained overnight.

Benefit to society

- Natural processes help to protect our planet, e.g. flood plains act as natural release valves for rivers in flood: diversity of vegetation on mud flats and sand dunes reduces coastal erosion; woods and hedges act as wind breaks; upland vegetation is good at binding soil and lessening erosion, and beds of seaweed reduce wave action.
- Wetlands act as natural filters for surface waters and are being used for waste water treatment.
- There is considerable uncertainty about the value of species, for example some plants promise potential cures for different forms of cancer Since our knowledge is so limited, it makes sense to preserve as many species as possible.

Economic value

- Recent advances in biotechnology have pointed to the potential use of the genetic material contained in plants, animals and microorganisms for agricultural, forestry, health and environmental purposes.
- To maintain the productivity of our crops, we depend on there being a reservoir of wild relatives, and a pool of genetic material that we can go back to in order to reinforce our selection.
- Much of the countryside in the UK is of great beauty and is a focus for recreation and tourism. For example our National Parks receive well over fifty million visits each year, while research for the British Tourist Authority indicates that overseas visitors are attracted as much by our varied landscapes as by our history and culture.

> The overall goal in Biodiversity: The UK Action Plan is:
> *"To conserve and enhance biological diversity within the UK and to contribute to the conservation of global biodiversity through all appropriate mechanisms".*

Table 1 illustrates that these ***species*** losses have been going on for many years, but the loss of habitats is regarded as a fairly recent phenomenon. In past centuries it is likely that loss of part of a woodland would always be a temporary or local feature - another woodland nearby might be extended or better managed so that local loss was not so great a problem. As the human population grew and the demands for fuel, food and shelter became more extensive, pressure on wild places grew. Woodlands became restricted to heavier, difficult to cultivate soils (note the current concentration of woods on the heavy clays of the Weald in south east England) and pressure to bring land into cultivation created challenges which Man reacted to by inventing new ways of draining land. Species such as the Great Bustard (*Otis tarda*) began to react to a new phenomenon, the reduction in area of habitat. The problems of habitat loss have been accelerated tremendously in the past fifty years and led to many more species losses, both locally and nationally, and resulted in the extremely damaging phenomenon of habitat fragmentation.

The radical review of agricultural policy in the 1940's, deemed necessary to make us self-sufficient in food, created many of the problems we face today. Foremost in this review was the development of new methods of cultivation and husbandry. The availability and extended use of inorganic fertilisers, pesticides and ever-more powerful machinery revolutionised the British countryside. The pre-war landscapes of small fields, hedges and flowery hillsides rapidly changed to intensive arable production with large hedgeless fields. The booklet "Nature Conservation in Great Britain" (*NCC*, 1984) was the first comprehensive attempt to bring together statistics on the decline of wildplaces and species of these islands - the conclusions gave great cause for concern (see opposite, Table 2).

Table 1:

Examples of species that this century have almost certainly become extinct in the UK largely due to human activity.

Species	*Suspected main reasons for loss in the wild*	*Date of last record*
Vertebrates		
Burbot (*Lota lota*)	This fish is assumed to have been lost through river pollution	1972
Mouse-eared bat (*Myotis myotis*)	Excessive disturbance at, and destruction of, nursery sites	1990
Sea eagle (*Holiaetus albricilla*)	Persecution through poisoning. shooting and egg collection. Subsequently re-introduced	1916
Invertebrates		
Large blue butterfly (*Maculinea orion*)	Lack of grazing and destruction of its grassland habitat Subsequently re-introduced.	1979
Essex emerald moth (*Thetidia smaragdario*)	Coastal defence works leading to a population with a too limited pool for successful reproduction	1991
Viper's bugloss moth (*Hadeno irregularis*)	Loss of Breckland heath to agriculture and development	1979
Blair's wainscot (*Sedino buettnei*)	The sole site. a coastal marsh. was destroyed by draining and burning	1952
Norfolk damselfly (*Caenagrion armatum*)	Degradation of the small marshy pools it inhabited through reed, willow or alder growth, or through desiccation	1957
Orange-spotted emerald dragonfly (*Oxygastra curtisii*)	Pollution from a sewage treatment plant caused its loss from the river where it was most numerous	1951
Exploding bombardier beetle (*Brachynus scolapetus*)	Lack of management of calcareous grassland	1928
Horned dung beetle (*Copris lunaris*)	Ploughing-up of pastures on chalky or sandy soils	1955
A click beetle (*Melanotus punctolineatus*)	The last site was destroyed during golf course construction	1986
Aspen leaf beetle (*Chrysomela tremula*)	Decline of woodland coppicing	1958
Plants		
Thorow-wax (*Bupleurum rotundifolium*)	This annual cornfield weed was lost through the improved cleaning of seed corn	1960s
Lamb's succory (*Arnoseris minima*)	A weed of arable fields. this annual became extinct probably due to agricultural intensification	1970
Hairy spurge (*Euphorbia villosa*)	Cessation of woodland coppicing at its only site	1924
Summer lady's tresses (*Spironthes aestivalis*)	This orchid became extinct as a result of the drainage of the bogs in which it occurred	1959

Table 2:

Wildlife habitats which have the most species of conservation concern

An analysis has been carried out for all 37 broad habitats and most key habitats to see how many species of conservation concern they each contain.

The 15 broad habitats which are primary habitats for the greatest number of species of conservation concern are:-

Broad habitat	Number of extant species
Broadleaved woodland	232
Standing open water	136
Natural rock exposure and caves	135
Calcareous grassland	112
Maritime cliff and slope	91
Lowland heathland	82
Running open water	75
Upland heathland	74
Fen and swamp	73
Arable and horticulture	72
Montane	70
Boundaries	65
Open coast	61
Estuaries	54
Sand dune	52

In terms of numbers of threatened species present broadleaved woodland is clearly of high importance, reflecting both its high degree of structure, which provides many ecological niches, and also the fact that it covered most of the country before man started to clear the land for agriculture It is also the habitat type from which most species have become extinct in the last 100 years. with 46 species being lost. and the one with most globally threatened and rapidly declining species (78 species).

Key habitats other than those shown in the table which support large numbers of species of conservation concern include hedges (47 species). upland oak woodland (47), vegetated sea cliff (45), lowland wet grassland (44), lowland wood pasture and parkland (38), and native pine woodland (37)

No conclusions should be drawn from this analysis about the importance of marine habitats for conservation because pertinent information on species within these habitats is very poor. Also. although some habitats may support only low number of species of conservation concern, nevertheless these species may be of exceptional conservation importance. Other habitats may contain assemblages of plants or animals which are especially species rich.and so are very important for biodiversity, without containing many special species.

HABITAT LOSS IN BRITAIN SINCE THE 1940's

Flower-rich meadows: 95% lost to the plough or to agricultural improvement

Chalk and limestone grasslands : 80% lost to agriculture arid mineral extraction

Heathland: 40% loss through planting of conifers, building development or neglect

Ancient lowland woods : 30 - 50% loss through conversion to conifer plantation

Fens, marshes and other wetlands : 50% loss or significant damage through drainage, industrial pollution or water extraction.

SPECIES LOSSES SINCE THE 1940's

Plants : 10 species have been lost and 19% of all flowering plant and fern species have declined in distribution and abundance

Dragonflies : 4 species have become extinct, with a further 11 in decline

Butterflies : dramatic reduction in the distribution of fritillaries and chalk downland species. Both Large Blue and Chequered Skipper extinct in England.

Bats : several of the 15 British species considered endangered

Reptiles and amphibians : four out of 12 British species endangered

Birds : at least 36 species of breeding bird have suffered long-term decline

Other surveys offer similarly disturbing data - the example which follows illustrates **the close cooperation between different bodies and organisations** in the gathering of such vital information.

The British Trust for Ornithology's Common Birds Census (CBC) has measured population fluctuations among common species since the early 1960s. It provides an example of how broadly based surveillance can identify important new trends. Fieldwork is carried out by skilled volunteers and covers farmland and woodland habitats using a census method which identifies territorial birds. The CBC provides an estimate of annual change in the size of UK populations of common bird species. In 1994 censuses of the bird populations of 87 farmland plots and 113 plots of other habitats were used to estimate changes.

The declines among farmland birds have been striking as is shown in the table. The declines appear to be driven by the loss of spring-sown cereals and crop rotations, the intensification of grassland management, and the increased use of chemical pesticides; further work is required for a better understanding of these factors and their effects upon birds.

RECENT DECLINES IN COMMON FARMLAND BIRD SPECIES IN THE UK

Species	*% decline in numbers in 25 years; 1969-1994. Source BTO CBC 'farmland Index'*
tree sparrow	-89
grey partridge	-82
corn bunting	-80
turtle dove	-77
bullfinch	-76
spotted flycatcher	-73
song thrush	-73
lapwing	-62
reed bunting	-61
skylark	-58
linnet	-52

Note that corn bunting is now so rare that it is found on too few CBC farmland plots to construct a farmland' index. Instead CBC plots from all habitats have been used to calculate the decline.

The need for improved information on population trends is reflected in the recent introduction of the Breeding Bird Survey which is jointly supported by BTO,JNCC and RSPB. It is a volunteer-based survey which sets out to increase the coverage of regions. Habitats and species over existing schemes, including the CBC, using a formal sampling strategy. Survey methods are simple and efficient, and volunteers record details of both the birds they encounter and the habitats they live in. The new survey provides tremendous potential to identify population declines at a UK or finer level, to provide pointers as to likely causes and either suggest remedial action or identify the need for targeted research.

The wholesale losses and declines of the meadows, woods, plants and animals must be fully appreciated and their causes understood if we are to build a sustainable future for British wildlife. It is not sufficient merely to maintain the present extent of the remaining habitats or populations of plants and animals, we must look towards reversing some of the losses and turning our declines into gains...

...and here we can offer some POSITIVE ACTION!

The British Government, as signatories of the Biodiversity Convention at the Earth Summit in Rio de Janeiro in June 1992, pledged to examine possibilities for nature conservation and the maintenance of biodiversity in Britain. To this end they set up a Biodiversity Steering Group which has published a major report which brings together findings and recommendations from a wide variety of interests including academics, the nature conservation agencies, the collections, business, farming and land management, voluntary conservation bodies and both local and central Government.

The Report contains in particular:

1. action p!ans for over 100 species and 14 habitats
2. proposals for a United Kingdom biodiversity database
3. recommendations for raising public awareness of biodiversity
4. proposals for local actions, including guidance on the preparation of local biodiversity action plans.

The publication of this report has received much sympathetic attention, and promises hope of a more settled future for many of our wild species and places.

LOSS AND DECLINE IN BRITAIN
why have species disappeared or diminished?

COMPETITION: introduced species have sometimes been more successful at exploiting the environment than native species. The Red Deer, for example, has declined in numbers due to competition from alien species such as sheep, goats and rabbits.

PEST CONTROL: initially species such as Red Deer, which inhibited tree regeneration, would have been hunted (with the bonus that they also provided meat!) but more recently the term 'pest' has included any species which affects Man's pleasure pursuits. Many predators, such as pine martens and red kites, have been ruthlessly hunted for this reason.

INTERBREEDING: native cattle (Aurochs) lost their genetic identity as they were interbred with domestic cattle brought from southern Europe. The same fate was suffered by the wild cats in Wales and England as it interbred with 'feral' domestic cats probably brought by settlers from Europe.

DANGEROUS TO MAN? Amongst the earliest species to disappear were bears and wolves, who were seen as a direct physical threat to humans. Wild bears may have survived until the 10th Century, wolves until the seventeenth.

COMMERCIAL EXPLOITATION: species with a product of direct financial value to humans have been extinguished by greed - the concept of sustainable rational cropping has not always been understood. The Beaver became extinct in the 16th Century as a result of hunting/ trapping for fur.

LOSS OF HABITAT: greater demand for agricultural land and greater technological skills in making land available (by drainage, for example) meant that species with a limited range no longer had a habitat which could supply their requirements for food, shelter and breeding sites eg the Crane from the Fens of East Anglia and the Great Bustard from the Brecks.

REINTRODUCTION OF SPECIES can only be successful if the reasons for their loss are understood and reversed

Populations and Population Pressure

Most organisms do not live as isolated individuals, but with other members of the same species in groups called **populations**.

A **population** is " a group of organisms of the same species living within a defined area of the environment"

Individuals in animal populations often interact with one another, such as in reproduction and the care of young, and may gain protection by living in herds, shoals or colonies. There may also be **disadvantages** in living as a member of a population - overcrowding or some other factor might cause shortage of food, light or some other resource, so that individuals **compete** with one another. Competition may cause the death of some individuals and result in a decline in numbers.

When ecologists study populations they are concerned not only with the **numbers** of a particular species at any given time, but also with the way in which this number **changes** in response to the environment. This study of **population dynamics** tells them how species are adapted to their particular way of life, and has various applications. It may be possible to predict the outbreak of pests, or to say whether useful species of plants or animals are likely to survive when introduced into new areas.

A population may increase in size as a result of **immigration** from neighbouring populations, or by **reproduction** of individuals already present within the population. A population may decrease in size as a result of **emigration** or by the death of individuals (**mortality** - see previous page).

We can see from this figure that the population does not increase indefinitely - eventually a balance is reached in which the number of individuals present is just supported by the environmental resources. In this situation the environment is said to have reached its **carrying capacity**, a figure determined by the **environmental resistance**

This type of growth curve is said to be **density-dependent** because growth rate is dependent on the density of the population - exhaustion of food and production of toxic wastes affect growth rate. This, then, is the importance of human population growth on conservation - a growing human population, or one which places increasing demands on environmental resources may reduce the carrying capacity of the environment for populations of other species. In other words, humans can out-compete other species. Some of the demands which the human population places on the environment are for

- food, and space in which to grow it
- reduced competition from predators and from pests - which means that these organisms must be killed or controlled
- water, particularly for irrigation
- dumping grounds for our pollutants

There is little doubt that these demands will be maintained, or more likely will increase. Even in Britain, where the population is stable in size, the demands for building land, for roads, for water, for variety of foods and for disposal of pollutants continue to increase. There is no doubt that the population pressure in Britain has caused enormous changes to our environment, but ***some of these are inevitable if a human population is to be maintained.***

A negative point of view might be that Britain has been 'spoiled', but a more positive view might be that more and more members of the British population are

a. aware of the need for a balanced use of our shared environment (almost 1 in 50 of the British population are members of a single conservation body, the R.S.P.B.)

b. able to offer skills which can be used to make a contribution to conservation measures in this country (more biologists and environmental scientists are trained than ever before)

Thus, in our survey of conservation in Britain we must

be AWARE, be REALISTIC and, perhaps most of all, be POSITIVE!

FACTORS AFFECTING POPULATION GROWTH

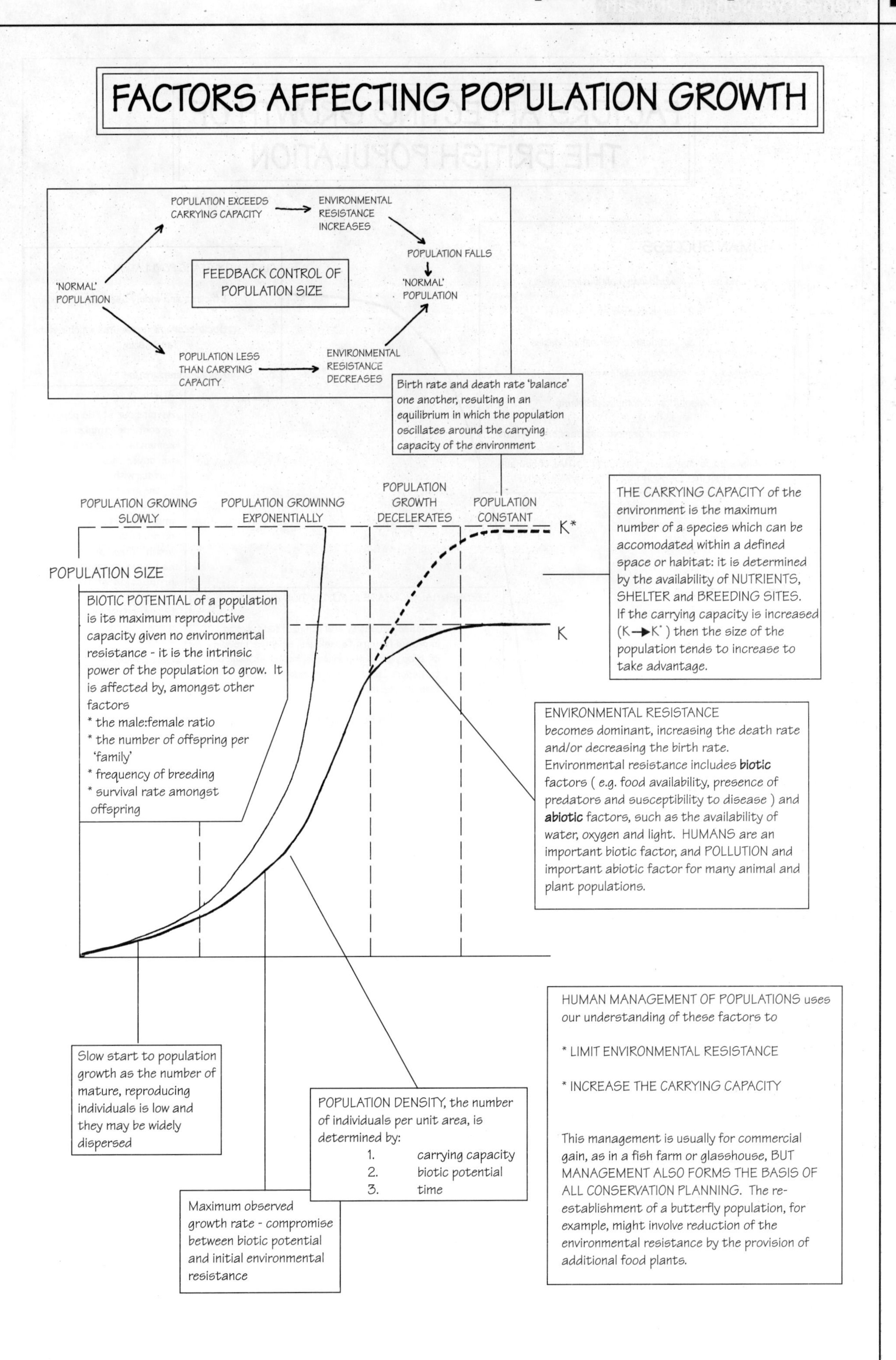

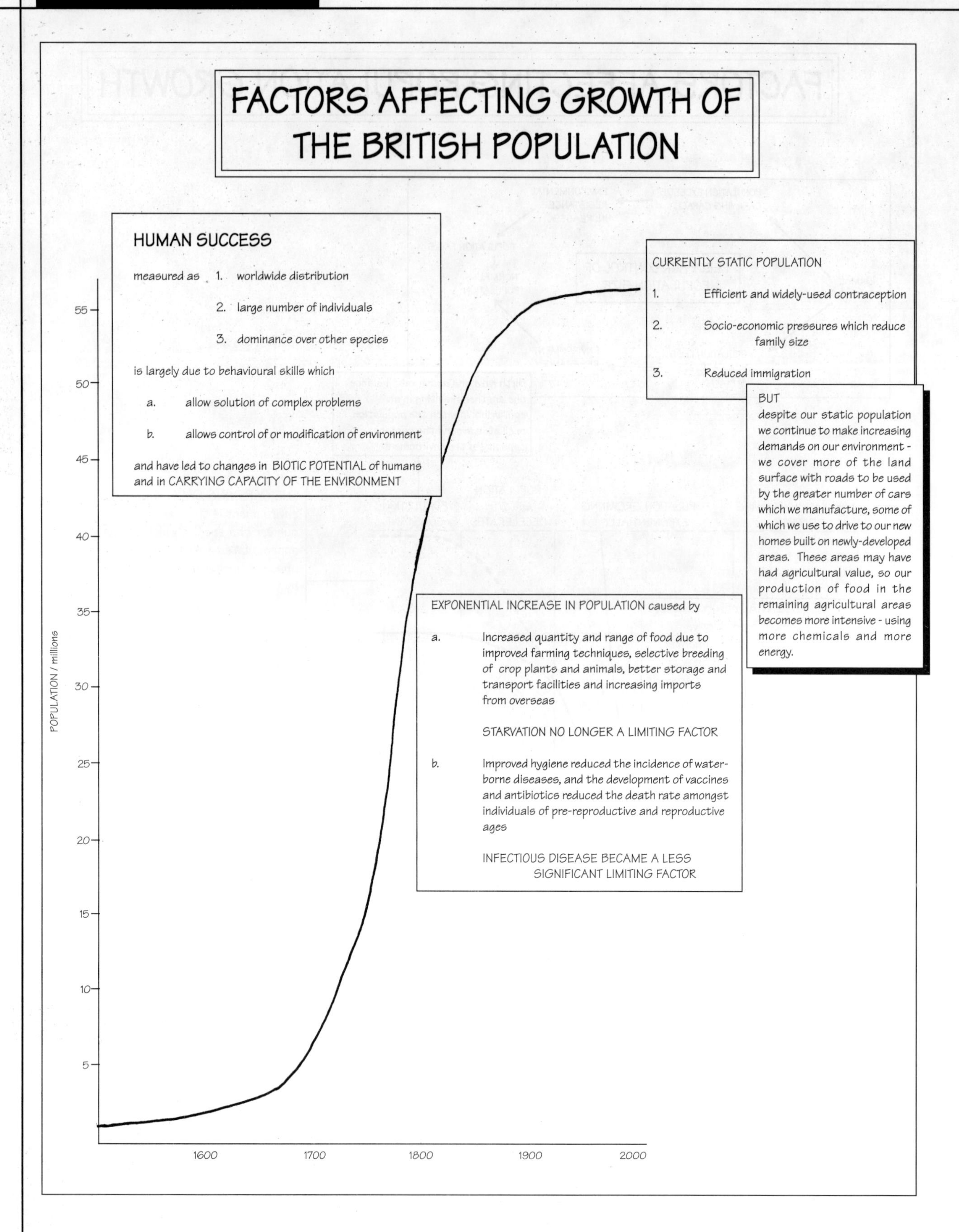
FACTORS AFFECTING GROWTH OF THE BRITISH POPULATION
HUMAN SUCCESS
measured as 1. worldwide distribution
2. large number of individuals
3. dominance over other species
is largely due to behavioural skills which
a. allow solution of complex problems
b. allows control of or modification of environment
and have led to changes in BIOTIC POTENTIAL of humans and in CARRYING CAPACITY OF THE ENVIRONMENT
CURRENTLY STATIC POPULATION
1. Efficient and widely-used contraception
2. Socio-economic pressures which reduce family size
3. Reduced immigration
BUT
despite our static population we continue to make increasing demands on our environment - we cover more of the land surface with roads to be used by the greater number of cars which we manufacture, some of which we use to drive to our new homes built on newly-developed areas. These areas may have had agricultural value, so our production of food in the remaining agricultural areas becomes more intensive - using more chemicals and more energy.
EXPONENTIAL INCREASE IN POPULATION caused by
a. Increased quantity and range of food due to improved farming techniques, selective breeding of crop plants and animals, better storage and transport facilities and increasing imports from overseas
STARVATION NO LONGER A LIMITING FACTOR
b. Improved hygiene reduced the incidence of water-borne diseases, and the development of vaccines and antibiotics reduced the death rate amongst individuals of pre-reproductive and reproductive ages
INFECTIOUS DISEASE BECAME A LESS SIGNIFICANT LIMITING FACTOR
POPULATION / millions
55
50
45
40
35
30
25
20
15
10
5
1600
1700
1800
1900
2000

Humans as Settlers

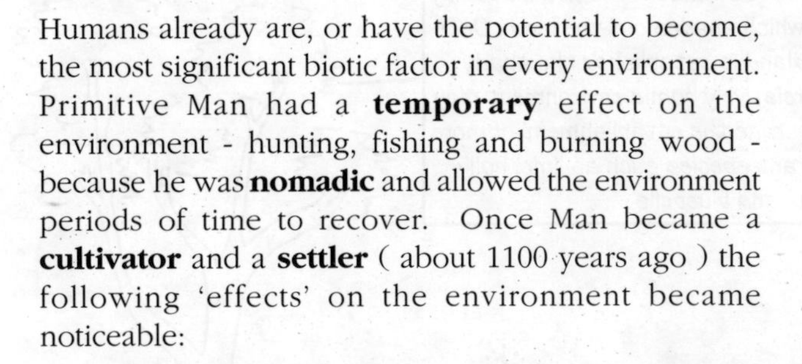

Humans already are, or have the potential to become, the most significant biotic factor in every environment. Primitive Man had a **temporary** effect on the environment - hunting, fishing and burning wood - because he was **nomadic** and allowed the environment periods of time to recover. Once Man became a **cultivator** and a **settler** (about 1100 years ago) the following 'effects' on the environment became noticeable:

1. The use of tools and the domestication of animals meant a more efficient agriculture and the ability to support a larger population.

2. The greater demands for shelter, agricultural land and fuel meant a greater rate of felling of trees.

3. The advent of fossil fuels lead to the development of machines, greater 'cropping', larger populations and an increasing demand for ever more efficient agriculture.

4. The careless use of fertilisers and pesticides, together with the ever - increasing consumption of fossil fuels, produced problems of pollution. These have been added to by the development of nuclear energy sources.

Because modern Man is *not* nomadic, and because the population density is so high, the environment does not have time to 'recover', so that these effects can easily become **permanent**. Conservation attempts to minimise the effects of these changes, but Great Britain is a series of relatively small islands with a long and continuing history of agricultural and industrial development so that there is inevitably competition for space and for biological resources. A current definition of conservation takes this competition into account:

" Conservation is the utilisation and management of environmental resources in order to have open, or create, the maximum number and kind of possible uses for the future "

Conservation may involve a number of strategies

Preservation : in its strictest sense this involves keeping some part of the environment *without any change.* This can only apply to very few areas, and in Britain is of less significance than....

Reclamation : involves the restoration of damaged habitats. In Britain this particularly applies to the recovery of former industrial sites, and....

Creation : involves the production of new habitats. In Britain this may extend from the digging of a garden pond to the planting of a national forest.

The key to conservation in this country is **management** - complex **management strategies** may be involved so that conservation can be considered alongside human involvement in industry, technology and the social sciences. As a consequence successful conservation involves **scientific and technical knowledge** as well as **qualities of judgement** with which to assess conflicting human requirements.

To summarise,

> conservation is dynamic and must be a compromise.

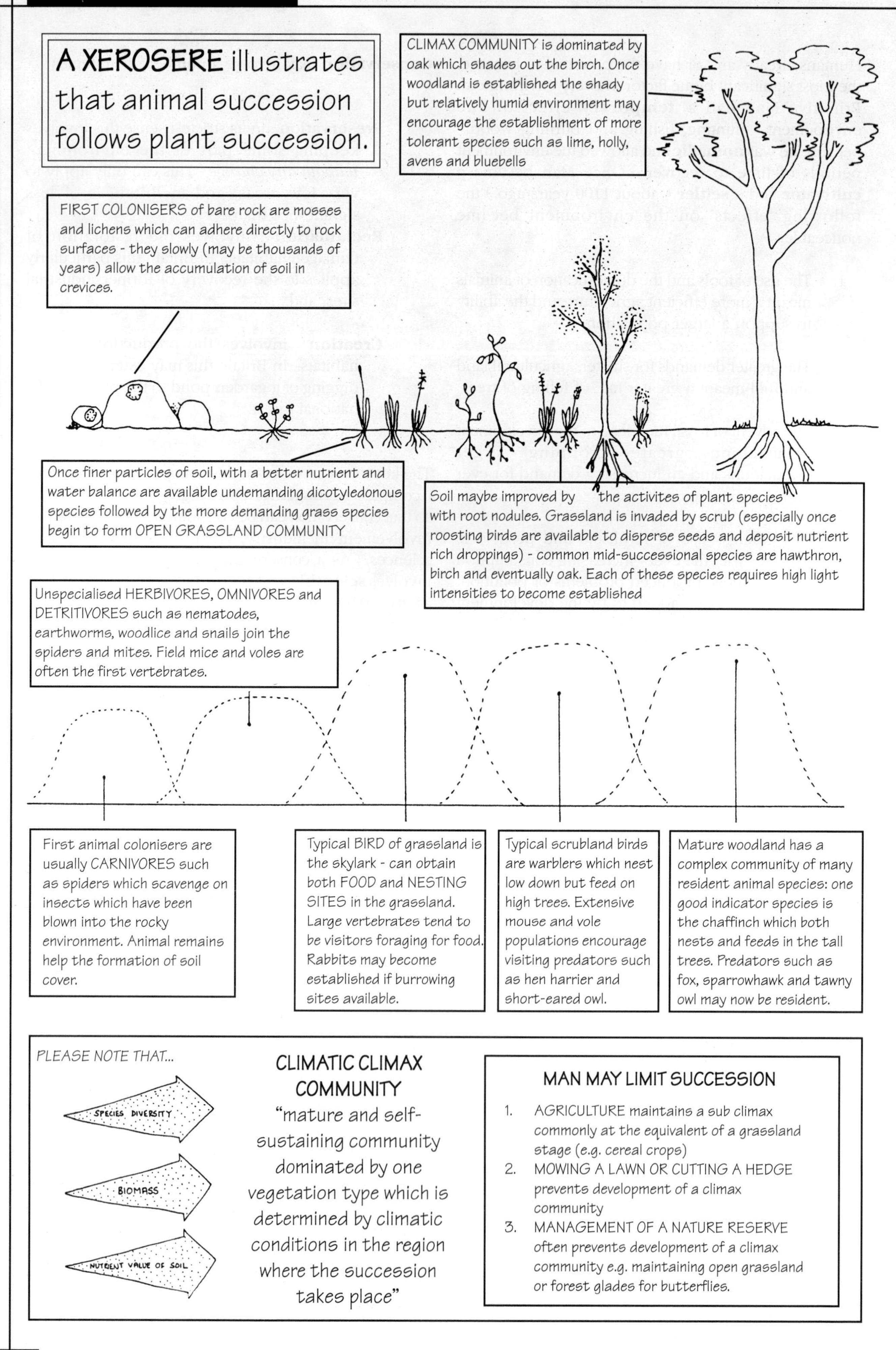
A XEROSERE illustrates that animal succession follows plant succession.
CLIMAX COMMUNITY is dominated by oak which shades out the birch. Once woodland is established the shady but relatively humid environment may encourage the establishment of more tolerant species such as lime, holly, avens and bluebells
FIRST COLONISERS of bare rock are mosses and lichens which can adhere directly to rock surfaces - they slowly (may be thousands of years) allow the accumulation of soil in crevices.
Once finer particles of soil, with a better nutrient and water balance are available undemanding dicotyledonous species followed by the more demanding grass species begin to form OPEN GRASSLAND COMMUNITY
Soil maybe improved by the activites of plant species with root nodules. Grassland is invaded by scrub (especially once roosting birds are available to disperse seeds and deposit nutrient rich droppings) - common mid-successional species are hawthron, birch and eventually oak. Each of these species requires high light intensities to become established
Unspecialised HERBIVORES, OMNIVORES and DETRITIVORES such as nematodes, earthworms, woodlice and snails join the spiders and mites. Field mice and voles are often the first vertebrates.
First animal colonisers are usually CARNIVORES such as spiders which scavenge on insects which have been blown into the rocky environment. Animal remains help the formation of soil cover.
Typical BIRD of grassland is the skylark - can obtain both FOOD and NESTING SITES in the grassland. Large vertebrates tend to be visitors foraging for food. Rabbits may become established if burrowing sites available.
Typical scrubland birds are warblers which nest low down but feed on high trees. Extensive mouse and vole populations encourage visiting predators such as hen harrier and short-eared owl.
Mature woodland has a complex community of many resident animal species: one good indicator species is the chaffinch which both nests and feeds in the tall trees. Predators such as fox, sparrowhawk and tawny owl may now be resident.
PLEASE NOTE THAT...
SPECIES DIVERSITY
BIOMASS
NUTRIENT VALUE OF SOIL
CLIMATIC CLIMAX COMMUNITY
"mature and self-sustaining community dominated by one vegetation type which is determined by climatic conditions in the region where the succession takes place"
MAN MAY LIMIT SUCCESSION
1. AGRICULTURE maintains a sub climax commonly at the equivalent of a grassland stage (e.g. cereal crops)
2. MOWING A LAWN OR CUTTING A HEDGE prevents development of a climax community
3. MANAGEMENT OF A NATURE RESERVE often prevents development of a climax community e.g. maintaining open grassland or forest glades for butterflies.

The earliest Humans in Britain would have been confronted by an environment which would be unfamiliar to most of us today. Much of the low-lying area of the East and South-east would have been marsh or swamp, and most of the rest of the country would have been woodland. This woodland (the wildwood) would have developed over thousands of years following a well-established sequence of changes ending in the establishment of a community of animals and plants in equilibrium with one another and representing the most productive community that the environment can sustain. This sequence of changes is called a **succession**, and the end product is called a **climax community** (see opposite).

Man has influenced the British environment for such a long time that little remains of the original climax community, which for much of lowland Britain would have been oak woodland, or a mixture of oak and beech. Poorer soils and upland areas might have been covered with pine and birchwood, and alder and willow would have dominated the wetter sites. From Neolithic times onward there was a tendency to increase the proportion of forested land dominated by oak, for the reasons outlined in the figure below.

Forest clearance was a result of Man's increasing population and consequent demands for agricultural land, so much so that there are very few 'relic' woodlands remaining in Britain today. However, if Man were to abandon an area of land to natural forces of regeneration it remains likely that Britain would have the potential to return to a largely oak-dominated climax community. If a philanthropist donated a chalk hillside with its wildflower and insect communities to a conservation body, the body would undoubtedly have to prevent the re-establishment of a climax community. As noted previously, CONSERVATION IS A COMPROMISE - leave well enough alone and return the country to oak forest, or 'interfere' to maintain a wide range of diverse habitats?

This country is so small and so densely populated that conservationists almost inevitably must 'interfere'.

In summary

> conservationists must be managers, and the key to successful conservation is informed and responsible management

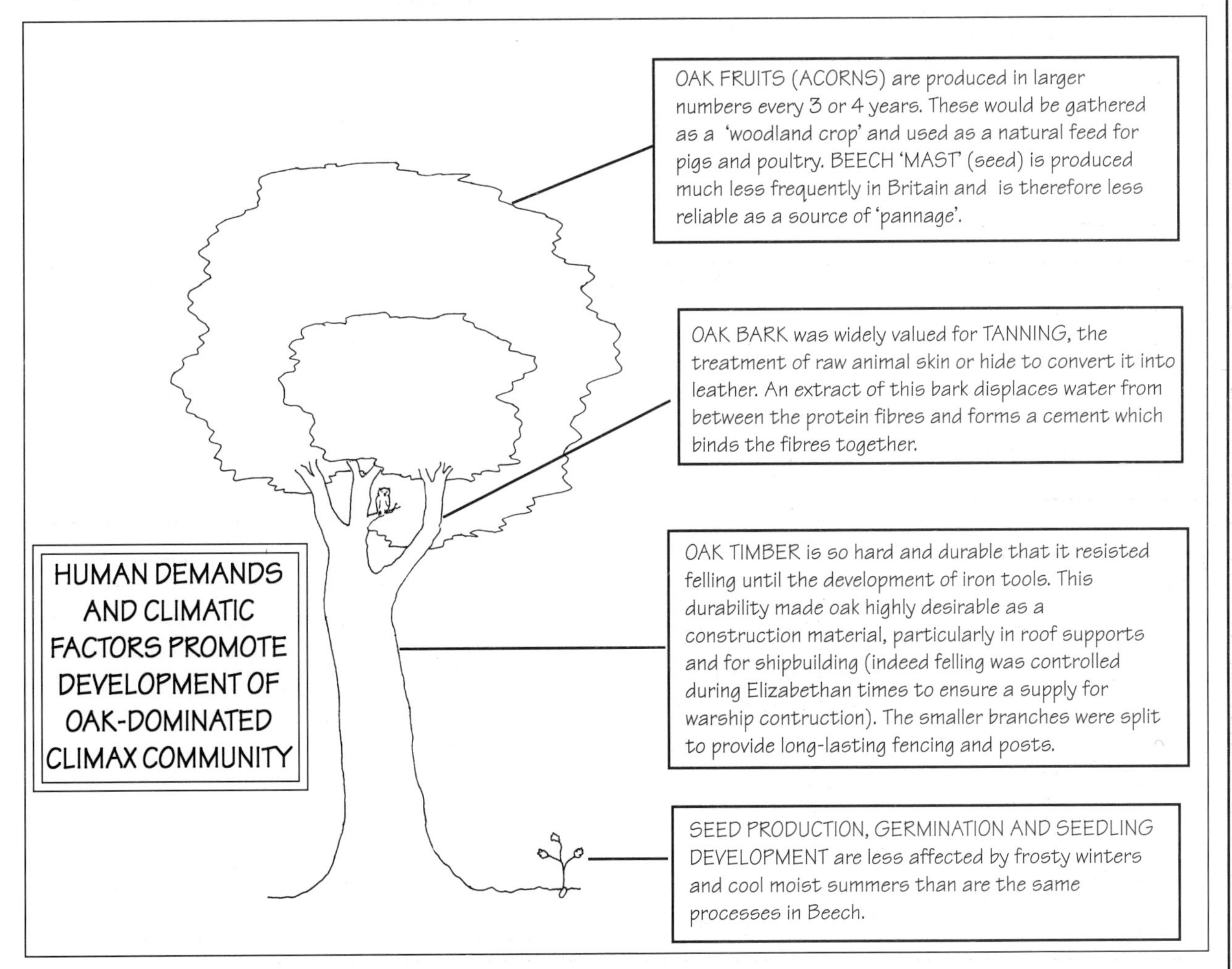

What could happen to London if everyone left...

Page 6 Daily Mail, Thursday, July 18, 1996

Wolves at the door of a wild London abandoned by Man

HOW NATURE WOULD EVENTUALLY RECLAIM A CITY

1 YEAR Dandelions and other weeds take hold as fine topsoil layer is created

5 YEARS Turf and clover carpet all level surfaces

10 YEARS As soil builds up, shrubs and deeper rooted plants take hold

20 YEARS Widespread flooding as embankments are eroded and marsh-land created

30 YEARS Birch woodland fills open spaces as buildings begin to crumble

40 YEARS Bridges collapse without maintenance and salmon spawn in pollution-free river

200 YEARS Concrete and steel structures collapse

500 YEARS City reverts to flood plain forest

What could happen to London if everyone left

MAIL GRAPHICS

LONDON: 24th CENTURY

WILD animals roaming by crumbling tower blocks, floods, swarms of insects and wolves howling beside the Great Leaning Tower of Canary Wharf.

That could be the future of a London without people hundreds of years from now, its seemingly indestructible steel and concrete structures crumbling as nature claims back its own. The glimpse into the future comes from New Scientist magazine, which projected what would happen if everyone left the capital this weekend.

In five years, the city would be carpeted with a green turf rich in clover, feeding off composted leaves. Ten years on, grasses and shrubs would have spread over the city with deeper-rooted plants and trees taking hold as soil levels rose.

Without humans to operate the Thames barrier, floods would be inevitable, according to author Laura Spinney. Without maintenance, river banks would be eroded, resulting in the formation of marshes and ponds.

With plants come swarms of butterflies, bees and other insects. Bats, hedgehogs, foxes, toads and newts would proliferate with London Zoo's grey wolves breeding with pet dogs gone wild. German shepherd dogs could survive well, possibly on a diet of smaller dogs. Cats would rediscover their wild side, but without people to provide for them, sewer rats would disappear.

After 30 years, birch woodland would fill open spaces. In the 50 years between 2006 and 2056, bridges would collapse without maintenance, and salmon spawn in the pollution-free Thames. Concrete and steel structures would begin to rot and collapse after 200 years. Canary Wharf would succumb as the clay on which it stands became waterlogged and steel reinforcements corroded.

Eventually, in the mid-24th century, the Great Leaning Tower of Canary Wharf could become a tourist attraction.

WILD animals roaming by crumbling tower blocks, floods, swarms of insects and wolves howling beside the Great Leaning Tower of Canary Wharf. That could be the future of a London without people hundreds of years from now, its seemingly indestructible steel and concrete structures crumbling as nature claims back its own. The glimpse into the future comes from New Scientist magazine which projected what would happen if everyone left the capital this weekend.

In five years, the city would be carpeted with a green turf rich in clover, feeding off composted leaves. Ten years on, grasses and shrubs would have spread over the city with deeper-rooted plants and trees taking hold as soil levels rose.

Without humans to operate the Thames barrier, floods would be inevitable, according to author Laura Spinney. Without maintenance, river banks would be eroded, resulting in the formation of marshes and ponds. With plants come swarms of butterflies, bees and other insects. Bats, hedgehogs foxes toads and newts would proliferate with London Zoo's grey wolves breeding with pet dogs gone wild. German shepherd dogs could survive well, possibly on a diet of smaller dogs. Cats would rediscover their wild side, but without people to provide for them, sewer rats would disappear. After 30 years, birch woodland would fill open spaces. In the 50 years between 2006 and 2056, bridges would collapse without maintenance, and salmon spawn in the pollution-free Thames. Concrete and steel structures would begin to rot and collapse after 200 years. Canary Wharf would succumb as the clay on which it stands became waterlogged and steel reinforcements corroded. Eventually, in the mid-24th century, the Great Leaning Tower of Canary Wharf could become a tourist attraction.

Daily Mail Thursday 18th July 1996

Estimating Populations

To study the dynamics of a population *or how* the distribution of the members of a population is influenced by a biotic or an abiotic factor, it is necessary to estimate the population size. In other words, it will be necessary to count the number of individuals in a population. Such counting is usually carried out by taking SAMPLES (in which the organisms are in the same proportion as in the whole population) because

1. counting the whole population would be extremely laborious and time-consuming

2. counting the whole population might cause unacceptable levels of damage to the habitat, or to the population being studied

The samples must be representative. They should be

1. of the same size (e.g. a *0.25* m^2 area of grassland)

2. randomly selected - for example. samples may be taken at predetermined points on an imaginary grid laid over the sampling area. The coordinates of the points may be selected using random numbers generated by a calculator

3. non-overlapping.

Quadrat sampling

Quadrats are sampling units of a known area. They are most often square and are usually constructed of wood or metal. The quadrat can be used in simple form, or it may have wire subdivisions to produce a number of sampling points.

Reliable sampling with quadrats requires answers to three questions

1. What size of quadrat should be used?

2. How many quadrats should be used?

3. ***Where*** should the quadrats be positioned?

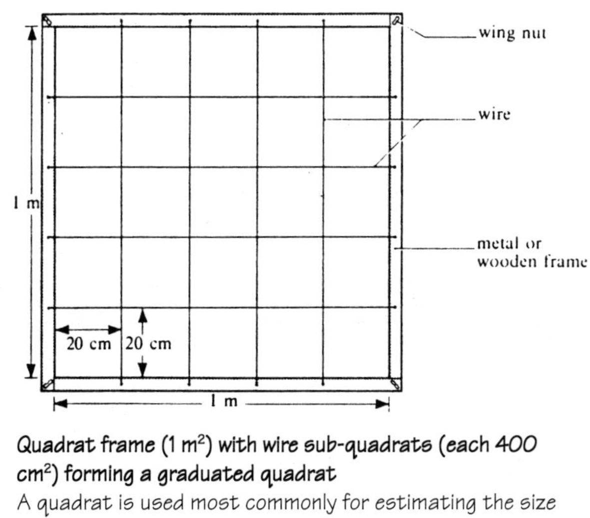

Quadrat frame (1 m^2) with wire sub-quadrats (each 400 cm^2) forming a graduated quadrat
A quadrat is used most commonly for estimating the size of plant populations, but may also be valuable for the study of populations of sessile **or** slow-moving animals (e.g. limpets)

The occurrence of a species within a quadrat can be expressed in several ways:

1. DENSITY : count the number of individuals in a fixed number of quadrats. and express results as average number of individuals per unit area

2. PERCENTAGE COVER : proportion of the ground area covered by the above ground parts of the species

3. PERCENTAGE FREQUENCY : percentage of the quadrats in which the species occurs

WHAT SIZE QUADRAT?

If individuals within a population are truly randomly dispersed, then any quadrat size should be equally efficient in the estimation of that population. However, environmental factors are rarely evenly distributed so that the living organisms dependent on them tend to occur in an aggregated distribution. Small quadrats are more efficient in estimating populations (more can be taken, and they can cover a wider range of habitat than larger ones) but there are practical considerations to be taken into account (a small quadrat might not include a dominant tree in a woodland). Optimum quadrat size is determined by counting the number of different species present in quadrats of increasing size.

The optimum quadrat size - 1% increase in quadrat size produces no more than a 0.5% increase in the number of species present.

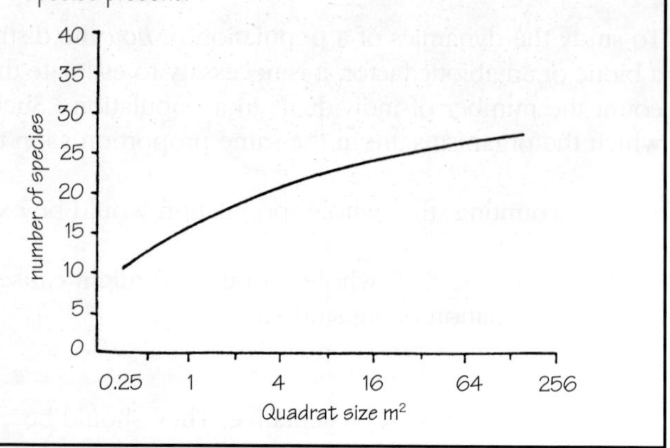

HOW MANY QUADRATS?

Too few might be unrepresentative, and too many might be tedious and time-consuming. To determine the optimum number, a series of quadrats of the optimum size is placed randomly across the sampling area - the cumulative number of species is recorded after each increase in quadrat number

The optimum quadrat number - 1% increase in quadrat number produces no more than a 0.5% increase in the number of species present.

number of species: 70, 60, 50, 40, 30, 20, 10, 0

Number of Quadrats: 1, 4, 8, 12, 16

RANDOM POSITIONING OF QUADRATS
The position can be chosen using random coordinates, as described earlier.

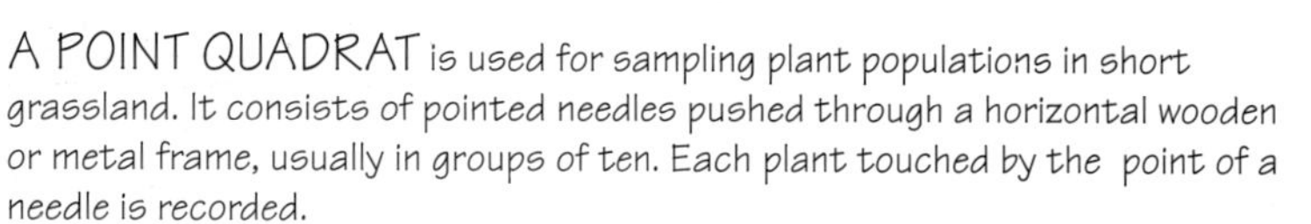

A POINT QUADRAT is used for sampling plant populations in short grassland. It consists of pointed needles pushed through a horizontal wooden or metal frame, usually in groups of ten. Each plant touched by the point of a needle is recorded.

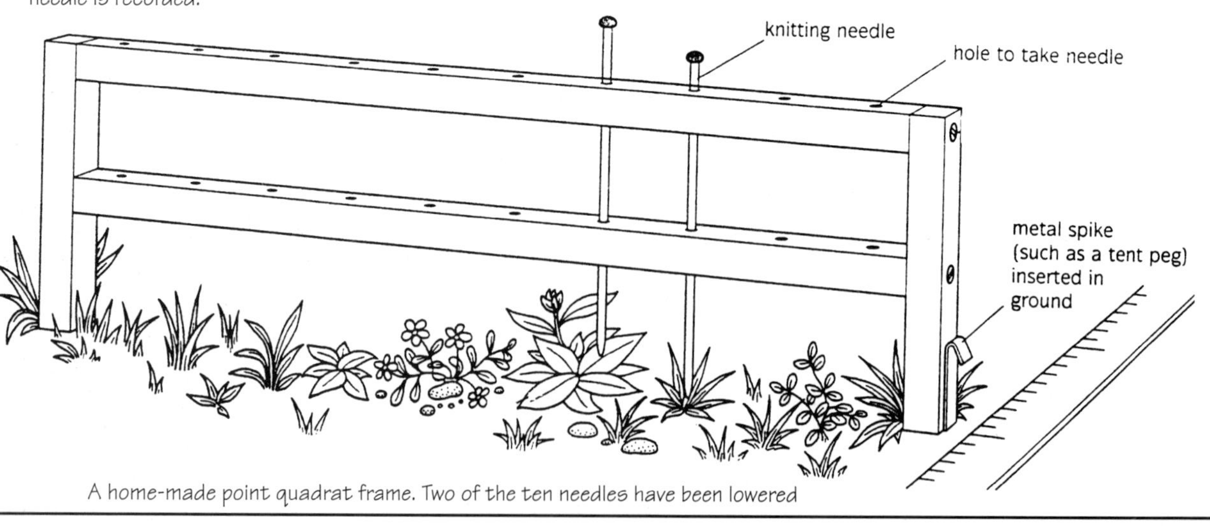

A home-made point quadrat frame. Two of the ten needles have been lowered

TRANSECTS are used to describe the distribution of species in a straight line across a habitat. Transects are particularly useful for describing zonation of species, for example around field or pond margins, or across a marsh. A simple LINE TRANSECT records all of the species which actually touch the rope or tape stretched across the habitat, a BELT TRANSECT records all of those species present between two lines (perhaps 0.5 m² apart) and an INTERRUPTED BELT TRANSECT records all of those species present in a number of quadrats placed at fixed points along a line stretched across the habitat.

CONSERVATION IS A COMPROMISE. AND CONSERVATION MANAGERS NEED A WIDE RANGE OF SKILLS

Conservationists have a part to play in education. It *may* not seem terribly significant, but it should be the duty of the media to inform accurately - the great crested newt is an *amphibian*, not a *reptile*!

Page 34

Daily Mail, Friday, July 14, 1995

Newts v new town

Rare reptiles may die if £500m homes plan evicts them, say conservationists

BRITAIN'S largest colony of rare great crested newts could be destroyed under plans to move them to a new site, it is claimed.

Some 30,000 of the endangered reptiles are to be relocated to a specially-created reserve because their present habitat is earmarked for a new £500million township.

By TRACEY HARRISON

The scheme has the blessing of the English Nature conservation group. But the World Wide Fund for Nature has branded it 'appalling', claiming many newts could die.

It now plans to appeal to the European courts to save the animals, designated an endangered species by the European Union.

Up to 30,000 live on the 2,250-acre site on the outskirts of Peterborough, in pools formed after clay extraction.

The land is to be developed into 5,200 houses, offices, industrial parks, shops and leisure facilities by the Peterborough Southern Township, a subsidiary of the giant Hanson Trust business empire.

Under a plan thrashed out with English Nature, the company has set aside 80 acres at the edge of the site as a reserve for the newts.

But the WWF says such large-scale relocation is bound to end in many dying.

'These creatures simply should not be moved from the habitat they are used to,' said spokesman Simon Forrester. 'It would be a massive disturbance and it is likely many would not survive.'

The WWF is drawing up a legal case arguing that the developers are failing to protect an endangered species.

But English Nature, which has designated the land a site of special scientific interest, insists the newts will be perfectly safe and content in their new home.

'The colony will not be destroyed,' said a spokesman.

'They are being moved a minimal distance to an identical habitat which will be specially patrolled.'

Even conservation bodies sometimes cannot agree amongst themselves! A conservation management plan will have to satisfy a number of groups which may have widely differing views on the current strategy

Legislation is increasingly significant in carrying out a conservation strategy

Note that this particular battle is being fought over an area which has developed from a previous industrial site

The major conflict in Britain is between those who perceive a need for continuing development and those who would like to preserve the environment

RARE REPTILES ARE MOVED TO MAKE WAY FOR £300m PLANT

What's clean and green but costs a fortune? Newt-clear power

Daily Mail Reporter

THE marshland was the ideal site for a £300million generator, power company bosses agreed.

But unknown to them, it was also the ideal site for a colony of great crested newts — and they were there first.

The newts are protected by law, so having discovered their existence, InterGen could not proceed without guaranteeing their future — and it proved no small task.

Conservationists from the Cheshire Wildlife Trust, who had discovered the colony while surveying the site at Rock Savage for Halton Borough Council, were drafted in to capture almost 600 newts in special traps. The reptiles were carried to an isolated pond on the site where they will remain until construction is completed in 1998.

American-owned InterGen had to promise to dig a new pond and to landscape a safe environment for the newts alongside the gas-powered generator before English Nature would license the removal operation.

The company will not reveal how much the delay and the extra work have added to the cost of the 750megawatt plant, which will feed adjoining ICI factories in Runcorn, although one project manager at the site said: 'We have spent thousands upon thousands of pounds to move the newts.'

InterGen spokesman Alex Doyle would only say: 'The important thing is that the newts are being protected during the construction process. We have done the right thing environmentally.'

Great crested newts, which are black with a speckled orange underside, can grow up to 5in long.

Their natural habitat is vanishing as ponds and lakes are drained. But English Nature said: 'This site will be managed and should be an even better environment for the newts than they have at the moment.'

Co-existence: Great crested newts and a photo mock-up of the power station

Sampling animal population: Motile species

Quadrats and line transects are ideal methods for estimating populations of plants or sedentary animals. Motile animals, however, must be captured before their populations can be estimated. Once more, a representative sample of the population will be counted and the total population estimated from the sample. One important technique is the **mark-recapture** (also known as mark - release - recapture) **method.** This method involves

1. capturing the organism
2. marking in some way which causes no harm (e.g. beetles can be marked with a drop of waterproof paint on their wing cases, and mice may have a small mark clipped into their fur)
3. releasing the organism to rejoin its population
4. a second sample group from this population is captured and counted at a later date.
5. the population size is estimated using the **Lincoln Index**

Lincoln Index

$$\text{Population size} = \frac{n_1 \times n_2}{n_m}$$

where n_1 is the number of individuals marked and released ("1" because it was the first sample), n_2 is the number of individuals caught the second time round ("2" because it was the second sample) and n_m is the number of marked individuals in the second sample ("m" standing for marked).

This method depends on a number of assumptions - failure of any of these to hold up can lead to poor estimates being made. These assumptions are:

a. the marked organisms mix randomly back into the normal population (allow sufficient time for this to occur, bearing in mind the mobility of the species)

b. the marked animals are no different to the unmarked ones - they are no more prone to predation, for example

c. changes in population size due to births, deaths, immigration and emigration are negligible

d. the mark does not wear off or grow out during the sampling period

TULLGREN FUNNEL

used to collect small organisms from the air spaces of the soil or from leaf litter. The lamp is a source of heat and dehydration - organisms move to escape from it and fall through the sieve (the mesh is fine enough to retain the soil or litter). The animals slip down the smooth-sided funnel and are immobilised in the alcohol. They may then be removed for identification.

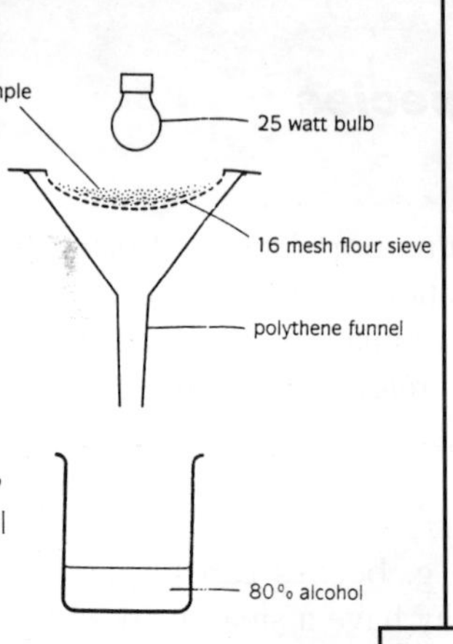

BAERMANN FUNNEL

works on a similar principle to the Tullgren funnel, but extracts organisms living in the soil water. The heat source drives the animals out of the muslin bag and into the surrounding water. Samples of water can be released at intervals, and the organisms in the sample collected and identified.

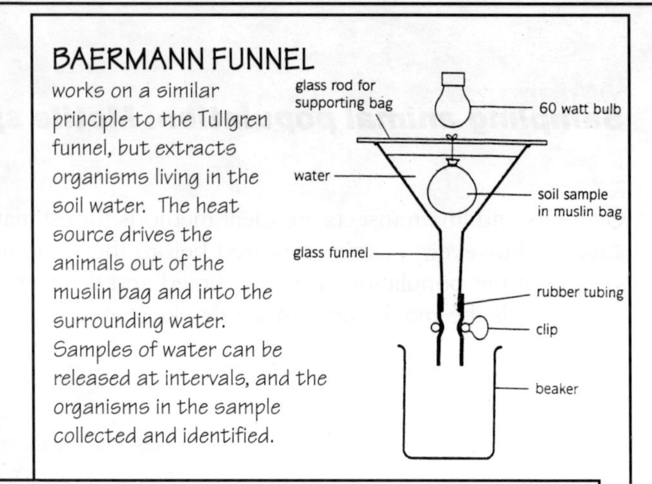

With both Tullgren and Baermann funnels it is essential that samples are treated in identical fashion if results are to be comparitive - for example, use fixed sample size, length of exposure to heat source and wattage of lamp.

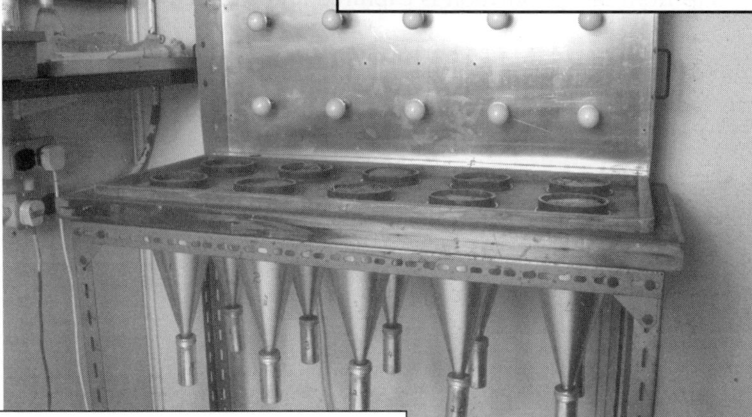

A group of Tullgren funnels in use

PITFALL TRAPS

used to sample arthropods moving over the soil surface. The roof prevents rainfall from flooding the trap, and also limits access to certain predators. The activities of trapped predators can be prevented by adding a small quantity of methanal to the trap. Bait of meat or ripe fruit can be placed in the trap.

Pitfall traps are often set up on a grid system to investigate the movements of ground animals more systematically.

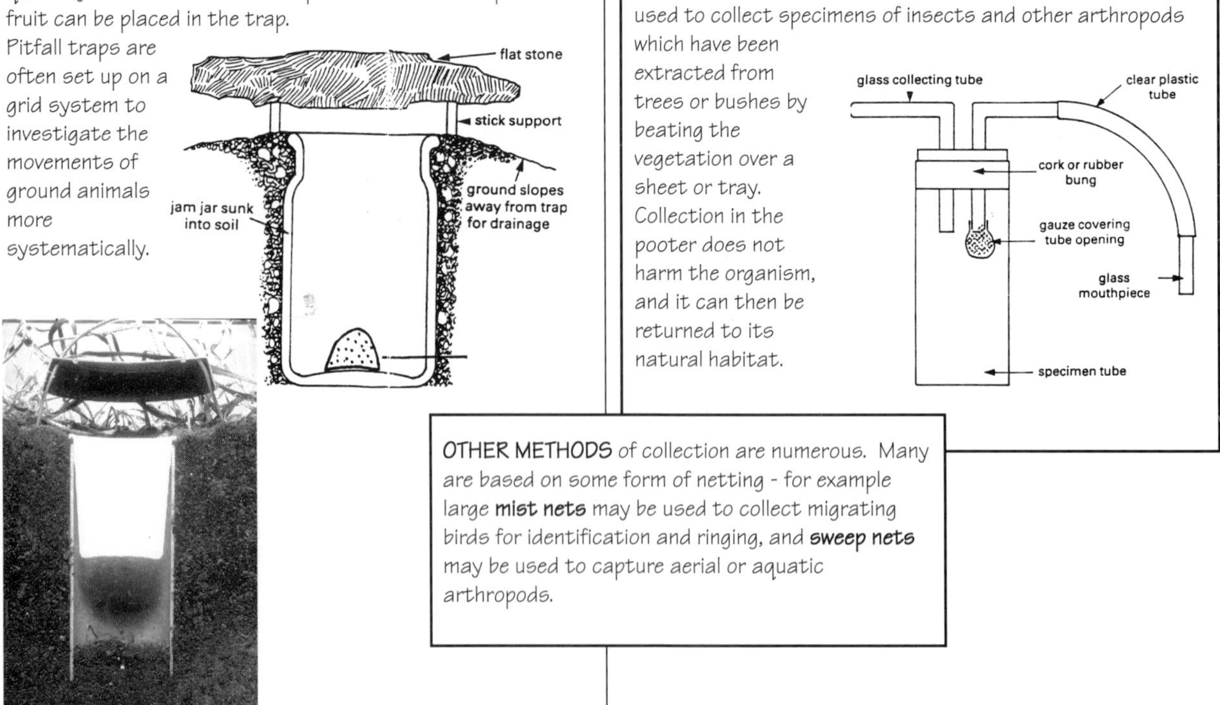

POOTER

used to collect specimens of insects and other arthropods which have been extracted from trees or bushes by beating the vegetation over a sheet or tray. Collection in the pooter does not harm the organism, and it can then be returned to its natural habitat.

OTHER METHODS of collection are numerous. Many are based on some form of netting - for example large **mist nets** may be used to collect migrating birds for identification and ringing, and **sweep nets** may be used to capture aerial or aquatic arthropods.

Management in action

The basis of successful management is **information.** The collection of information about biological resources, biological monitoring, can provide data with at least four major uses in the development of conservation strategies:

1. **the status (number and distribution) of plant and animal species :** for example, the Common Birds Census, undertaken by the British Trust for Ornithology, is based on information collected from woodland and farmland habitats. It provides an index of population changes relative to an arbitrary datum year (1966 for most specis) where the index is set at 100. The scheme provides a most valuable set of data for the analysis of changes of populations of birds, especially with regard to loss of habitat and pollution.
   Similar schemes exist for monitoring of butterfly and vascular plant populations.

2. **optimum management of living resources :** for example, the control of pest species such as aphids or blackfly has been has been made much more efficient using data gathered by the Rothamstead Insect Survey. Similarly management of commercially important species depends upon the gathering of basic information - the National Game Census monitors population trends and fluctuations in red grouse, grey partridge and brown hare amongst others.

3. **environmental protection :** chemical monitoring (such as the measurement of atmospheric acid gas levels) is supplemented by biological monitoring since the biological environment may manipulate chemical pollutants. For example, pesticides such as DDT were subject to bioaccumulation - the build up of chemicals as they travel along a food chain - and the absorptive activity of plant roots may significantly alter measured concentrations of nitrate in the environment. Good examples of biological monitoring include the use of lichens for measurement of levels of atmospheric pollutants, the assessment of aquatic invertebrate populations to determine water quality (the Trent Biotic Index) and the exciting use of remote sensing in, for example, monitoring populations of surface phytoplankton which provides valuable information on the 'Greenhouse Effect'.

4. **impact of environmental damage:** oil spills such as occurred with the grounding of the Torrey Canyon represent just one example of a 'pollution incident'. Following such an incident, monitoring may provide data on the level, extent and duration of the effects of the incident - this data will be of particular value if baseline information is available for comparison. Baseline information is available for the Milford Haven (much of it gathered by the Field Studies Centre at Dale Fort) and might be used to monitor the effects of oil pollution incidents such as occurred at this site in 1990.

Of course, the basis of biological monitoring is the availability of appropriate survey and census methods. Some of these survey methods, and their application to conservation are described in this Chapter and later in this book - in each case the sequence of operations can be seen to be:

a. survey the habitat / determine the status of the species
b. devise a management plan
c. initiate the funding of the plan
d. carry out the plan
e. repeat the survey to determine success of plan
f. review management plan

Thus successful conservation is likely to involve the co-operative activity of biologists, technologists, landowners, farmers, accountants and fundraisers, and will **inevitably be a compromise.** As an example of this compromise in action, study the figure below, which summarises the management of a island nature reserve in this country.

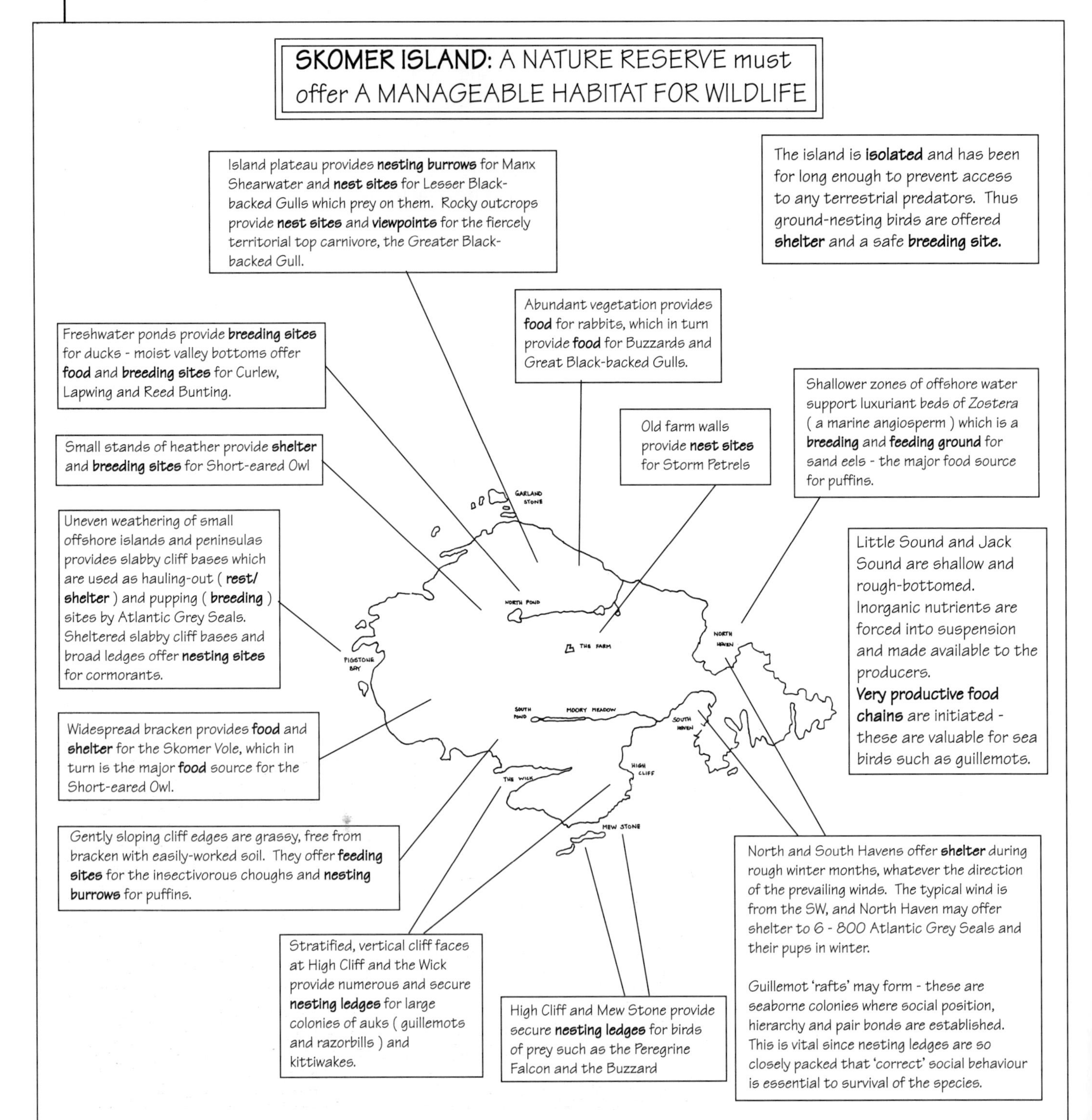

Why and how

One species dominates all others - the biomass of humans, at almost 200 million tons, may only be surpassed by the krill of the southern oceans. This places Man in a unique situation - humans have a total responsibility to consider what they are doing to other living organisms and to themselves. It has been estimated that the final quarter of this century will witness the loss of up to one million species, many of them unknown to science. This would work out at about 40 000 each year, or about 100 each day.

Does it matter if a species becomes extinct? Possible arguments supporting the view that Man should conserve species are as follows:

1. Ethical. It could be argued that Man has no right to exterminate other species. He is just one of millions of species on Earth, and is not special in any way other than that he has developed the power to control the destinies of other species. Man should use this power responsibly. A culture which encourages respect for wildlife is preferable to one that does not.

2. Aesthetic. Every species is unique and irreplaceable, having its own particular beauty (like a work of art). Once extinct, it can never be recreated, and its beauty is destroyed. Humans should conserve species and their habitats because they enrich our lives.

3. Economic. Reserves, zoos and wildlife farms can be profitable. For example, Kenya's wildlife is very important to its economy.

4. Scientific. Animals and plants provide research material which may be vital in the advancement of medicine, food production and industry. Living organisms also provide a bank of genes, which may eventually be incorporated into other species, with enormous potential benefits to Man. This situation has been summed up by Tom Lovejoy of the WWF

> " If we were preparing for a new Dark Age, and could take only a limited number of books into the monasteries for the duration, we might have to determine which single branch of knowledge would have the greatest survival value for us. The outstanding candidate would be Biology, including its applied forms such as medicine, agriculture, forestry and fisheries. Yet we are doing just the contrary, by busily throwing out the biology books before they have been written "

5. Ecological. Extinction of a species is a symptom of deterioration of the natural environment, and tends to produce ecological instability. Any instability ultimately affects mankind, since the Earth is his environment too. Stability is essential in the long term for sustained food production.

Because your arguments would be more convincing if you take a **balanced** view, try to take each of these points in turn and suggest arguments which might be put against them. For example, how might a starving person in the third world, or a non-biologist at a planning enquiry in this country, argue convincingly against each? If you were arguing for species conservation, which of the five points do you think would stand up best?

Strategies for the preservation of endangered animal species.

1. **Captivity:** species may be kept alive and bred in captivity until conditions in the wild improve enough to offer them a chance of survival. For example, Barn Owls , Sand Lizards and British Field Cricket have all been bred in captivity and released to supplement wild populations.

2. **Partial Captive Rearing**: provides protection during the most vulnerable stages of the life cycle. e.g. eggs are collected, incubated and hatched to reduce predation losses, then the young are released.

3. **Cross-fostering**: give endangered birds' eggs to a similar, but more common, species for rearing. Original parents re-lay (thus increasing number of potential chicks) - up to 3 or 4 clutches.

4. **Movement** of whole population to a safer location.

5. **Re-introduction to habitats** where former dangers have been removed.
   e.g. **White-tailed Eagle** to the island of Rhum, from Scandinavia, after its original persecution to extinction in Scotland by gamekeepers and egg-collectors.
   Salmon to the Thames, after the reduction of levels of pollution.

6. **Improving and expanding breeding areas**
   e.g. islands and platforms built for breeding terns, away from human disturbance and foxes. Roosting boxes, even an artificial cave, provided for bats. Extra ponds dug for **Natterjack Toads.**

IN GENERAL,
PRESERVATION/RESTORATION
OF HABITAT IS VITAL.

The following pages detail some examples of the application of these methods to endangered British species. It is most important to remember that large, attractive species such as the Barn Owl and the Red Squirrel will always attract attention and conservation effort, but less 'attractive' species - perhaps slugs, mosses or biting insects - also deserve attention. The two examples chosen are to some extent FLAGSHIP SPECIES i.e. their conservation attracts public attention, and the management strategies which can then be implemented will inevitably protect habitat which can then support other, less 'attention-grabbing' species.

BARN OWL

Captive breeding and release

The Barn Owl (*Tyto alba*) has been recorded roosting and breeding in most rural habitats in Britain - it is believed that much of its success has been its ability to live in habitats which have been modified for farming. It has long been regarded as the "farmers' friend", but changes in farming methods may well be one of the reasons for its current decline in this country.

The Barn Owl roosts and breeds in most types of farm building providing appropriate sites exist and the building remains undisturbed. Evidence of their presence includes the analysis of regurgitated pellets - Barn Owls swallow their prey whole and the low acid content of their stomach prevents the digestion of bones, teeth and claws which are expelled wrapped in the fur or feathers of their prey. The collection of such pellets is an important part in determining the success or otherwise of captive breeding and release programmes.

Conservation measures

As is typical for a conservation strategy, the collection of data is vital. For example, ringing returns show that most barn owls remain within about 20 km of their ringing site which suggests that local populations are contained within an area about the size of an English county. Any survey of populations should therefore take place over an area of about that size. Such a survey would include

a. records of barn owl sightings

b. pellet analysis

c. identification of isolated barns and other suitable buildings

d. identification of suitable trees with large cavities

e. identification of suitable foraging areas

Where suitable foraging - rough grassland - exists breeding boxes might be installed in suitable buildings , and if such buildings are absent boxes can be positioned in trees or on poles.

If suitable feeding grounds exist, and after a period of twelve months no sites have been used and no breeding has been recorded, captive bred owls may be released. Different methods have been used in such release programmes. Evidence, in the form of pellets which indicate successful rates of feeding from the wild, suggests that if the programme is carried out by responsible and informed groups reintroduction can be successful in boosting barn owl populations. Many critics of these programmes have been quick to point out that not all reintroduction programmes are organised and carried out by responsible organisations - to keep some check on what might otherwise be counterproductive exercises (the 'public' will hardly be converted to conservation by the sight of many poorly fed or dead owls) the Department of the Environment has, since 1993, assumed legal control of all barn owl releases. Any organisation wishing to undertake a reintroduction programme must obtain an appropriate licence and keep meticulous records of the progress of their programme.

It seems likely that the fate of the barn owl population of this country depends largely on the availability of suitable habitat (such as might be available under set-aside schemes) coupled with carefully controlled and monitored release of captive-bred birds.

Reasons for the decline in Barn Owl Populations

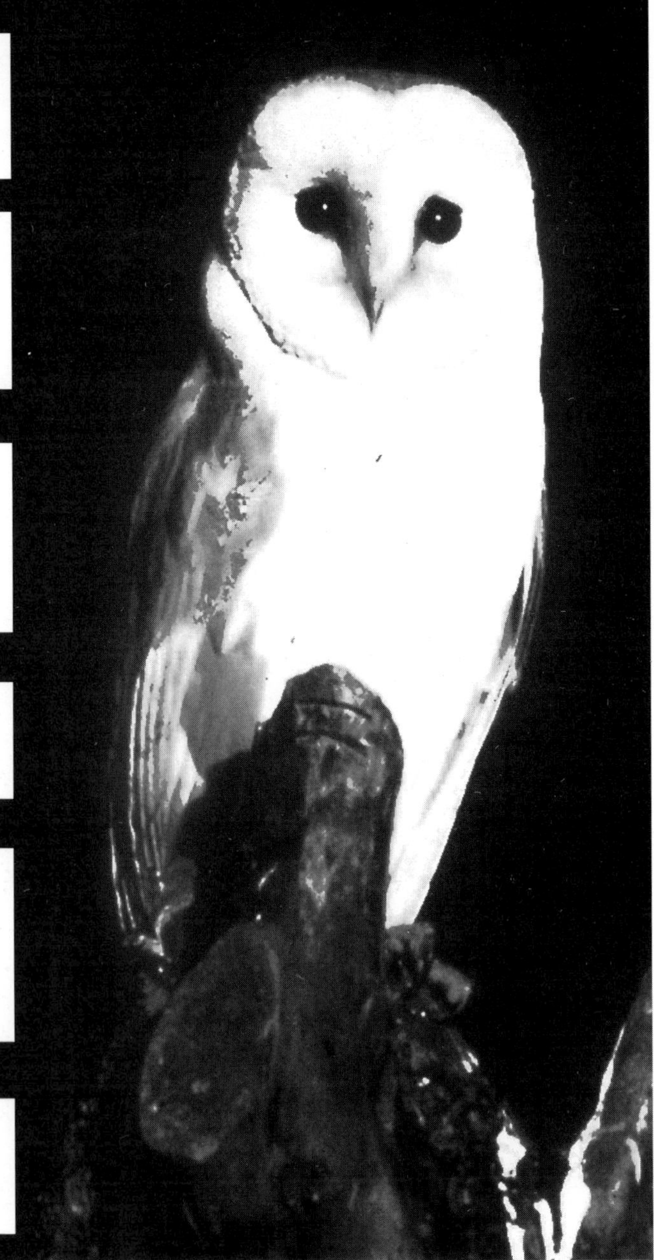

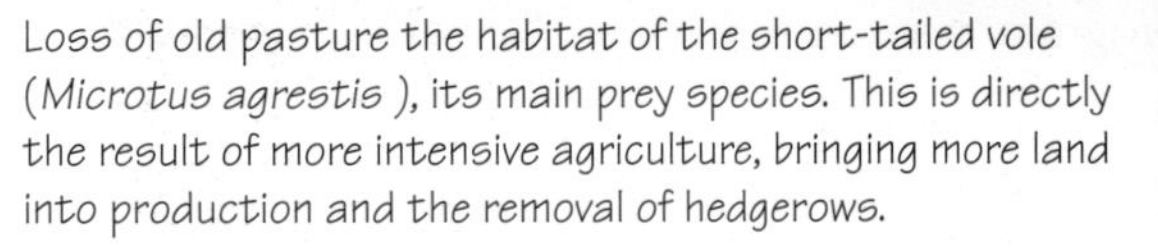

Loss of the elm tree whose large cavities offered both secure roosting and nest sites. This is principly the result of Dutch Elm Disease, but also the removal of old hedgerows for more mechanised and intensive farming practices.

Loss of suitable farm buildings - traditional barns have been replaced by more efficient modern constructions which do not offer nest or roosting sites. The more suitable barns have often been demolished or have been converted into human habitations, thus disturbing traditional owl sites.

Harsh weather conditions, including deep snow and drought, which have caused a reduction in food supplies and damaged already vulnerable owl populations.

Pesticide use - like all predatory species the Barn Owl is vulnerable to accumulation of these compounds at the top of the food chain. DDT, Aldrin and Dieldrin will all have had their effects, and rodenticides such as difenacoum and brodifacoum continue to limit breeding success of this species.

The increase in road traffic, causing an estimated 3,000 to 5,000 deaths each year. Many Barn Owls hunt alongside road margins, and their flight close to the ground makes them particularly vulnerable,

Possible conservation measures to increase Barn Owl populations

YOUNG CLUTCH RELEASE involves placing a clutch of owlets, approximately five weeks old, in a nestbox in a suitable building. There are no adults to feed the young, and the young are not confined. They fledge at about eight weeks of age, and supplementary feeding encourages the birds to disperse gradually or remain at the release site.

LONG-TERM RELEASE involves confining a pair of captive-bred owls in a suitably adapted building and allowing them to breed. The adults are released when the owlets are six to seven weeks old in the expectation that the parent birds will not desert the site because of their instinct to feed their young. Supplementary feeding with day old chicks is continued until pellet analysis indicates that the released birds have converted to a 'wild' diet -usually after a further three months or so.

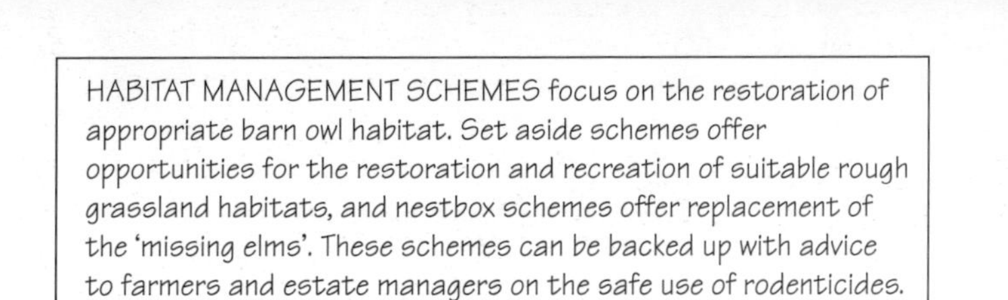

HABITAT MANAGEMENT SCHEMES focus on the restoration of appropriate barn owl habitat. Set aside schemes offer opportunities for the restoration and recreation of suitable rough grassland habitats, and nestbox schemes offer replacement of the 'missing elms'. These schemes can be backed up with advice to farmers and estate managers on the safe use of rodenticides.

Grey squirrels are popular garden visitors, but they are increasingly replacing Britain's native red squirrels

RED SQUIRREL

Habitat management and control of competition

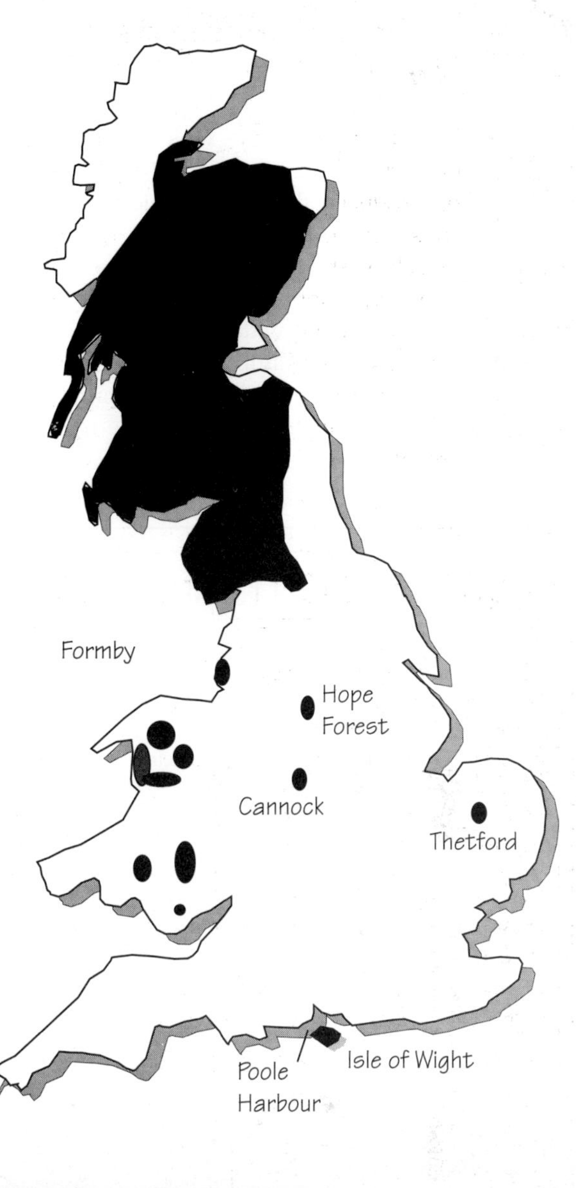

The Red Squirrel (*Sciurus vulgaris*) was originally distributed widely throughout the British Isles but it has now disappeared from much of England, surviving in only a few discrete populations. In most areas it has been replaced by the larger Grey Squirrel (*Sciurus carolinensis*) - there are just 160 000 reds left compared with an estimated 2.5 million greys. The grey is a far less fussy eater than the red, which feeds predominantly on conifer seed, and has for some time seemed able to out-compete the red in broadleaved woodland. Now the greys are encroaching on the red's last refuges of the extensive conifer plantations of Scotland and Northern England. Because of its endangered status the Red Squirrel has full protection under the Wildlife and Countryside Act, 1981.

Conservationists and timber growers, working within the government's joint Nature Conservation Committee, have mobilised volunteers to monitor Red Squirrel populations and have attempted to persuade owners of broad-leaved woodland to support a strategy to "Save the Red".

The management plan involves three broad strategies:

1. adjustment of habitat to suit existing red populations
2. provision of supplementary food for reds
3. control of populations of greys, particularly those close to red squirrel strongholds.

In addition there may be trial introductions of red squirrels to boost declining or sparse local populations.

Without action it is likely that the red squirrel would disappear completely from mainland southern and central England within 10 - 20 years. The plans described illustrate close co-ordination between the commercial interests of the Forestry Commission, the direct conservation interest of English Nature and the academic research efforts of workers at Queen Mary and Westfield College and the University of Sheffield.

Possible reasons for the decline of the red squirrel

Competition with the grey, which is particularly important in broadleaved woodland. The red feeds on conifer seeds, producing the characteristic stripped 'core' of pine cones, and only supplements its diet with hazelnuts, beech mast, acorns, fruits and berries. The grey can survive on a monotonous diet of a wider range of foods - they can cope with a diet which is almost exclusively acorns, for example. The greys are also more willing to feed at ground level, and can thus take advantage of food sources which may be ignored by the more strictly arboreal reds.

Disease may be significant. It is believed by veterinary scientists that the grey squirrel carries a virus which usually only causes disease and death in red squirrels. Thus in mixed populations the reds are at a disadvantage.

Habitat loss has occurred. Although the red survives better in coniferous forest it must have access to trees of different ages to provide food throughout the year. Many recent conifer plantings have been a. composed of trees all of the same age and b. of Sitka Spruce, which produces small seeds and sheds them early in the year, leaving little food for reds in the winter.

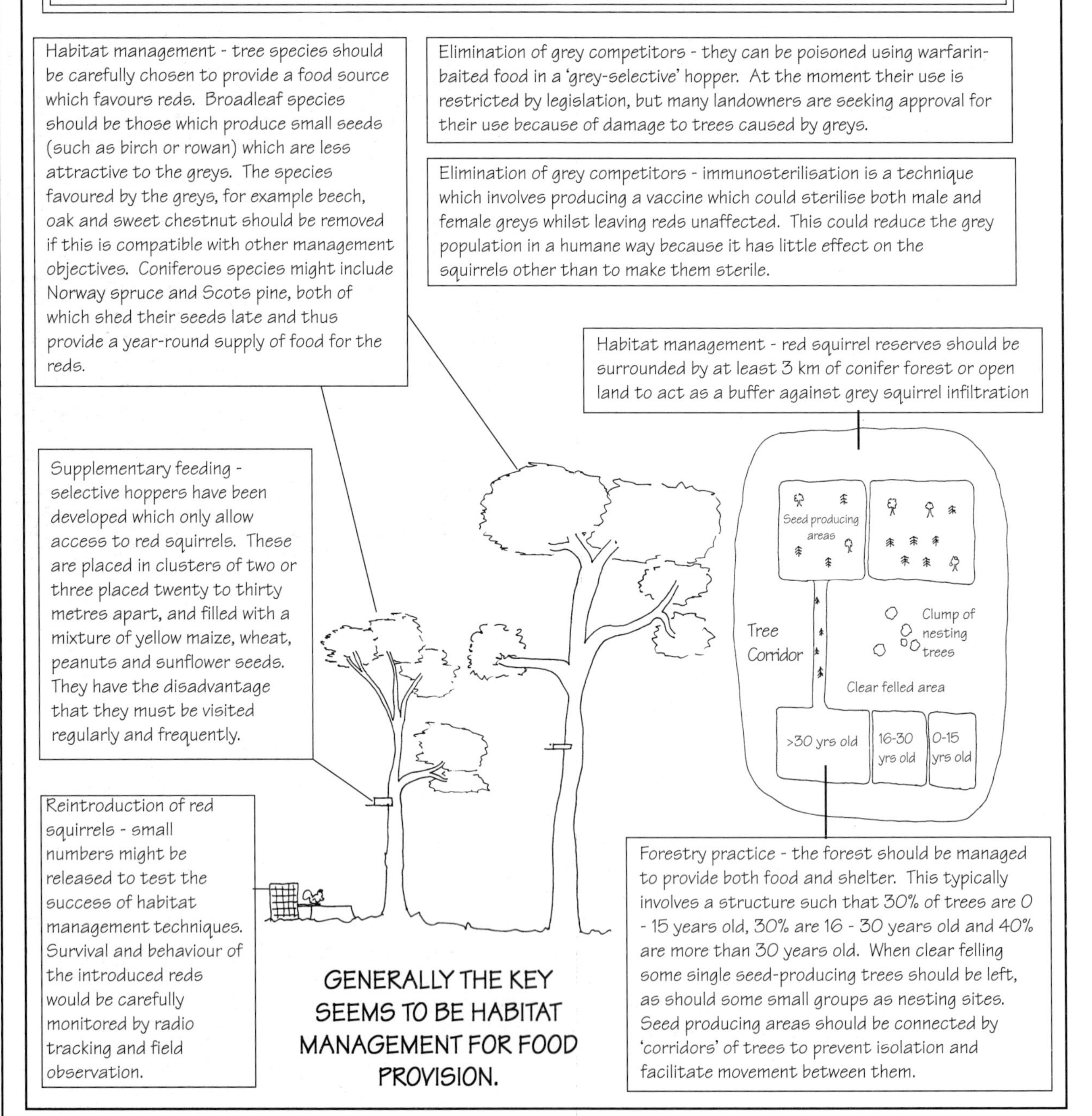

The management of ecosystems for profit

As we have stated previously, conservation is a compromise. In a country as crowded as ours there will inevitably be conflict and competition for land. Some areas of land may be managed in such a way that they provide a profitable product for the landowner, but at the same time provide some benefit to wild populations.

Game rearing

In recent years the management of game-bird populations has had a poor public image - in part this reflects the association of shooting for sport with the rich, landowning classes. Despite this, the management of game-bird populations has played an important role in shaping our landscape, in a manner which has generally been beneficial to wildlife.

The successful management of game relies upon a detailed understanding of their ecology and habitat requirements. These requirements have dictated the way in which game estates have been managed, and are responsible for the retention of hedgerows, coppice woodland and rough grassland. Given the economic climate of today it seems unlikely that these habitat features would be retained on estates if game shooting were to cease.

We can now examine some of the management strategies that are employed and how they benefit wildlife in general.

Woodland management

Woodland plays an important role in the management of pheasants (*Phasanius colchicus*). Where a shoot relies on the release of hand-reared birds, woodland provides a release site. The young birds (poults) are placed in release pens at about six weeks of age and later, with the development of their flight feathers, the poults move out into the wood itself. The woodland is also important for wild populations of pheasants - the cock birds establish territories along the edges of woodlands, to which they attract the hens. Woodland edges rich in shrubby cover (30 - 200 cm in height) are favoured over those where there is a sharp divide between the wood and the adjoining field. Woodland edge bordering arable fields holds three times as many territories as edge bordering grassland.

The structure of the woodland is critical. Pheasants prefer areas with good ground cover interspersed with large trees in which to roost. If the ground cover is too sparse then the pheasants are at an increased risk of predation, while if it is too dense then it becomes too difficult to drive the birds from the wood and onto the guns. The coppicing of small areas within a wood creates a mosaic of vegetation types.

Areas of bramble and hazel are cut back when they become too dense and this opens up parts of the wood, thereby allowing the dormant seeds of ground flora to germinate.

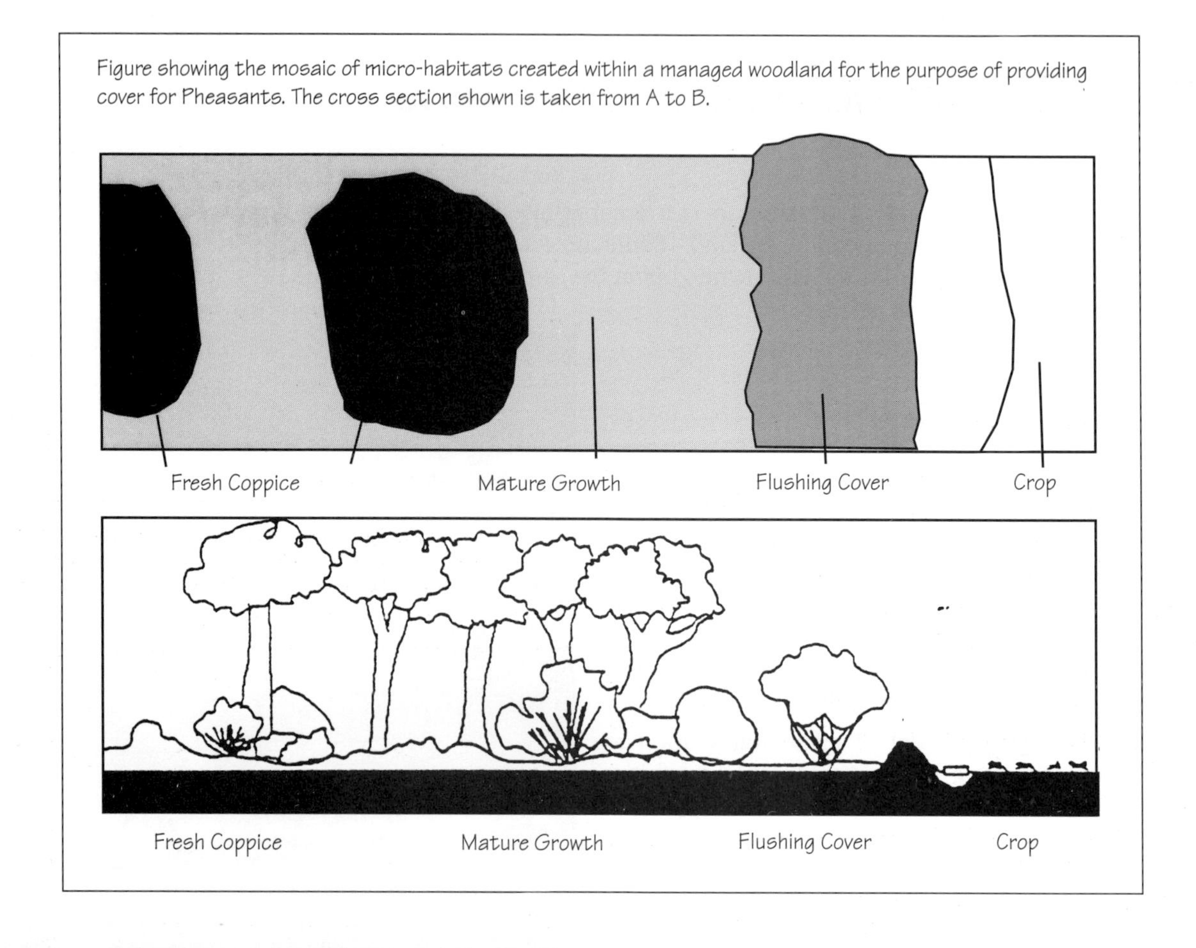

Figure showing the mosaic of micro-habitats created within a managed woodland for the purpose of providing cover for Pheasants. The cross section shown is taken from A to B.

Many estate woods contain a range of plant species typically associated with ancient woodland. These species, including Solomon's Seal (*Polygonum multiflorum*) and Butcher's Broom (*Ruscus acueatus*), are usually of limited distribution.

The mosaic of vegetation types allows a range of bird and mammal species to exploit the wood. Willow Warblers (*Phylloscopus trochilus*) and Blackcaps (*Sylvia atricapilla*) nest in the dense bramble cover, while Dormice (*Muscardinus avellanarius*) will use the bramble as a hibernation site in winter. In the summer the Dormice will feed on the Hazel (*Corylus avellana*) and Honeysuckle (*Lonicera periclymemum*) which are favoured by coppicing.

Hedgerow Management

Hedgerows are important for pheasants and partidges, both for nesting and for feeding. The length of permanent field boundary correlates closely with the breeding density of both species of partridge (*Perdix perdix*, the grey partridge and *Alecoris rufa*, the red-legged partridge), thus reflecting the clear preference for hedgerows as nesting habitat. Indeed, the decline of both species has been partly attributed to a loss of suitable nesting habitat as a result of hedgerow removal. The quality of the hedgerow and adjoining vegetation is also important. Female Grey Partidges use dead grass to cover their eggs before incubation, and the quantity of dead grass was shown to be the most important factor in predicting where Grey partridges chose to nest and the likelihood of the nest being predated. Red-legged partridges show a clear preference for nesting in nettles (*Urtica dioica*).

The quality of the hedgerow also influences the survival of chicks. Pheasants and both partridge species benefit from the high invertebrate populations in weedy and rough grass areas.

In modern farmland many of the hedgerows have been removed, and those that remain are usually of poor quality and affected by herbicide sprays. The Game Conservancy, through its Cereals and Gamebirds Research Project, has examined ways in which the quality of field boundaries can be increased (see overpage). The effects on crop yields are small, but the use of such headlands increases the densities of invertebrate prey species by a factor of 2.5 and chick survival by a factor of 1.8. The effect of this on population size is shown below:

Plot showing densities of Grey Partridges (Perdix perdix) at the Mannydown Estate in northern Hampshire where 'Conservation Headlands' were introduced in 1962. (A). The solid line shows the density found in these headlands while the broken line shows the density in control fields where the headlands were missing.

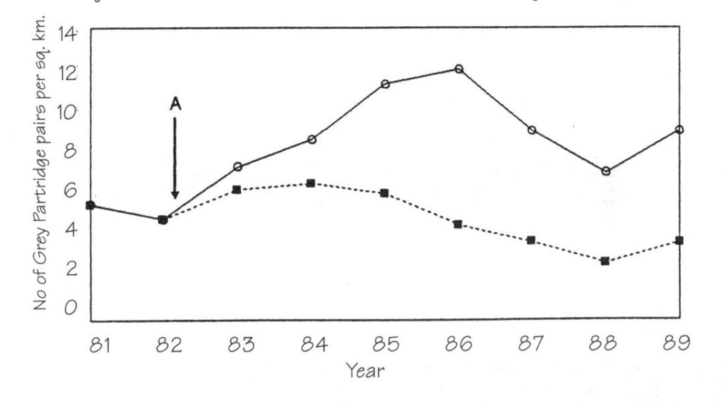

Rough field margins are attractive to partridges

Although these headlands have been established to increase game-bird densities and breeding success they have been of great value to other species

- ground nesting birds such as skylark (*Alauda arvensis*) and reed bunting (*Emberiza schoeniculus*)
- small mammals such as field vole (*Microtus agrestis*) and bank vole (*Ciethrioriomys glareolus*)
- insectivores such as hedgehog (*Eririaceus europacus*) and common shrew (*Sorex caecutiens*)

In addition the features associated with hedgerows, including at least some dead timber, and their availability as 'corridors' between adjacent habitats tends to increase the diversity of species using them.

Vermin Control

This element of game-bird management is probably the most emotive of all - even the use of the term 'vermin' rather than 'predator' is judgemental. Game managers maintain that the ultimate aim of vermin control is not to remove all of the predators from an area but to maintain their populations at a level which does not adversely affect game populations - unfortunately some can be non-selective in the application of their control regimes. Despite the fact that birds of prey are currently on the list of most protected species in the 1981 Wildlife and Countryside Act some landowners are seeking licences to cull them, particularly the peregrine falcon (*Falco peregrinus*)and the hen harrier (*Circus cyaneus*). According to the RSPB up to 700 offences against birds of prey take place every year, but it is often difficult to prosecute the perpetrators as evidence is difficult to obtain. The landowners openly condemn illegal killing of birds of prey - many realise that in a conservation - conscious country such as Britain such law-breaking is bad public relations - but seek the legal right to control predators which they suggest are limiting grouse and pheasant populations.

Scientific evidence *does not* support the landowners view - there is no doubt that harriers and peregrines prey on game birds *and* their chicks, but there are other factors which have a greater effect. It has been demonstrated that territorial disputes influence red grouse (*Lagopus lagopus*) populations more than the presence or absence of birds of prey. A study by Adam Watson, formerly of the Institute of Terrestrial Ecology, suggests that the major cause of the decline in grouse populations is the loss of heather habitat, and that better habitat management (e.g. by rotational burning) is the most cost-effective method of raising game-bird populations.

The control of predator populations can cause widespread effects in complex food webs - the removal of a 'top' predator may allow increase in the populations of subdominant animals, and the elimination of a predator may allow its prey species to become pests (some pheasant-rearing concerns have discovered that rodent populations increase uncontrollably, causing enormous damage to food stocks, if predators are removed from the ecosystem). Supporters of predator control point out that wildlife other than game species will benefit - small mammals and nesting songbirds will benefit from localised reductions in the number of stoats (*Mustela erminea*) and weasels (*M. nivalis*).

In summary

- game management should incorporate an understanding of how ecosystems work and how habitat quality determines productivity of species
- certain habitat types are dependent upon the continuation of land management for game shooting e.g. small coppiced woodlands are probably commercially unviable without game-rearing.
- benefits to wildlife other than game-birds are probably incidental, but would not exist without game management

Britain's persecuted birds of prey

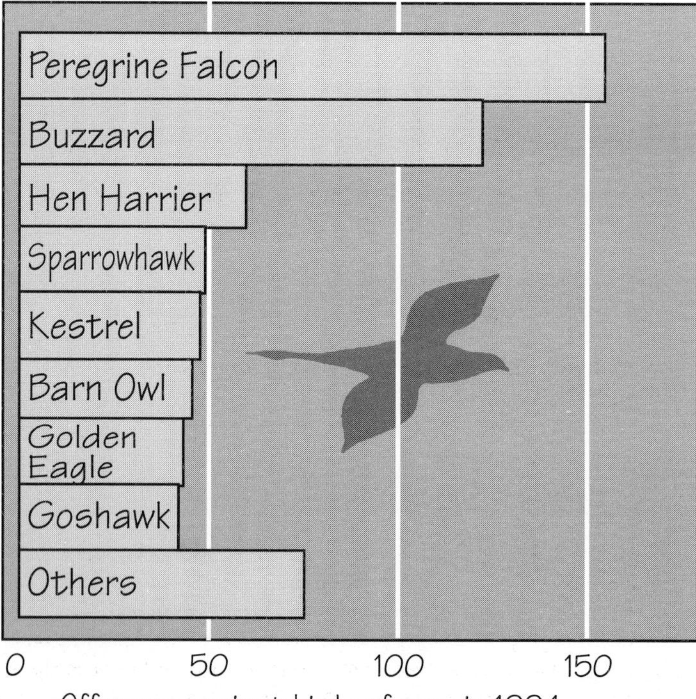

The Game Conservancy's Field Margin

"Conservation through wise use"

Guidelands for the Management of Cereal Field Margins 1992/93

(Conservation Headlands and Field Boundaries)

Hedge

Trim hedges every 2 to 3 years and keep to an approximate height of 2m. Do not allow hedge to overgrow adjacent grassy strip which is the vital area for nesting.

Conservation Headland

The area between the crop edge and the first tramline (usually 6m wide according to boom width). This is an area of crop treated with selective pesticides (see guidelines) to control grass weeds, cleavers and diseases whilst allowing most broad-leaved weeds and beneficial insects to survive. Ploughing of headlands is recommended especially on heavy soils or where grass weeds are a problem. Avoid turning furrow onto grassy strip as this can create ideal conditions for annual weeds.

Choose headlands next to good nesting cover. Avoid headlands infested with difficult weeds (especially barren brome and cleavers).

Sprayed Crop

Treat as normal. Avoid drift into headlands. Use only safer aphicides. (See guidelines.)

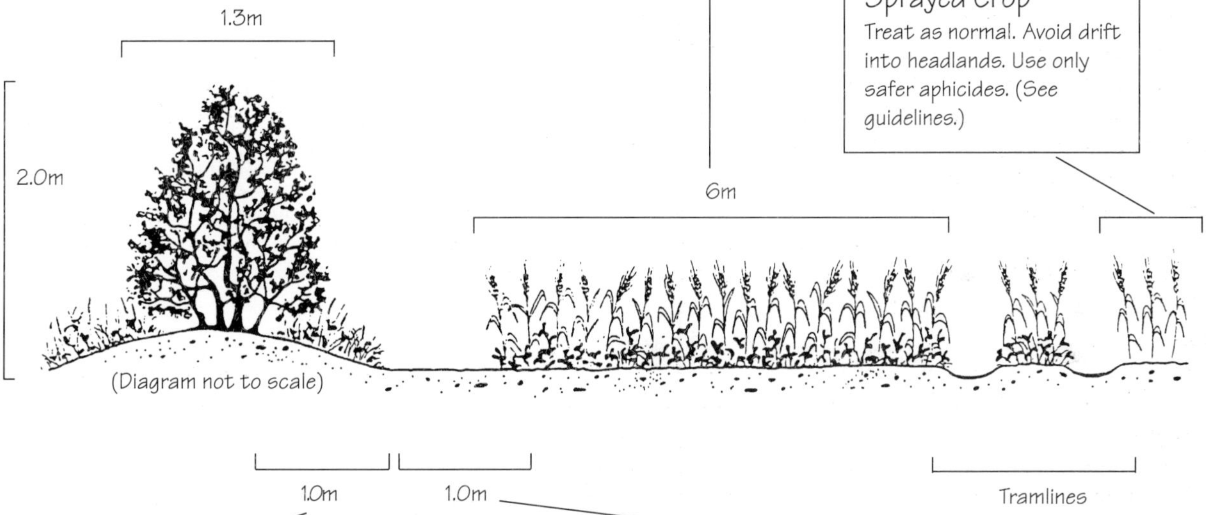

Grassy Bank/Nesting Strip

The area used for nest sites by gamebirds and for overwintering by beneficial insects. At least 1m wide and preferably sited on a bank. Should be composed of perennial grasses and other non-weedy herbaceous species. Avoid spray and fertiliser drift into this area. Allow build up of dead grass material essential for successful nesting, but top the vegetation if necessary every 2-3 years to avoid scrub encroachment.

Boundary or Sterile Strip

Purpose is to prevent invasion of crop by cleavers and barren brome where they have become abundant. Should be at least 1m wide. Maintain by rotavation or a herbicide application. Do not spray out grassy bank. Drill crop further out into the field to leave area of bare cultivated ground for the sterile strip. Avoid spray drift by shielding nozzle down to ground level (NB: sterile strip is not essential for conservation purposes: purely intended for weed manaagement).

Machinery

A specially designed sprayer is now available which can selectively spray a six-metre strip along the headland while spraying the main crop with standard chemicals. Each part of the machinery is independent of the other, thus saving the need for a separate run along the Conservation Headland.

While spraying sterile strips it is vital to prevent drift into crop and hedge bottom. A very useful device, which applies the chemical safely and accurately from the tractor, has been designed for this purpose.

For further information on these two pieces of equipment contact the Conservation Headlands Field Officer.

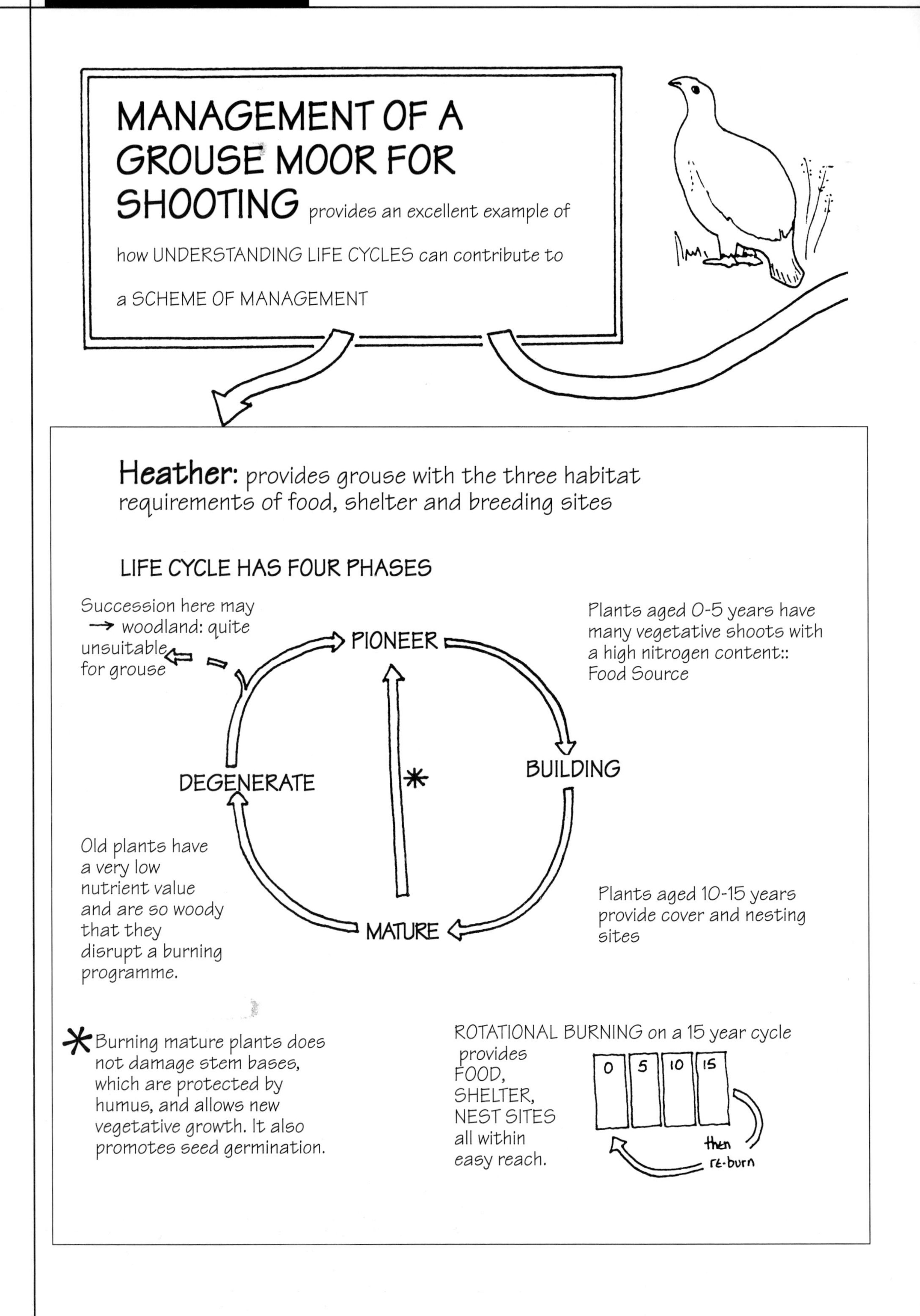
MANAGEMENT OF A GROUSE MOOR FOR SHOOTING provides an excellent example of
how UNDERSTANDING LIFE CYCLES can contribute to
a SCHEME OF MANAGEMENT
Heather: provides grouse with the three habitat requirements of food, shelter and breeding sites
LIFE CYCLE HAS FOUR PHASES
Succession here may → woodland: quite unsuitable for grouse
PIONEER
Plants aged 0-5 years have many vegetative shoots with a high nitrogen content:: Food Source
BUILDING
DEGENERATE
*
Old plants have a very low nutrient value and are so woody that they disrupt a burning programme.
MATURE
Plants aged 10-15 years provide cover and nesting sites
* Burning mature plants does not damage stem bases, which are protected by humus, and allows new vegetative growth. It also promotes seed germination.
ROTATIONAL BURNING on a 15 year cycle provides FOOD, SHELTER, NEST SITES all within easy reach.
0
5
10
15
then re-burn

GROUSE: populations show some self-regulation due to TERRITORIAL AGGRESSION DURING COURTSHIP

MAXIMUM GROUSE POPULATION = MAXIMUM COMMERCIAL VALUE

Grouse population could be affected by: a) Nutrient availability
b) predators
c) intraspecific aggression

and a management programme aims for OPTIMUM <u>SUSTAINED</u> POPULATIONS

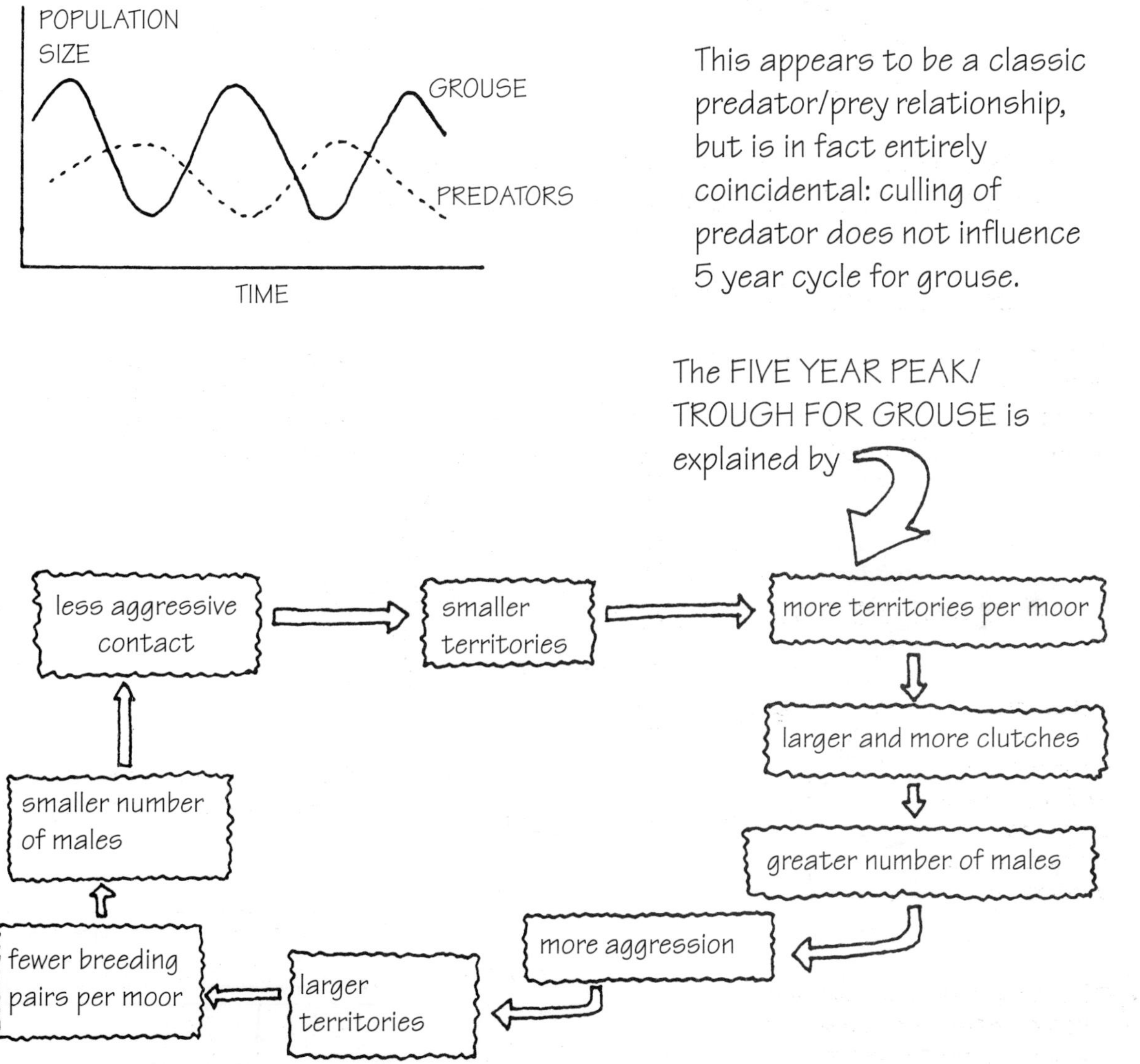

BEST MANAGEMENT PLAN: £££'s SPENT WISELY

1. Rotational heather burning: December - February
2. Controlled shooting: post breeding season August - December
3. Development of access and amenities
4. Predator control

Managing a woodland coppice

The basic principle of the coppice system is that each coppice stand grows mainly from shoots which spring from the cut shoots of the previous stand. Commercial coppice yields three main products

- sticks, poles and brushwood from the underwood
- timber from standard trees scattered among the underwood
- pasture from the herbaceous field layer beneath the underwood and in grassy rides and clearings

The management system should be highly systematic, with the underwood cut on a rotation of 5 - 25 years and the standards cut on a different rotation which is a multiple of the underwood cutting. Grazing is prevented in newly-cleared areas until the new growth of wood is tall enough to resist damage (typically after 4 - 7 years, depending on species . This management scheme produced the 'coppice-and-standard' woodland so familiar in southern, south eastern and eastern England. Today there is little commercial value in coppicing, although there is still some call for sweet chestnut palings and there are proposals for small-scale local power stations fuelled by coppiced wood. If coppice is to be maintained for its wildlife value there must be some financial return to the woodland owner - the maintenance of coppice for game-bird rearing (see above) is highly significant.
Some important **coppiced** species are Ash (*Fraxinus excelsior),* Sweet Chestnut, (*Castanea sativa),* Hornbeam (*Carpinus betulus) and* Hazel (*Corylus aveliana).* Important **standards** include Oak (*Quercus robur),* Ash and Beech (*Fagus sylvaticus).*

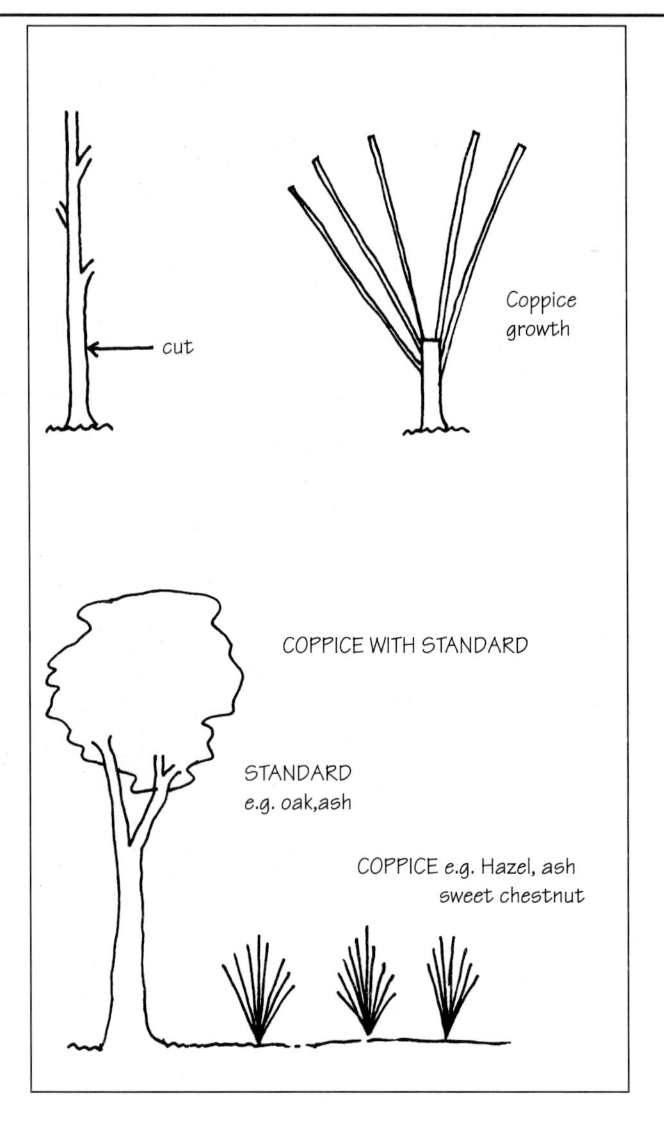

For details of species conservation programmes which include coppice management see pages 20 and 22.

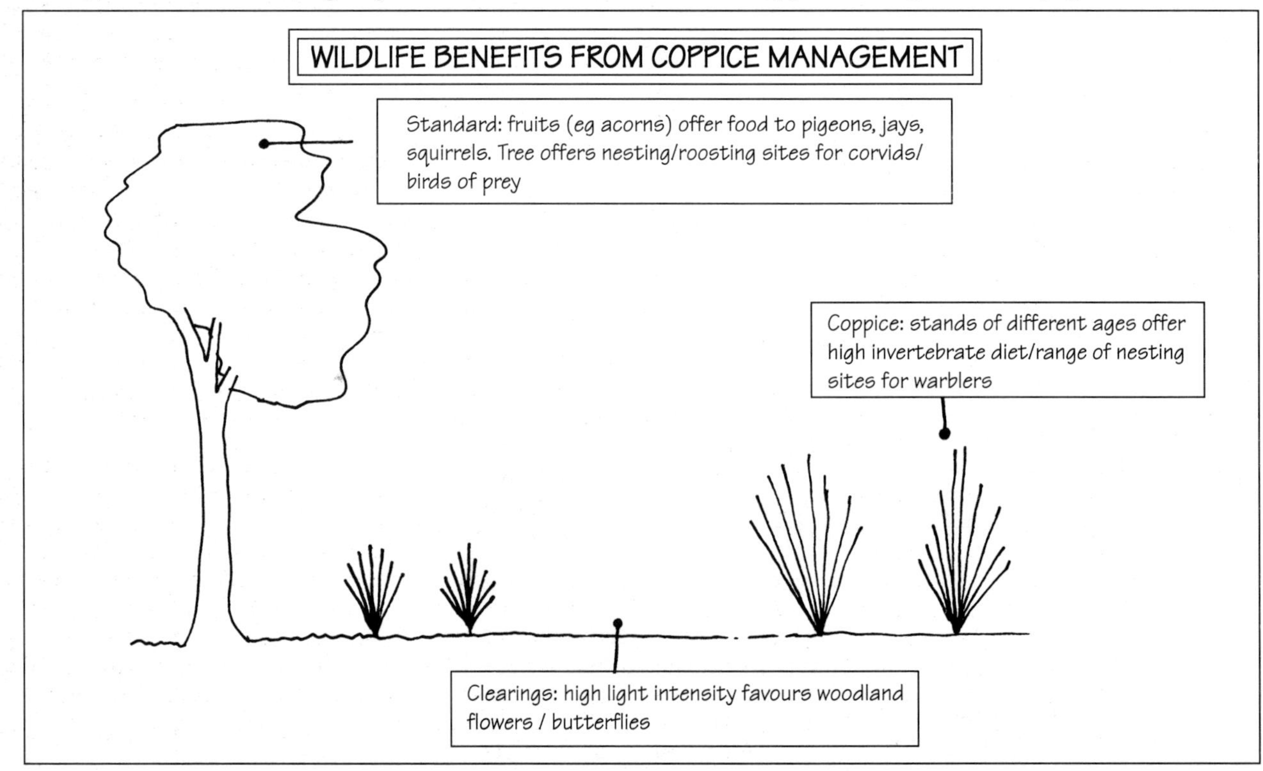

Woodland management could still save our most attractive insects, says Sanjida O'Connell

On a butterfly wing and a prayer

Butterflies in Britain are under serious threat. Four species have become extinct, seven more are on the brink of extinction and the total loss stands at 40 per cent, says Martin Warren, senior conservation officer for Butterfly Conservation and the author of a recent survey on butterfly populations.

Butterflies are the "miner's canary" of the natural world- "They're early warning indicators," says Dr. Warren. "They'll disappear before other species." Butterflies are highly sensitive to any disturbance to their habitat and will start to decline in numbers within five to 10 years after a particular site is disturbed. And by the time butterflies die out, other plants and animals will already be treading the same path to extinction. The next species to go may be even more sorely missed: the British dormouse, for instance, may survive for a few years where the resident butterfly species have disappeared, but it too, will eventually be wiped out.

One of the major reasons butterflies are dying out is mismanagement of their natural habitat. What many butterflies need are sunny woodland clearings. Over half the woodland sites in which butterflies are found are completely unmanaged or only partially managed, yet almost half are designated as sites of special scientific interest, supposedly protected and maintained by law. However, it's not just bad management that is to blame but also a change in our use of wood.

In the past, small woodlands of hazel were grown and trimmed for firewood but these have now given way to woods composed of larger, slower-growing trees. As a consequence, active coppicing of wood has been reduced by 94 per cent since the turn of the century. And the dense woodland which has replaced the coppiced hazel has few sunny clearings.

After the Second World War, wood was desperately needed and whole tracts of ancient woodlands were replaced with fast-growing conifers. As these trees are all of the same age, they create even more shade than they would have done had the trees been planted at different times. Because they prevent light from filtering through to the forest floor, plants that are vital for butterflies and other insects cannot grow.

It is not just woodland butterflies that have suffered, but also those associated with more open habitats. Development and intensive agriculture have reduced grasslands by 92 per cent in the past 52 years. In a few cases, changing land use has actually benefited butterflies. Bracken is normally the scourge of conservationists, because it spreads so quickly and little animal and plant life is associated with it. But the high brown fritillary butterfly is actually encouraged by bracken as it depends on violets found near the edges of bracken stands. In addition, the dead litter retains warmth which allows the caterpillars to grow better.

Young conifers that are widely spaced and still small also provide suitable sunny, open habitat, but Dr Warren stresses that this is only temporary. Living on the margins of areas that have resulted from human intervention is not enough to outweigh the destruction of suitable, more traditional habitat; despite the increase in bracken-infested areas, the number of high brown fritillary has still decreased by 97 per cent.

One solution would be to open tracts in the forest, known as rides, and to resume coppicing. However Dr Warren says that opening rides in coniferous forests is difficult: conifers do not put forth fast-growing shoots in the way that trees such as hazel do, and so the rides become dominated by grasses rather than the plants butterflies and other animals need. Moreover, a few rides in a few forests does not provide an extensive enough area to maintain a viable population of butterflies. Coppicing is also expensive in terms of staff and because it rarely serves any useful purpose to local people who no longer need firewood.

But the situation is not completely hopeless. "Many sites where butterflies are left are small, but if they were well managed, butterflies could be saved," Dr Warren says. There have been some successes: at Gait Barrows in Cumbria, butterflies that are extinct in most other areas have started to return following an increase in coppicing. The Forestry Commission is changing its policy and has agreed to provide grants to enable coppicing to be carried out.

"Up to now the emphasis has been on protecting sites from the bulldozer - simply emergency measures - but even if you put a fence up, most butterflies will still disappear," he says. We may not want to go buck to heating our homes with hazel twigs, but if we want to protect British butterflies as well as the rest of our woodland wildlife, we need to conserve and manage our woods properly.

Fish farming may conserve wild fish populations

Humans have been catching fish for food for many years - certainly far longer than they have managed domestic animals and grown crops. The relationship between human and fish populations has followed a classic predator-prey relationship, and it has become apparent in recent years that wild fish populations have fallen below sustainable levels. To allow stocks of wild fish, particularly cod and herring, to recover a number of proposals have been made

- catch fewer fish, by operating quota systems
- catch only bigger fish, allowing smaller fish to reach breeding age
- substitute 'farmed' fish for wild-caught species

FISH FARMING has become a rapidly growing industry, especially on the west coasts of Scotland and Ireland. In this country, production costs are high so that the product fish must be able to command a high price. For this reason commercial fish farming has concentrated on Salmonids, especially Rainbow Trout. Some efforts have been made to farm plaice and dover sole, but there have been difficulties in feeding the fish in captivity (they do not eat prepared pellets) and the adult fish do not command high prices. There has been a little more success with Turbot, which thrives at high densities, has a good conversion ratio and grows quickly, as well as being an expensive fish.
There is no doubt that salmonid farming provides many fish for eating or for sport without damaging wild populations, but there are environmental costs such as pollution and disturbance of natural food chains. The basic principles of fish farming, together with some perceived advantages and disadvantages are explained on the following pages.

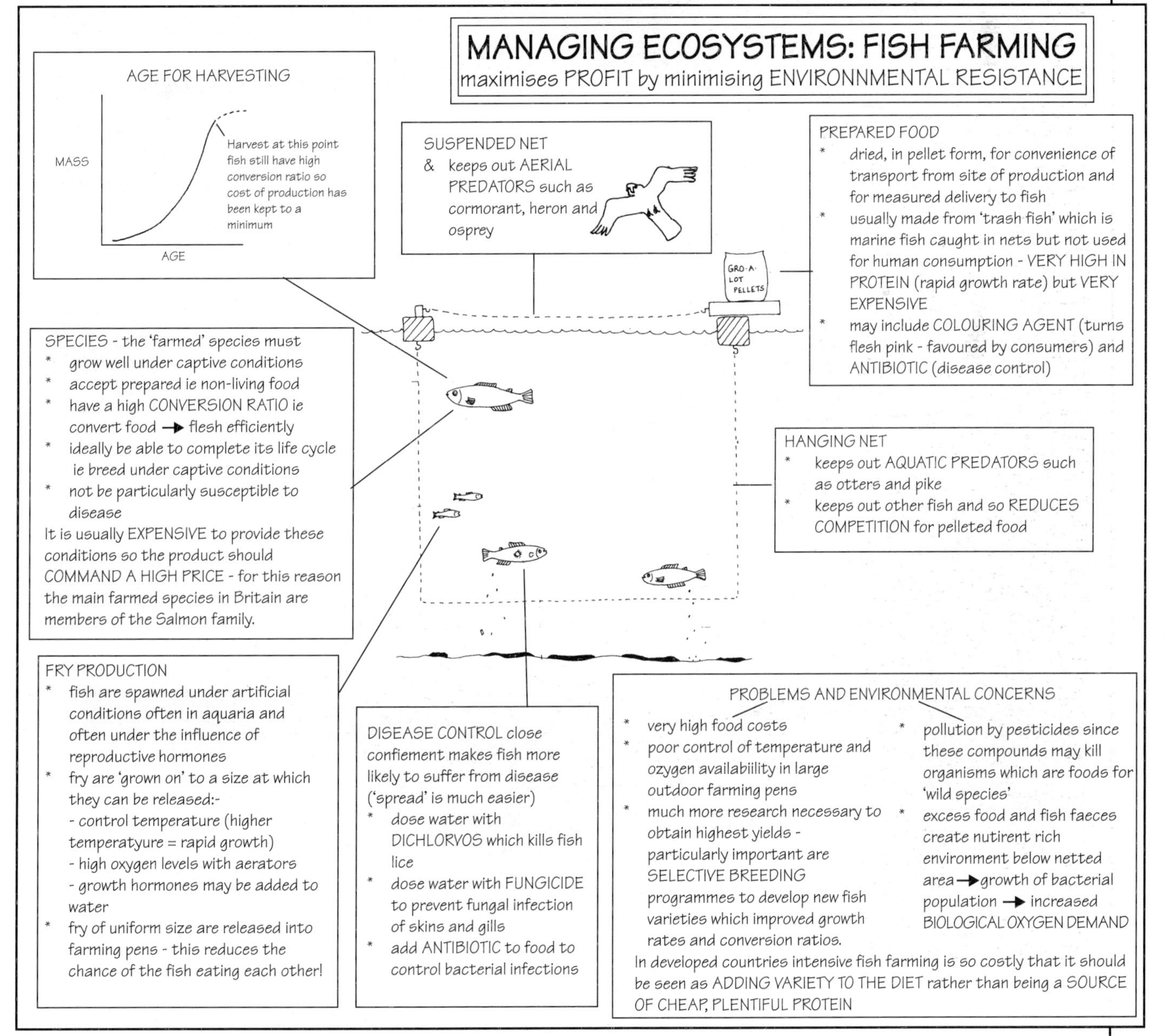

NEW SCIENTIST

FOCUS

Can we make supersalmon safe?

The transgenic salmon in tanks by a Scottish Loch are becoming a problem. Should the British government allow the fish to grow up?

The tiny fry swimming in high-security tanks next to Loch Fyne in Scotland all look alike. Salmon fry do. But in a few months' time some of them will stand out. They will be noticeably bigger than the other fish-and growing much faster. These salmon have been genetically modified. A year later, they will be many times the size of normal fish the same age.

The salmon, at the Otter Ferry salmon hatchery on Loch Fyne, have been hatched from eggs that had been injected with a gene for salmon growth hormone, plus a promoter sequence from the ocean pout. In just one year, the altered salmon can grow up to fifty times the size of normal year-old fish, although on average they are more likely to be five times as big.

What will happen to these rapidly growing fish? Ideally, fish farmers would like to use them to breed a lucrative race of supersalmon. But what are the consequences of these fish escaping from a fish farm? Are the risks too great? The British government could soon have to decide whether the experiment should be allowed to continue. Its decision will affect not just fish farming, but the whole biotechnology industry in Europe. The industry fears that any safety mishap could further damage its public image.

Any plans to farm transgenic fish would have to be looked at by the Advisory Committee on Releases to the Environment. The committee advises the environment secretary who then has to decide whether to approve the plans. The committee's guidelines on transgenic fish, "give salmon with an extra growth hormone gene as one example of the kind of fish that might need to be regulated"

The future of the Scottish fish, or any like them in future, revolves around two questions. Would escaped transgenic salmon cause any further damage to stocks of wild salmon? If so, is it possible to protect wild salmon so that transgenic salmon can be farmed safely?

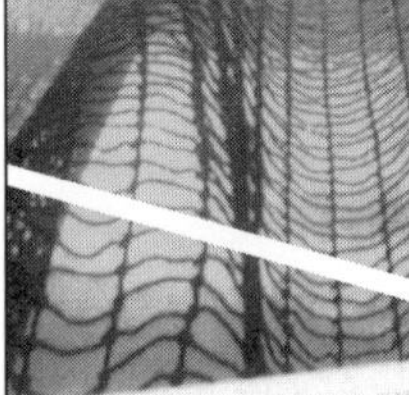

If the transgenic fish are less fit, but escape in such numbers that they dominate wild populations despite their lower survival rates, then the whole stock could become more vulnerable.

That has already happened with normal salmon that have escaped from farms. There are five times as many farm fish as wild salmon in some Norwegian rivers, the Norwegian Institute for Nature Research in Trondheim. Yet farm salmon competing with wild types in tanks and streams seem to have only a quarter as much survival and breeding success.

There are benefits in making all farmed fish sterile, because this would reduce the impact of escaped fish on wild stocks. It would also be good for the hatcheries, making it easier to control the supply of improved stock. The profit could be enough to pay for rearing nonsterile breeding stock inland, thus removing any threat of escapes.

Restoration: the repair of damaged ecosystems

There can be no doubt that human activities will alter and can damage ecosystems. Remember that human exploitation of the land and sea will inevitably be a compromise - possible human benefits must be balanced against possible environmental damage. In this section we can examine how human skills may be used to help restore habitats which have been damaged by human exploitation - we should note how a satisfactory outcome depends upon a close relationship between knowledge of biological and chemical phenomena, and the application of mechanical and technical skills. We shall consider three examples:

- gravel pit management - repair to systems damaged by the extraction of roadbuilding materials
- conservation headlands - 'temporary' repair to habitats damaged by hedgerow removal
- bioremediation - repair to systems damaged in the exploitation of energy sources

Gravel pits - new habitats from extraction industries

The digging of pits for the extraction of sand and gravel has a highly visible effect on the landscape. Although extraction of minerals by the digging of pits has gone on for over 2 000 years, recent requirements for sand and gravel for roadbuilding and other construction have resulted in a proliferation of pits over the last forty years or so, particularly based on the deposits in the Thames and Trent valleys and the floodplains of the Ouse and its tributaries. Worked out extraction sites may give rise to wet gravel pits which cover a considerable area - it was estimated that in 1980 there were approximately 2 700 ha of wet pits just in the six counties of Berkshire, Greater London, Cambridgeshire, Leicestershire, Norfolk and Surrey, and that half of this area had been created in the previous twenty years.

The conservation of purely natural wetlands in Britain is not enough to protect threatened species because too much has been lost already. We must create new sites, and the management of gravel extraction sites presents an excellent opportunity for re-establishment of animal and plant populations. Gravel pit wetlands range from 1 - 100 ha in area, can be 3 - 30 m in depth and most are less than 50 years old. They are characteristically flat-bottomed, steep-sided and have fluctuating water levels and, as the gravel is usually extracted from one part of the area at any one time, they usually contain some relatively shallow water, numerous pools and sometimes islands and peninsulas. The perimeter : water area ratio is high, and as most of these pits are in fertile river valleys a range of aquatic and marginal plants will naturally recolonise, albeit slowly. The process can be accelerated by adding organic matter and by planting.

Techniques of gravel pit management : the most successful gravel pits for wildlife will have been managed with the following factors in mind:

SECURITY : the species which are to benefit from the reserve will only do so if they can be protected from natural predators, such as stoats and foxes human visitors, who might unwittingly disturb them

To offer this security both ISLANDS and MOATS are of importance. Islands will be considered in the section on breeding sites, but moats and the banks produced from the ensuing spoil are described in the diagram below.

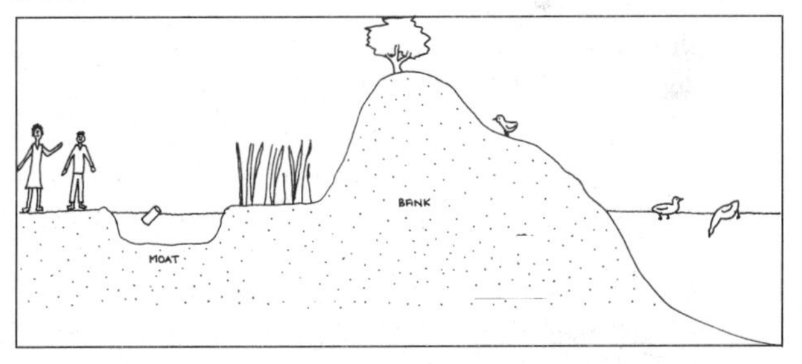

In a very large pit, of at least 100 ha, sailing and other leisure activities must be limited to well-defined areas. Even then the total wildlife population will be lower than without these activities. Birdwatchers must only be allowed in certain areas where there are good views over open water or at roosting/feeding sites, and the watchers must be screened from the birds by vegetation, embankments or hides.

RESTING AND MOULTING SITES : wildfowl require a large sheltered area free from emergent aquatic plants where the birds can remain far from shore in calm conditions. These areas are best provided by forming long islands or peninsulas in the lake with their long axis at 90 degrees to the prevailing wind. They can be planted with tall shelter trees and, if the island can slope upwards towards the downwind side, the islands will deflect the wind upwards to be filtered by the trees giving a larger area of sheltered water downwind. The water needs to be sheltered otherwise in windy weather birds would waste a lot of energy just "keeping station" i.e. avoiding being blown to the downwind shore.

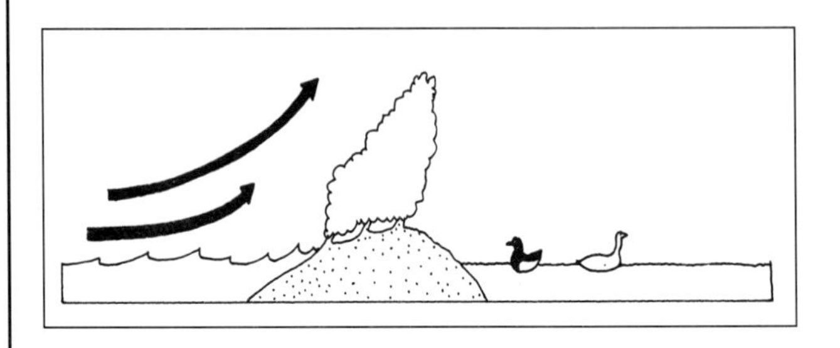

In an ideal situation these islands should have bare rocky or shingle beaches on the downwind side for "loafing" birds, and should be staggered across the lake so that the shelter from one island overlaps that of the next one downwind:

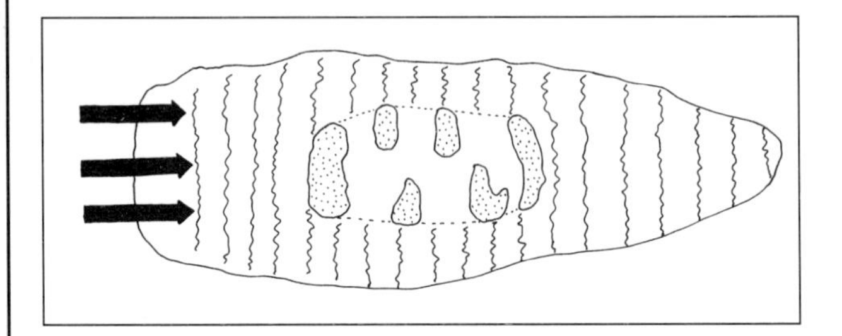

As well as open water roosts, shore-based loafing areas are required as these are used during rough weather and during the midsummer period when the birds are flightless. They can be produced by allowing cattle or sheep to graze certain areas of the shore, or by covering an appropriate area with 500 gauge black polythene sheet which is then covered with 20 - 30 cm of fine gravel. The sheeting and gravel can be retained with rough concrete, and suppress plant growth allowing the birds a good all-round view. Ideal spots are South facing (for maximum sunshine), sheltered, narrow peninsulas where open water is never very far away.

BREEDING HABITAT : gravel pits can provide excellent nesting sites for ground nesting species such as waterfowl and terns. Nesting sites can be protected by tall vegetation - densely growing nettles, willow herb, brambles and rushes provide good cover. Islands provide the safest nesting sites as the principal ground predators (foxes, stoats and badgers) will rarely risk swimming. Gravel pits which have been worked dry can provide overburden to make small islands in the future lake. If the island planning is completed in advance of overburden stripping the restoration costs can be reduced as the amount of earth-moving required is very much reduced.

The ideal shape for an island is as a semi-circular atoll, or horse-shoe shape, with the mouth of the horse-shoe facing away from the prevailing wind:

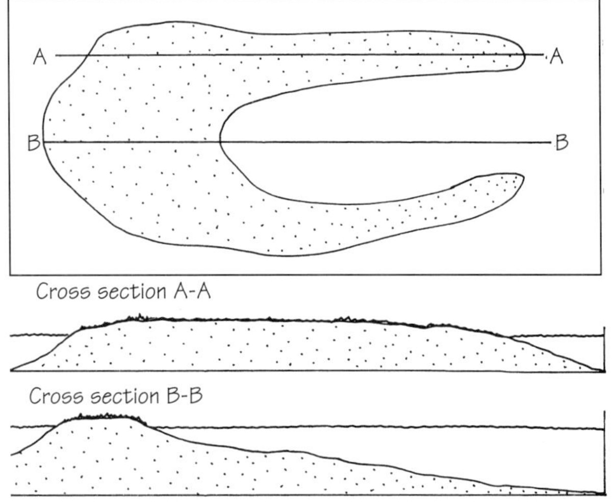

The shoreline should be irregular and the atoll should enclose an area of shallow water. The highest side of the island should be upwind to increase the shelter effect of the inner lagoon. This shape also provides a long, productive water's edge in relation to the area of the island and it encloses a shallow, sheltered, productive lagoon out in the security of a deeper lake.

Islands can be constructed so that a ring of encircling vegetation offers protection but does not encroach on nesting sites by incorporating a buried sheet of polythene.

FEEDING AREAS : these fall into a number of categories:

- deep water for fishing species, such as Great Crested Grebe, and for diving ducks such as Goldeneye.
- shallow shelving areas for dabbling ducks such as Mallard, and 'stalkers' such as Heron
- scrubland for insectivorous species such as Willow Warblers
- grassland for grazers such as geese

Management techniques might include:

- control of water levels by sluices and gates
- planting of emergent plant species along edges
- purchase of adjacent fields, or payment of compensation to farmers of adjacent land

An excellent example of the management of a gravel pit for wildlife is the RSPB reserve at Dungeness in Kent. This area is an SSSI, supporting a rich and varied flora (including a particularly rich lichen flora) and a wide variety of breeding and visiting seabirds and waterfowl.

Important species include

- Common, sandwich and roseate terns. Mediterranean gull.
- Wintering mallard, teal, shoveler, tufted duck, pochard, goldeneye and smew.
- Grass snake, viviparous lizard, marsh frog, toad and smooth newt.
- Harvest mice, pygmy and common shrew.
- Marsh cinquefoil, Nottingham catchfly, yellow vetch, bulbous meadow grass and sheep's bit.

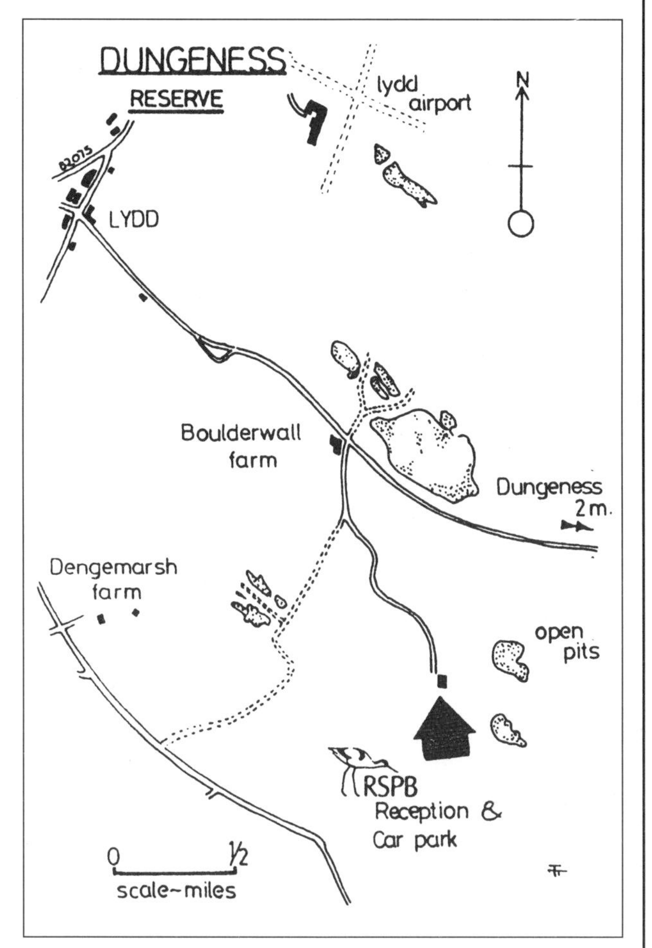

THE R.S.P.B. RESERVE AT DUNGENESS

is an excellent example of the management of an industrial wasteland for the benefit of wildlife.

From 1907 to 1938 the R.S.P.B. employed local men as 'watchers' to protect the Dungeness seabird colony from both human interference and natural predation. In 1931 some of the land was purchased with the help of a local benefactor - Mr. R.P.Burrowes of Lydd - making Dungeness the oldest of the R.S.P.B's reserves.

The Burrowes Pit is a co-operative venture between the R.S.P.B. and ARC Limited, the commercial extractors working on the site. In return for permission to extract gravel the management team have been able to lay down certain conditions, including depth of extraction, building of gravel islands and the recycling of 'uneconomic' sediment. As a result new nesting opportunities protected from ground predators have been established, rapid plant colonisation of pit margins has been achieved and the improvement of the reserve as a winter feeding site has been accomplished.

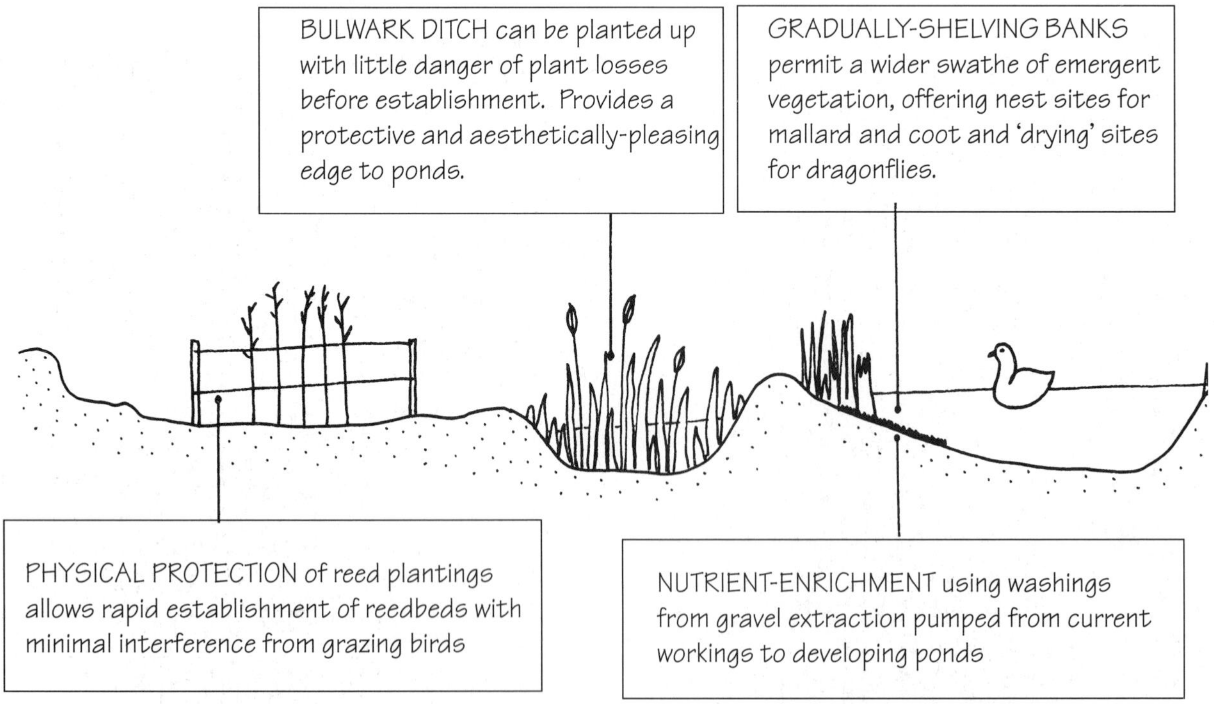

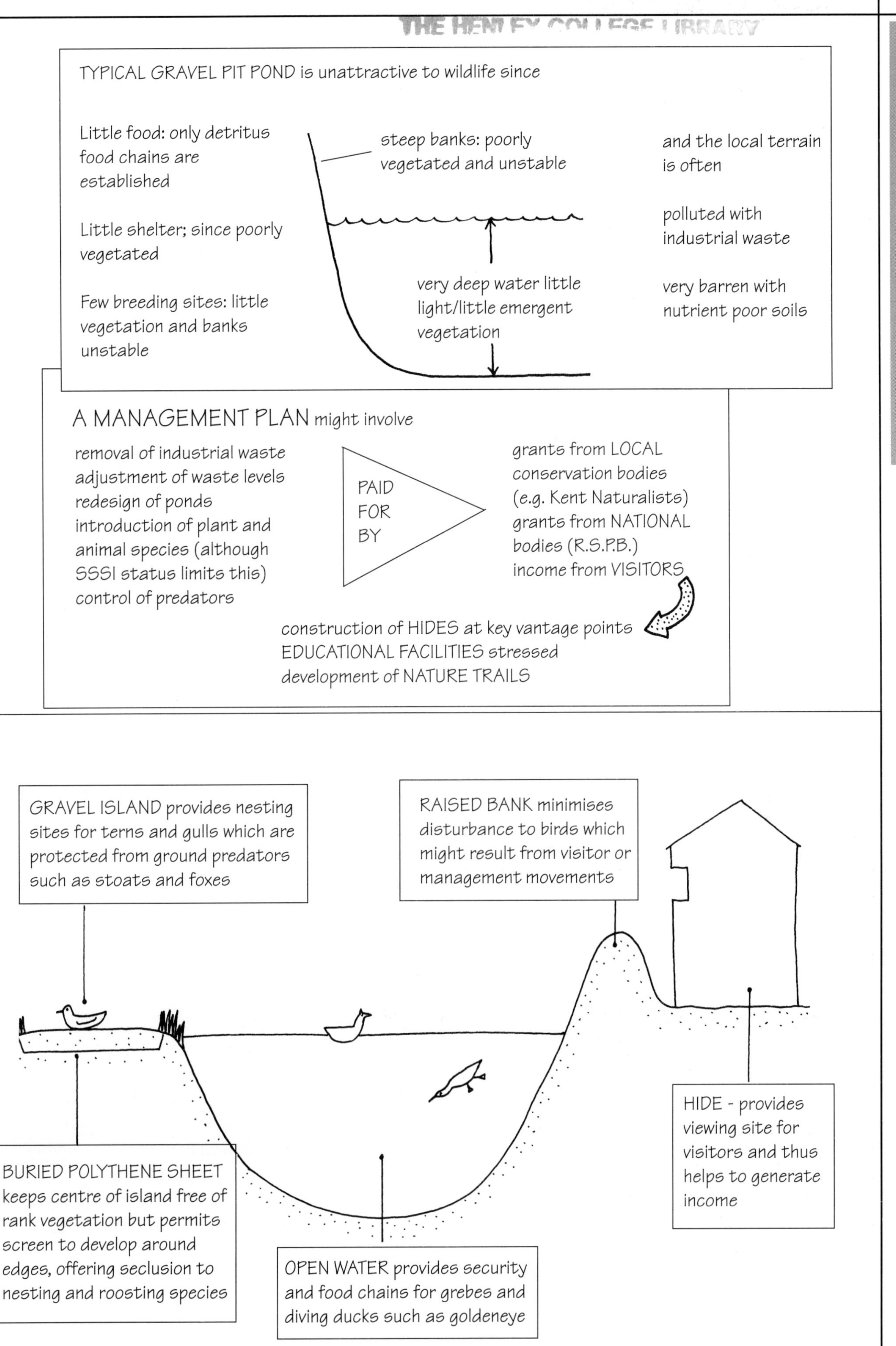
TYPICAL GRAVEL PIT POND is unattractive to wildlife since
Little food: only detritus food chains are established
Little shelter; since poorly vegetated
Few breeding sites: little vegetation and banks unstable
steep banks: poorly vegetated and unstable
very deep water little light/little emergent vegetation
and the local terrain is often
polluted with industrial waste
very barren with nutrient poor soils
A MANAGEMENT PLAN might involve
removal of industrial waste
adjustment of waste levels
redesign of ponds
introduction of plant and animal species (although SSSI status limits this)
control of predators
PAID FOR BY
grants from LOCAL conservation bodies (e.g. Kent Naturalists)
grants from NATIONAL bodies (R.S.P.B.)
income from VISITORS
construction of HIDES at key vantage points
EDUCATIONAL FACILITIES stressed
development of NATURE TRAILS
GRAVEL ISLAND provides nesting sites for terns and gulls which are protected from ground predators such as stoats and foxes
RAISED BANK minimises disturbance to birds which might result from visitor or management movements
HIDE - provides viewing site for visitors and thus helps to generate income
BURIED POLYTHENE SHEET keeps centre of island free of rank vegetation but permits screen to develop around edges, offering seclusion to nesting and roosting species
OPEN WATER provides security and food chains for grebes and diving ducks such as goldeneye

ARC excavating gravel pits for roadbuilding materials

RSPB directs excavations so that new pits will benefit wildlife

Following excavation and removal of machinery the pits appear more natural

Edges are enriched with silt to provide planting medium for introduced vegetation

THE R.S.P.B. RESERVE AT DUNGENESS

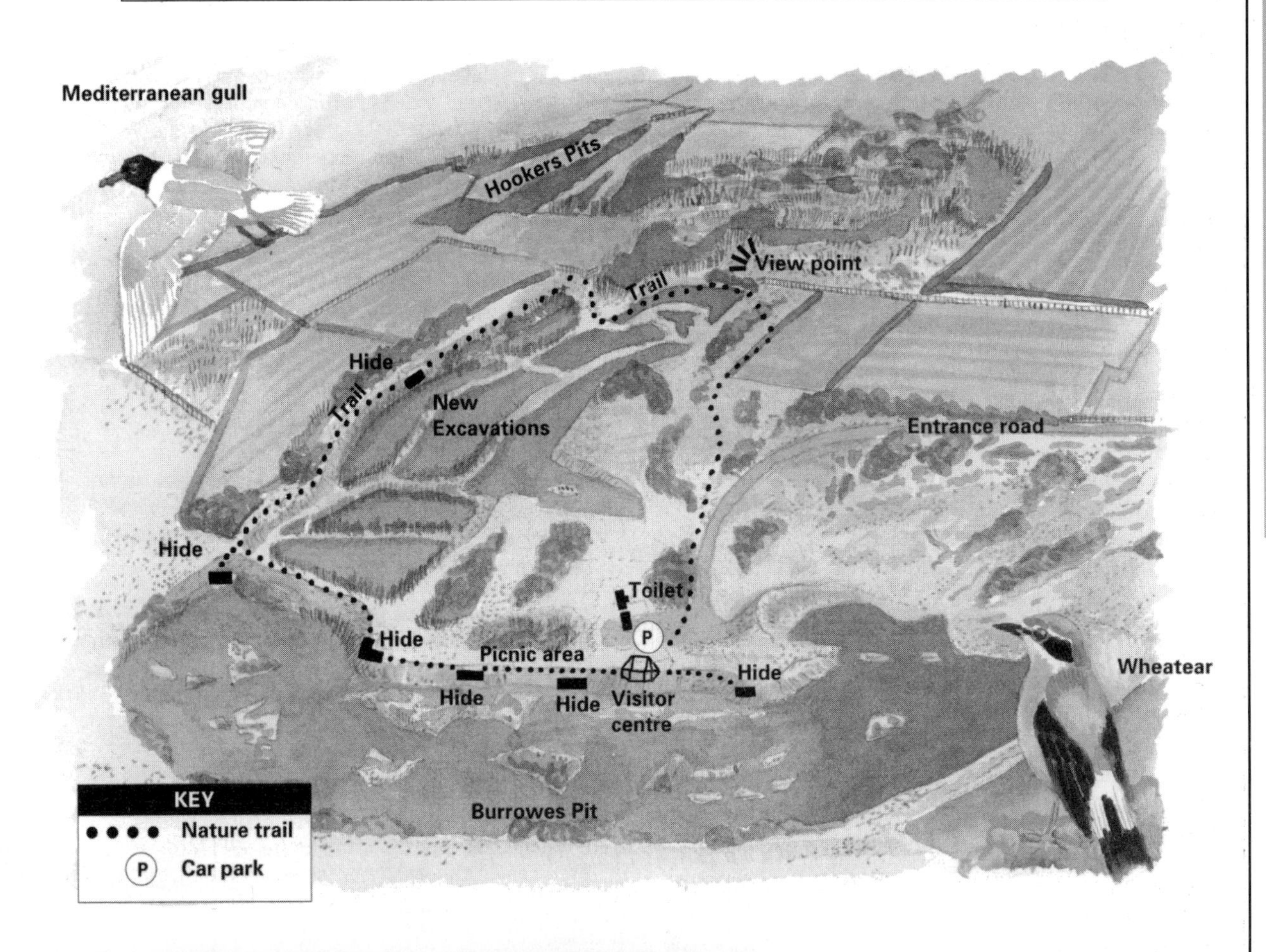

Volunteer labour is enlisted to prepare beds for planting: barriers prevent grazers removing young plants

The new reed beds are quickly established: 'hookers' (more mature plants) are able to survive without barriers.

Bioremediation: repair of ecosystems damaged by pollution

Localised pollution of the natural environment has traditionally been a sign of industrial and economic success. We now consider that excessive pollution is a signal that an industry is in decline, or has not been properly developed. One well-known example of a poorly managed commercial process which can lead to devastating damage to the environment is the loss of oil from tankers or storage units, by accident or by design. Most oil pollution is the result of the illegal washing at sea of oil tankers, although the running aground of such tankers is more 'spectacular'. Oil pollution has a number of effects

- it coats the feathers of seabirds, causing them to lose their waterproofing and insulatory properties - this prevents the birds flying and may cause death through hypothermia
- it covers seaweeds in the littoral zone, preventing photosynthesis
- it blocks the siphons of shellfish, preventing feeding and gas exchange
- it is unsightly and unpleasant to the touch, reducing the attraction to tourists who might be important to the local economy

Daily Mail, Saturday, February 17, 1996

BATTLE TO PREVENT ENVIRONMENTAL CATASTROPHE

Crippled on a

Fate of wildlife 'in hands of the gods' as stricken tanker spews oil

By PAUL HARRIS and JASON BURT

A WILDLIFE catastrophe was feared last night as an oil slick threatened birds and animals along one of Britain's most beautiful coastlines.

More than 4,000 tons of crude oil — a million gallons — spewed into the sea when a supertanker ploughed on to rocks off west Wales.

It formed an eight-mile slick which started to come ashore in stinking black patches yesterday despite a desperate race to keep it at bay.

At risk are some of the most important bird breeding sites in Europe, as well as the seals and porpoises which flourish in the area.

The unique concentration of animals — including some rare species — makes it potentially a worse disaster than bigger spills in the past.

'It couldn't have happened in a worse place,' said the Royal Society for the Protection of Birds. It could not have happened at a worse time, either, with the breeding season about to get into full swing.

Bird hospital worker Nancy Bryant said: 'The first waves of some 300,000 birds are arriving on cliffs around the coast. It could be devastating.'

Near Milford Haven are the world's second largest gannet colony and important concentrations of guillemot, fulmar, shag, cormorant and gulls.

Atlantic grey seals, harbour porpoises and bottle-nosed dolphins could also suffer.

As accident investigators tried to piece together how the Russian-crewed Sea Empress went aground, emergency teams fought to minimise the effects of the spill and stop more oil leaking out.

The stricken tanker, now afloat again, was being held in position just offshore by four tugs, while salvage experts and divers assessed the damage.

If weather conditions allow, a smaller tanker will be brought alongside to take off some of the Sea Empress's remaining 126,000 tons of oil — from the tanks most likely to leak again — before she is towed into Milford Haven for repairs.

The Department of Transport marine pollution control unit sent seven aircraft fitted with dispersant sprays over the main slick while protective booms were placed in front of vulnerable marshlands.

Co-ordinator Kevin Colcomb said about 200 tons of oil had already come ashore on beaches. Council workmen, contractors and Texaco staff were fighting to clear it.

Louise Tickle of the RSPB said volunteers would be standing by throughout the weekend to help clean oiled-up birds and animals.

The success of the battle against the oil depends on time, wind and tides. The future of the wildlife, said one expert, 'is in the hands of the gods'.

In Brussels, the European Commission announced that it had sent a task force of international experts to help.

It also promised as much as £250,000 in financial support for the area, with more cash for environmental organisations if necessary.

Disaster struck in a few seconds on Thursday evening as the tanker neared the huge Texaco refinery in Milford Haven after a routine two-day trip from the Firth of Forth.

Captain Eduard Bolgov was on the bridge, but had let the local harbour pilot take over control. Sea conditions were moderate, with 20mph winds, yet somehow, the Sea Empress ran on to rocks.

Transport Secretary Sir George Young, who flew over the stricken tanker yesterday, said: 'Clearly, there was either a loss of power or loss of steering.'

But Captain Bolgov rejected any suggestions of mechanical failure. He told his bosses: 'There was a great shuddering as the ship went through the entrance to the outer harbour. There was no problem with the steering gear or with the propeller system.'

It was the second time in five months that a tanker has run aground in the area, although on the last occasion the double hull of the Norwegian vessel Borga prevented any spillage.

Mick Green of the Cardigan Bay Conservation Society said: 'There seems to be a problem where they swing around to get into the harbour. Perhaps they should turn further out.'

The merchant navy officers' union NUMAST claimed that the accident was 'a disaster waiting to happen' because the Government was allowing far too many ships to sail in British waters under a flag of convenience.

The Government said a full inquiry was under way.

Salvage operation: The stricken Sea Empress yesterday Picture: HUW EVANS

The single hull that lacks a leak-stopper

CRITICISM will focus on the fact that the Sea Empress is single-hulled and, it is claimed, therefore more vulnerable to being pierced.

Such tankers do not have a second protective inner skin to stop leakage if the first is damaged.

The debate over single hulls has raged for years and intensified last October when another supertanker, the 122,655-ton Norwegian vessel Borga, ran aground in exactly the same spot. It suffered a steering failure but did not spill any oil — because there was a double hull.

The International Maritime Organisation said design amendments were adopted in 1992 and came into force in July 1993 for existing ships and July 1995 for new ships.

All new vessels now have to be double-hulled or 'an acceptable alternative', such as having greater division of the cargo space. But existing ships can operate for up to 30 years as single-hulled.

The Sea Empress, completed in February 1993, qualifies as an existing ship.

Captain Peter Cooney, managing director of Acomarit (UK), which manages the Sea Empress, said: 'A double-hulled ship did hit rocks not very far away from this ship, but conclusions shouldn't be drawn from this. Single-hulled ships are perfectly safe.'

One vessel, seven flags

THE complex history of the Sea Empress is typical of the shipping industry.

At least seven different nations are involved with the 147,000-ton vessel, which is 277 yards long and 43 wide — the equivalent to almost three football pitches.

Built in Spain, the single-hulled tanker operates under a Liberian flag and is owned by the Alegrete Shipping Company, part of the Cypriot Seateam group.

The 28 Russian crew are employed by Glasgow-based Acomarit (UK) Ltd which manages the vessel.

Its local agent is UK-based Inchcape and it was chartered by French firm Dreyfus Energy on behalf of the U.S. giant Texaco. The tanker gained its 'classification' in Norway with the DNV organisation.

Disasters that still leave their mark

THE Sea Empress disaster has not yet reached the scale of other major tanker catastrophes of recent years.

The last such accident in Britain occurred in January 1993 when the Liberian-registered Braer, carrying 619,300 barrels of oil, ran aground on the rocks in Quendale Bay, Shetland.

Some 80,000 tons of light crude oil was spilled into the sea, causing severe damage to property, livestock and health.

Oil was spread over the islands during several days of gales and the surrounding water was declared unfishable for months.

Outstanding claims by Shetlanders still exceed £50million.

In the worst oil spill in the U.S., the supertanker Exxon Valdez crashed into Bligh Reef in Alaska in 1989, discharging 11million gallons — 40,000 tons — of crude oil, coating 1,800 miles of coastline.

The Exxon Corporation was ordered to pay £3.2billion in punitive damages to fishermen and other groups.

Marine salvage companies recovered 1.25million tons of oil from 14 stricken tankers in 1994.

Daily Mail, Saturday, February 17, 1996 ** Page 7

AFTER SHIP RUNS AGROUND WASHING DEADLY SLICK ON TO BEACHES

tide of destruction

CORMORANT

Number in area: 350. **Food:** Small fish. **Description:** Long-necked, black, up to 3ft long. **Vulnerability:** Very high — they dive for fish; nest on low rocks. **Danger:** Oil can be ingested as they eat, and clog feathers.

GUILLEMOT

Number in area: 2,000. **Food:** Small fish, eg sand eels. **Description:** Type of auk. Looks like small penguin. **Vulnerabilty:** Very high — most of time spent on water. **Danger:** Oil on feathers can reduce buoyancy and insulation.

GREY SEAL

Number in area: 10-20. **Food:** Small fish. **Description:** Grey, smooth-skinned, 7ft long. **Vulnerability:** Medium — appear able to detect oil spills. **Danger:** Oil can stick to skin and be ingested when they preen.

GANNET

Number in area: Up to 10,000. **Food:** Fish. **Description:** Large, white, with yellow head. Up to 4ft long. **Vulnerability:** Fairly low — they fly most of the time. **Danger:** Can't fly if oil clogs their feathers.

SHAG

Number in area: 150. **Food:** Small fish. **Description:** Black with greenish sheen, distinctive crest. 30ins long. **Vulnerability:** High. **Danger:** Oil can be ingested with fish, also can stick to feathers.

Graphic: Philip Argent/ Adrian Black

Where city suits spell trouble

HIGH on a clifftop above the blackening sea, daylight picked out a man in a raincoat and city brogues shouting earnestly down a mobile telephone.

Behind him a giant oil tanker listed hopelessly in the water. Helicopters filled the air with noise and a few miles away the first black patches were beginning to appear on secluded sandy beaches around the coast. Locals in Milford Haven know that when the men in suits arrive, it usually means trouble. This time the man was from the shipping company and it was big trouble.

Since the Sea Empress hit the rocks a few hours earlier, its thoroughly modern commodity had became a potential destroyer of a coastline which took millions of years to evolve.

Before most of the suits had even been woken from their beds in London, a small navy of specialist emergency craft was trying to contain the spillage with all the technology and experience gained from a succession of such catastrophes. Even that was not enough.

By the time the man in brogues called his office, they were talking about a million gallons of spewed-out oil and a slick measuring eight miles long.

It was a race against time, and they were already losing.

Detergents can be used to break down spillages but environmentalists say that the chemicals can often cause more devastation than the oil. The priority yesterday therefore was confinement, then trying to keep the oil away from the beaches.

At West Angle beach, three miles from the site of the stricken tanker, stinking sludge came ashore with the tide, covering large areas of golden sand with a two-inch-thick coating of dark brown.

From 200 yards away the fumes made you choke. Up close it stuck to your shoes and found your clothes no matter what you did to prevent it. The rubber boots of the Dyfed council workmen were thick with it after only a few minutes' labour as they tried, Canute-like, to sweep and scrape back the filthy tide with shovels and wooden implements.

They knew there was never any hope of clearing it all and it showed in the weariness of their voices. 'It's a hell of a job,' said one. 'But we can't just stand here and do nothing.'

The oil *can be* dispersed from beaches or from the surface of water by detergents but these chemicals themselves may be directly toxic or may upset ecosystems by eutrophication. The removal of oil occurs naturally, as bacteria *decompose* the organic hydrocarbon compounds in the oil as part of their normal metabolic processes. This breakdown is, however, rather slow since the concentration of nitrogen-containing compounds can be rate limiting to bacterial metabolism. One method of pollution repair by biological methods i.e. by BIOREMEDIATION is thus to optimise the breakdown capabilities of bacteria by supplementing their growth medium with nitrogen- and phosphorous-containing compounds.

Other examples of the optimisation of microorganisms for bioremediation purposes are:

- bioaugmentation - in this process organisms are collected from the polluted site, grown in culture and inoculated back into the site
- specialised organisms known to contain specific degradative enzymes or biochemical pathways may be cultured in the laboratory and then injected into the polluted site
- organisms may be genetically engineered to contain the desired degradative enzymes and cultured in the laboratory before injection into the polluted site.

One use of bioremediation techniques which is assuming greater economic importance is the cleaning of contaminated water supplies - contaminants may be removed by the culture of the appropriate microbes in enormous underground chambers, as illustrated below.

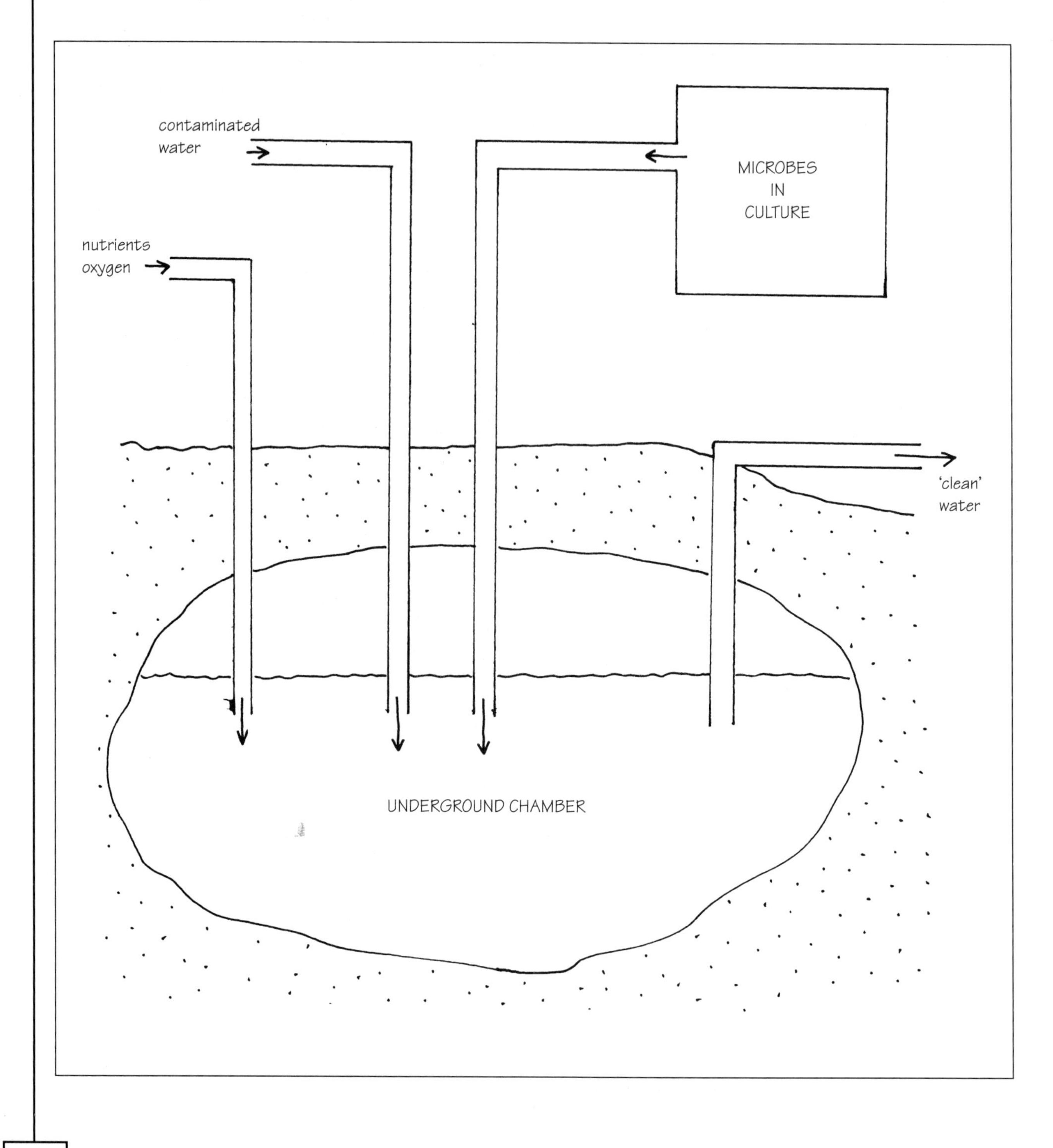

Conservation headlands: help for beetles and spiders

A strong argument for the maintenance of hedgerows is that the base layer of vegetation provides a habitat for predatory species which could help to control the populations of pest species in adjacent arable fields, a strong argument against the maintenance of hedgerows is that they consume space which might otherwise be occupied by crops. This latter argument is now largely redundant as a result of set-aside provisions, but the inconvenience of hedge boundaries for machinery movements remains significant on some farms. One possible solution which is of proven benefit to wildlife is a CONSERVATION HEADLAND, largely developed by Willmot-Pertwee.

Beneficial predatory species, such as spiders and carnivorous beetles, must search for their prey by walking on the ground or by climbing over vegetation. The purpose of a conservation headland is to offer access to fields and shelter from harsh winter conditions to these beneficial species.

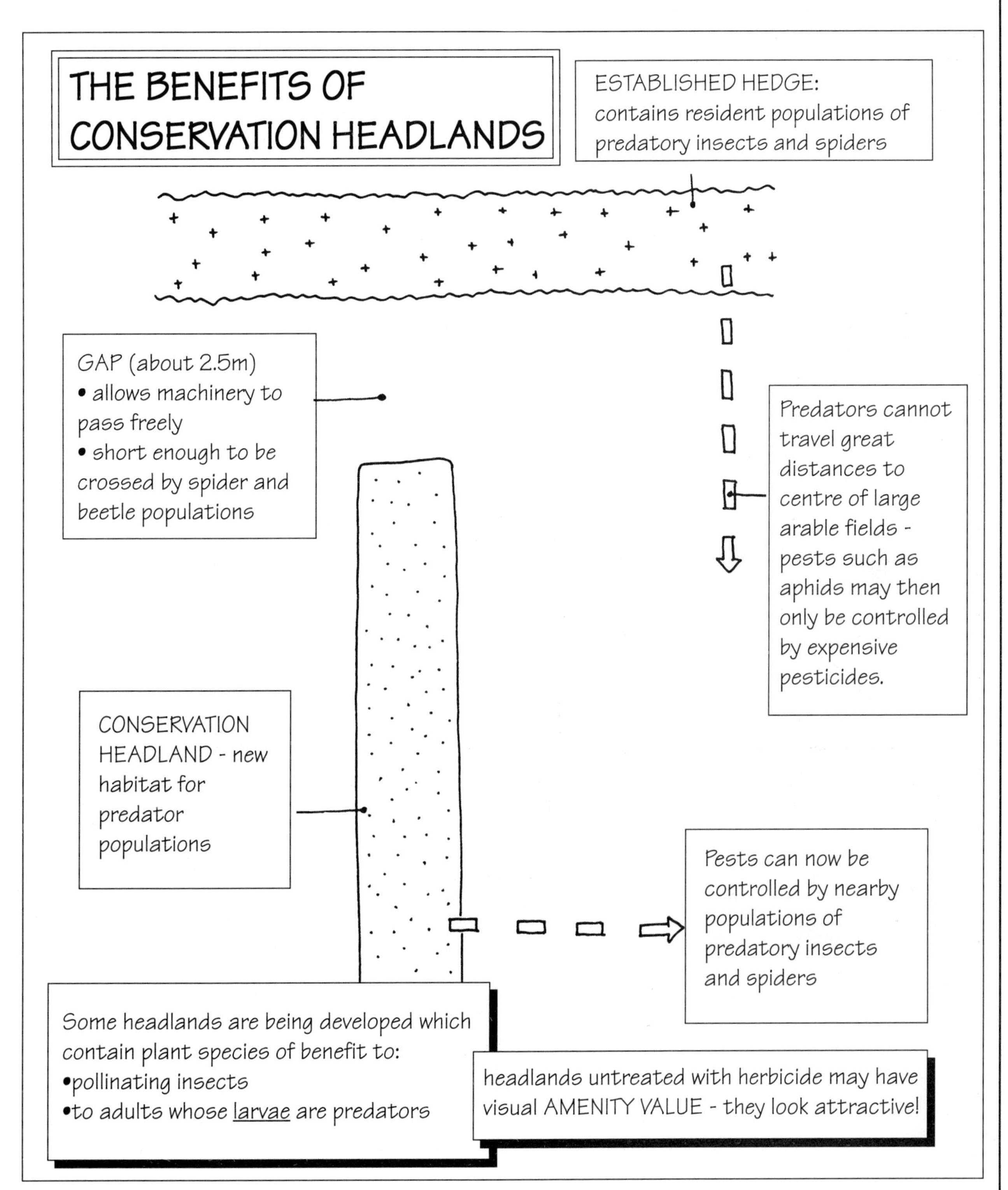

The establishment of such a headland offers the great benefit to the farmer that it is *easily reversible* - if a change of field use is necessary the farmer can easily plough in the headland.

Construction of a conservation headland

- during normal cultivation, careful two-directional ploughing can create a ridge or earth-bank about 0.4m high and about 2 m wide.

- a mixture of perennial grass seeds, containing tussock and mat-forming species such as cocksfoot and Yorkshire fog, is sown at a density of 3g per sq.m. The sowing can be immediately following the formation of the ridge or in the next Spring.

- treat the bank with a broad-spectrum, non-residual herbicide to remove any opportunist weeds which might infect crop areas or which might limit establishment of the grasses

- maintain a one metre sterile strip between the ridge and the crop - by rotavation or with a residual herbicide - to protect the ridge from grammicides applied to the crop

> "at 1995 prices it would cost less than £80 to establish a 400m headland on a 20 ha field and less than £30 per annum to maintain one - reduced pesticide usage would save up to five times this cost and offer great environmental benefit"

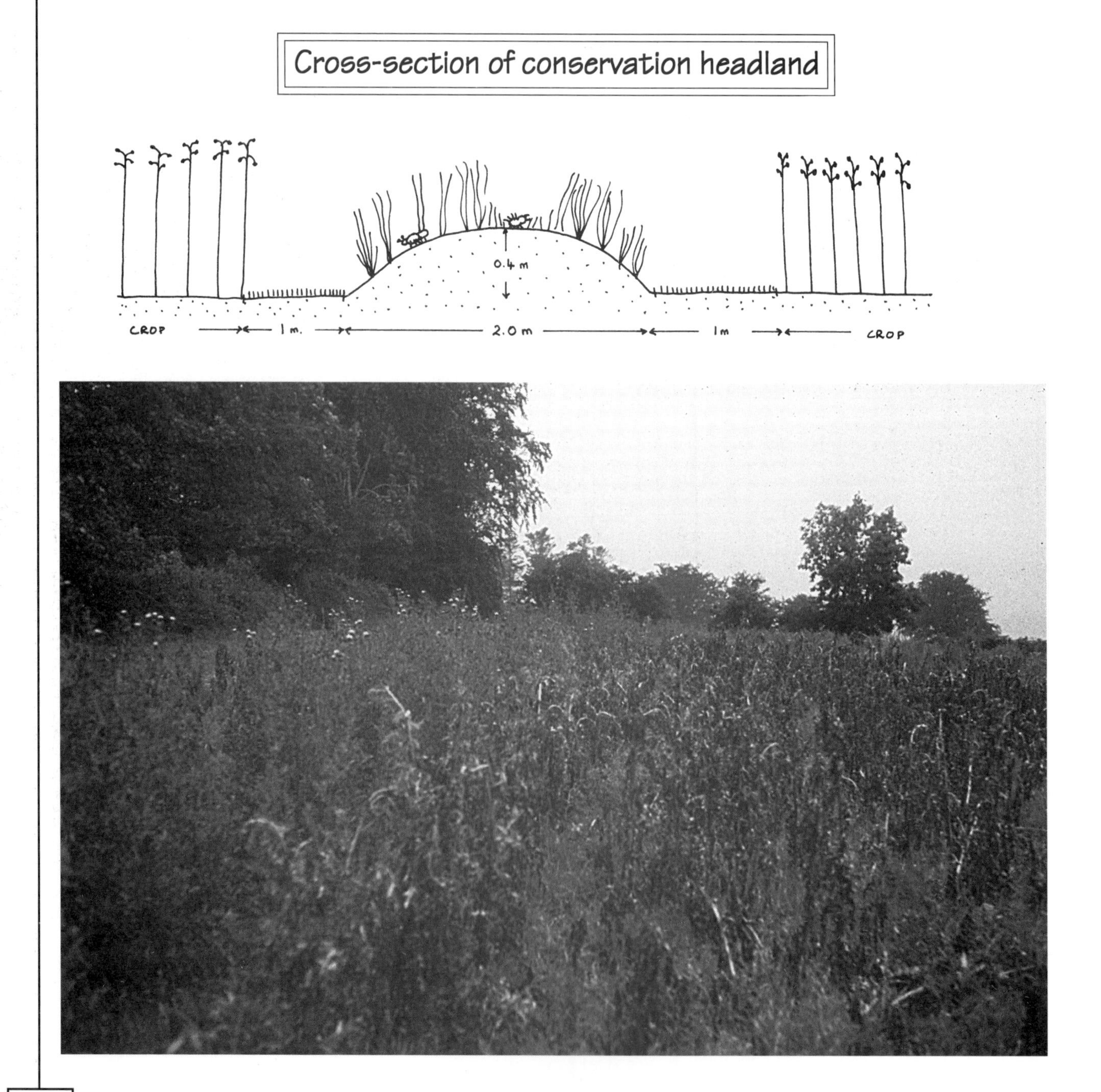

Cross-section of conservation headland

Almost any newspaper or scientific journal will contain an article or review of the effects of some pollutant. What is a pollutant? Broadly speaking we might define

a. a **pollutant** as any product of Man's activities which may be shown to have a harmful effect on the environment, and

b. **pollution** as the generation of any product which may have a harmful effect on the environment.

Pollutants can be classified into three types:

1. those which do occur naturally, but which are significantly increased in concentration as a result of Man's activities (carbon dioxide, for example)
2. those which do not occur naturally but which are produced as a result of Man's activities (phosphorus-containing detergents, for example)
3. those which are not themselves toxic but which go on to affect the environment in some harmful way (chlorofluorocarbon compounds, for example

Two major groups of pollutants are those which affect the **atmosphere** and those which affect **aquatic** ecosystems. As a student of conservation you might be concerned about atmospheric damage caused by **carbon dioxide** (and the **Greenhouse Effect)**, sulphur dioxide (and **acid rain**) or **CFC's** (and **disruption of the Ozone Layer**). You might also be interested in the effects on aquatic ecosystems of **metals** and of **nitrates** (the problem of **eutrophication**). This section contains information on all of these but note that the conservationist's requirement is twofold - not just a question of knowing/identifying the problem, but also making suggestions as to how the problem might be overcome.

Acid Rain: Precipitation of sulphur and nitrogen oxides in solution

The phenomenon of acid rain is not a recent one. The phrase was first used more than a hundred years ago by Britain's first air pollution inspector, Robert Angus Smith, who used it to describe the polluted rain in his home town of Manchester and its effects on trees and buildings.

Acid rain production

The problem is a regional rather than a global one, mainly affecting industrial regions such as Northern Europe, North-west USA and South-east Canada. These areas have been heavy consumers of fossil fuels and it is oxides of sulphur and nitrogen released into the atmosphere by fossil fuel combustion that are largely responsible for acid rain precipitation.

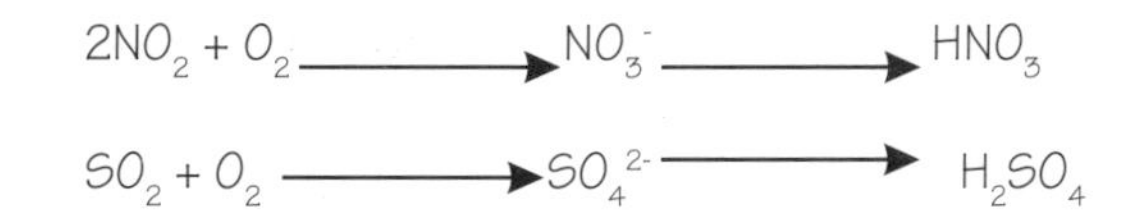

$$2NO_2 + O_2 \longrightarrow NO_3^- \longrightarrow HNO_3$$

$$SO_2 + O_2 \longrightarrow SO_4^{2-} \longrightarrow H_2SO_4$$

catalysed by minute airborne particles of iron and manganese, by unburnt hydrocarbons and by ammonia released from slurry tanks

Is there a solution?

There are prospects that both prevention and cure may eventually reduce emission of acid gases and restore some of the lakes and forests. **Preventative measures** attempt to reduce emissions from both industrial(with power station 'scrubbers', for example) and motor vehicle (catalytic converters) sources. The table on page 46 shows that since 1970 Britain has reduced its emissions of sulphur dioxide by almost 40%, although the UK remains the biggest source of this gas in Western Europe. In keeping with the European Community Directive on 'Large Combustion Plants' there has been considerable investment in cleaner plant and more modern equipment, but the UK is handicapped in comparison with other European countries since this country relies so much on coal burning for its electricity supply. Britain has been less successful in reducing nitrogen oxide (NOx) emissions - much of this is from car exhausts, and the increase in road traffic is hindering Britain's announced aim to reduce emissions by 30% by 1998. Britain is committed to do this through the UNECE (United Nations Economic Convention on Europe) Protocol on acid emissions, and since 1992 all new cars have had to have catalytic converters fitted. From November 1991 the MOT test has included measurement of the levels of acid emissions in exhaust gases.

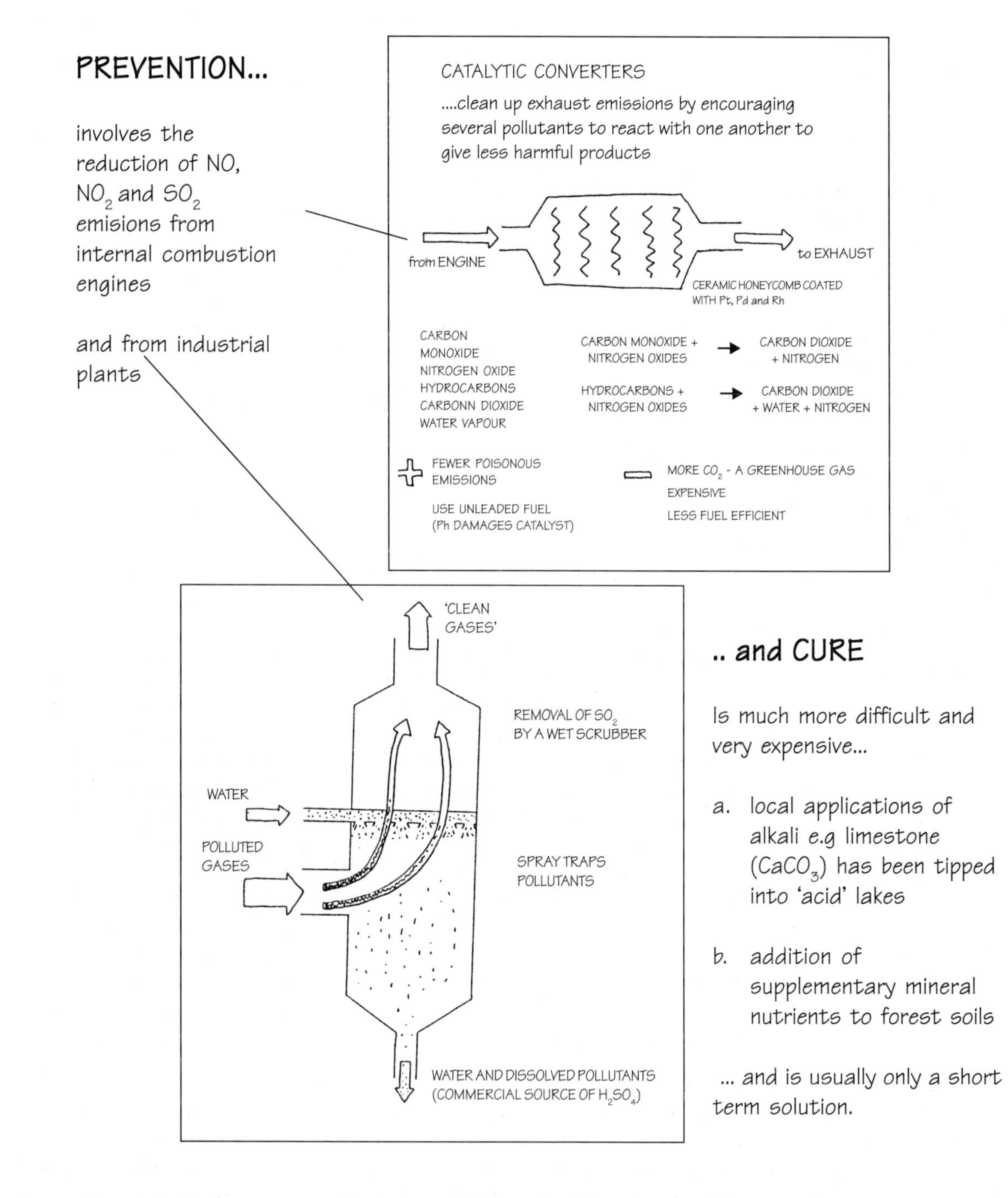

A **cure** for acid rain damage seems further away. The only short term possibility is to dump enormous quantities of limestone into lakes and rivers, and to add nutrients to forest soils. This would be enormously expensive - in Germany, for example, such a programme has been estimated to cost £15 000 million per annum.

Problems caused by acid rain

These arise in three areas - in the **soil**, in run-off **water** and in **trees**. Most **soils** in Europe are acidic, but the acids (largely carbonic and organic acids) are 'immobile' and do not readily transfer their acidity elsewhere. Acid rain, however, contains strong negative ions such as sulphate and nitrate which *do* mobilise hydrogen ions and transfer them efficiently to surface waters. Much of the nitrate is absorbed by plant roots, but the sulphate concentration can rise to the point at which it mobilises not only protons but also aluminium ions. The mixture of mobile protons and aluminium ions has had a profound effect on the ecology of **lakes and rivers** in areas subject to the deposition of acid rain. The most significant of these changes is the reduction in the rate of decomposition of organic matter - this limits the availability of ions for producers so that the productivity of the aquatic ecosystem is markedly reduced. Organisms higher up the food chain are also affected directly. Low pH allows the exoskeletons of crustaceans to soften and leaves them prone to fungal infections, and the high aluminium concentrations interferes with ion transfer in the gills of fish so that the gills become covered with a thick mucus which severely curtails the transfer of oxygen from water to blood.

Sulphur and nitrogen in fossil fuels are oxidised during combustion

$S + O_2 \rightarrow SO_2$

$N + O_2 \rightarrow NO_2$

Further oxidation occurs in the clouds

$SO_2 + O_2 \rightarrow SO_4^{2-}$

$NO_2 + \frac{1}{2}O_2 \rightarrow NO_3^-$

These reactions are catalysed by ozone, ammonia and by unburnt hydrocarbons ... and are followed by solution in water

$SO_4^{2-} + 2H^+ \rightarrow H_2SO_4$

$NO_3^- + H^+ \rightarrow HNO_3$

to make up ACID RAIN

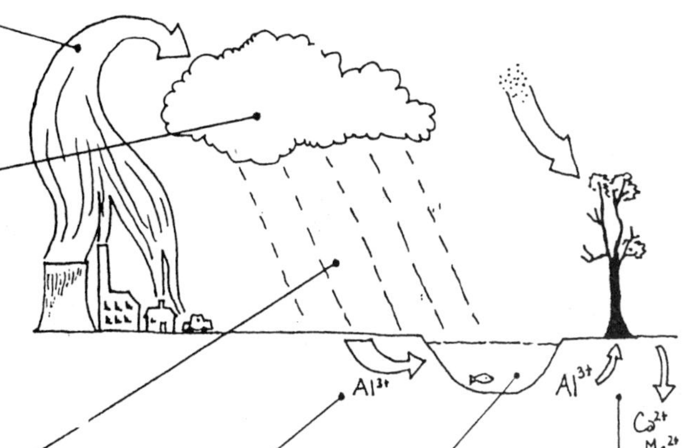

Al^{3+}

Al^{3+}

Ca^{2+} Mg^{2+}

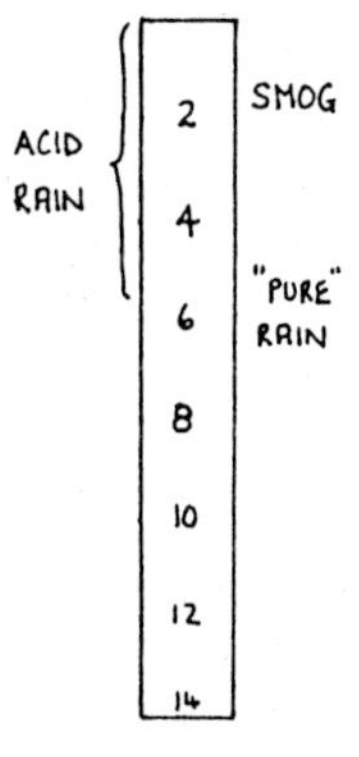

ACID RAIN

SMOG

"PURE" RAIN

2
4
6
8
10
12
14

pH SCALE is logarithmic: rain of pH 4 is 100 times more acidic than rain of pH6

PROBLEMS

SOILS: H^+ in soils are normally stable (bound to soil particles or to HCO_3^-) but the SO_4^{2-} ion in H_2SO_4 is very mobile and so transfers H^+ to the run-off waters. (NO_3^- would have the same effect but is rapidly absorbed by plant roots)

WATER IN LAKES AND RIVERS: SO_4^{2-} displaces Al^{3+} from soil. The aluminium ions washed into the water interfere with gill function in fish - 'sticky' mucus accumulates, limits oxygen uptake $\rightarrow$ DEATH OF FISH

Change in pH also causes soft exoskeletons $\rightarrow$ DEATH IN INVERTEBRATES

FOREST: the leaching effect of the acid rain removes Ca^{2+} and Mg^{2+} from the soil ($\rightarrow$ poor middle lamella and chlorophyll formation) Uptake of Al^{3+} occurs to toxic levels. Atmospheric SO_2 and NO_2 damage spongy and pallisade mesophyll $\rightarrow$ TREE STARVATION All made worse by ozone, ammonia and frost- trees are stressed and sensitive to fungal infections.

Aluminium may also contribute to the damage to trees in acid rain areas. The most obvious sign of this damage is defoliation, beginning with the crown of the tree - this may affect as much as 25% of the European tree population. Aluminium in the soil may be directly toxic to trees, and the associated acid run-off may leach essential nutrients (such as calcium and magnesium) from the soil so that the trees literally 'starve'. The atmospheric pollutants associated with acid rain are also harmful - sulphur dioxide damages spongy mesophyll and inhibits photosynthesis, ozone may cause developmental changes such as accelerated shoot growth and retarded root growth and high levels of nitrogen compounds may 'stress' plants by promoting rapid growth when other nutrients are in limited supply.

In general, the pH of rain is lowest nearest to its source and increases with distance from the source. However the normal wind pattern in Europe, from SW to NE, means that acid emissions from Britain may well be deposited over Northern Germany and Scandinavia.

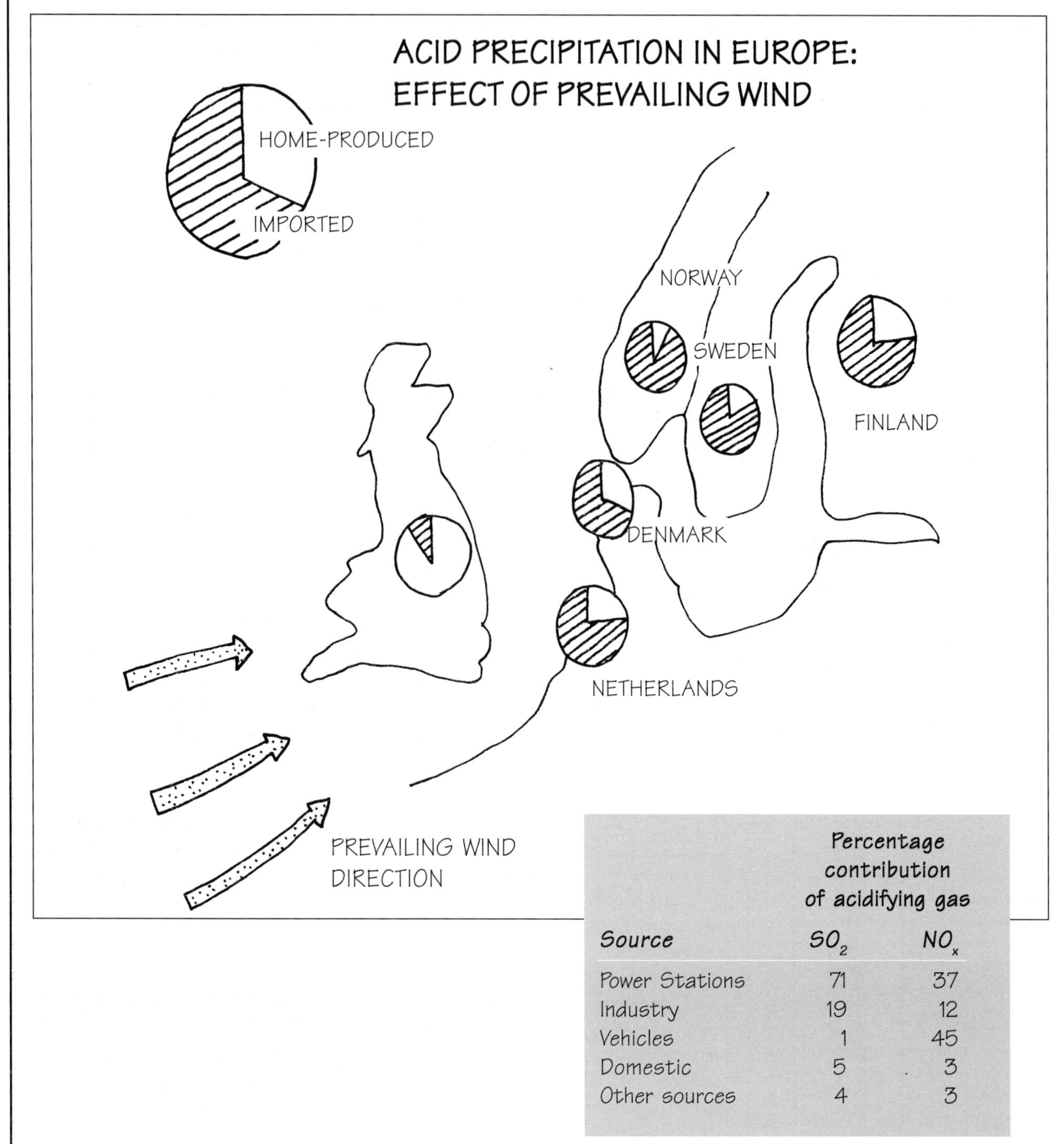

Source	Percentage contribution of acidifying gas SO_2	NO_x
Power Stations	71	37
Industry	19	12
Vehicles	1	45
Domestic	5	3
Other sources	4	3

Annual emissions of SO_2 and NO_x

(expressed as millions of tonnes of S and N per year)

Region	1900	1950	1960	1970	1980	1984	1987
United Kingdom							
SO_2	1.4	2.3	2.8	3.0	3.0	2.3	1.8 1.9
NOx	0.21	0.30	0.41	0.50	-.54	0.63	0.74
Europe (excluding USSR)							
SO_2	-	10.0	-	18.4	20.0	-	-

The Greenhouse Effect : Carbon Dioxide and Methane may cause global warming

The greenhouse effect is not a new phenomenon, nor is it necessarily harmful. It refers to the trapping of solar radiation close to the Earth's surface by some gaseous components of the Earth's atmosphere. These gaseous components act like the glass in a greenhouse and keep the temperature on the earth at an average of 15°C (ideal for photosynthesis and for maintaining the water cycle) - in their absence the temperature would fall to -18°C and there would be no life on Earth.

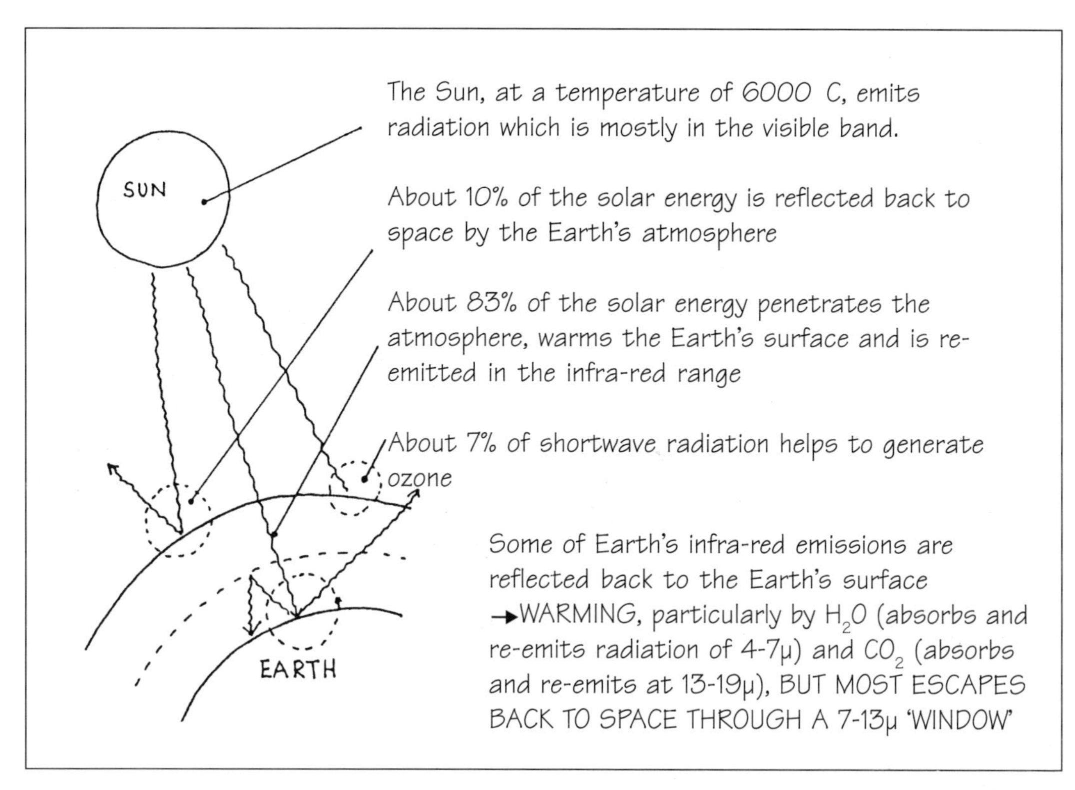

Sources of greenhouse gases : The burning of fossil fuels (wood, coal, oil) for power generation and as part of forest clearance probably contributes 50% of greenhouse gases. Carbon dioxide is the major greenhouse gas in terms of quantity, but synthetic compounds such as the CFCs (used as refrigerants, aerosol propellants and in the production of polystyrene) are far more effective as greenhouse gases

Gas	*Source*	*Proportion of total warming effect (%)*	*Effectiveness as greenhouse gas (relative to carbon dioxide)*
Carbon dioxide	Combustion of fossil fuels	50	1
Methane	Fermentation reactions	18	30
Water vapour	Combustion Evaporation	6	50
Nitrous oxide	Combustion of fossil fuels	8	150
Ozone	Effect of sunlight on air pollutants	12	2 000
CFCs	Aerosol propellants refrigerants polystyrene production	6	20 000

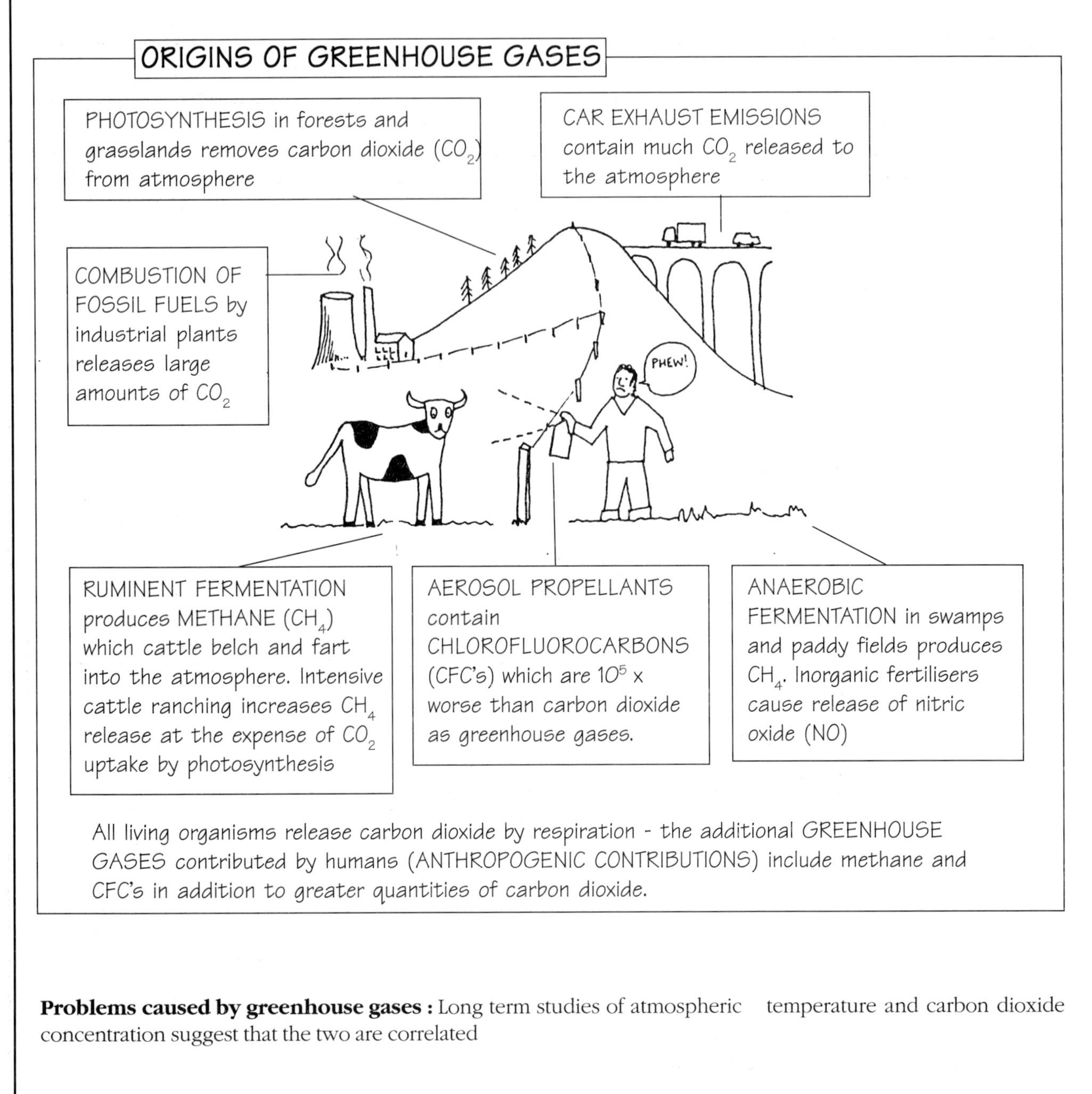

Problems caused by greenhouse gases : Long term studies of atmospheric temperature and carbon dioxide concentration suggest that the two are correlated

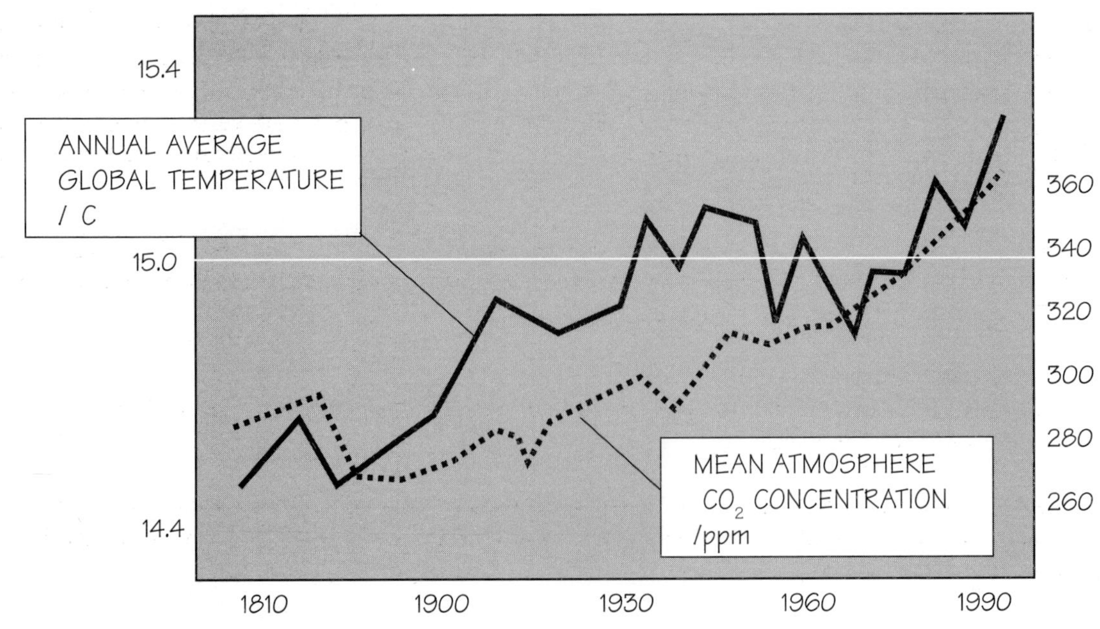

A major sink for carbon dioxide is the photosynthetic activity of phytoplankton. It is not clear whether the increase in temperature might promote growth of phytoplankton so that the carbon dioxide will be removed from the atmosphere, nor what the capacity of the oceans for heat absorption is. Some research workers have suggested that pollution of the sea by nitrates and phosphates may promote growth of phytoplankton and thus minimise the increasing CO_2 concentrations - clearly the emission of CO_2 and its effects on global warming are complex! Nonetheless there remains great concern about the possible effects of global warming - some computer studies have predicted that a doubling in atmospheric CO_2 concentration would cause a rise in temperature of 4.2°C. The effects of such a change in Britain are summarised below:

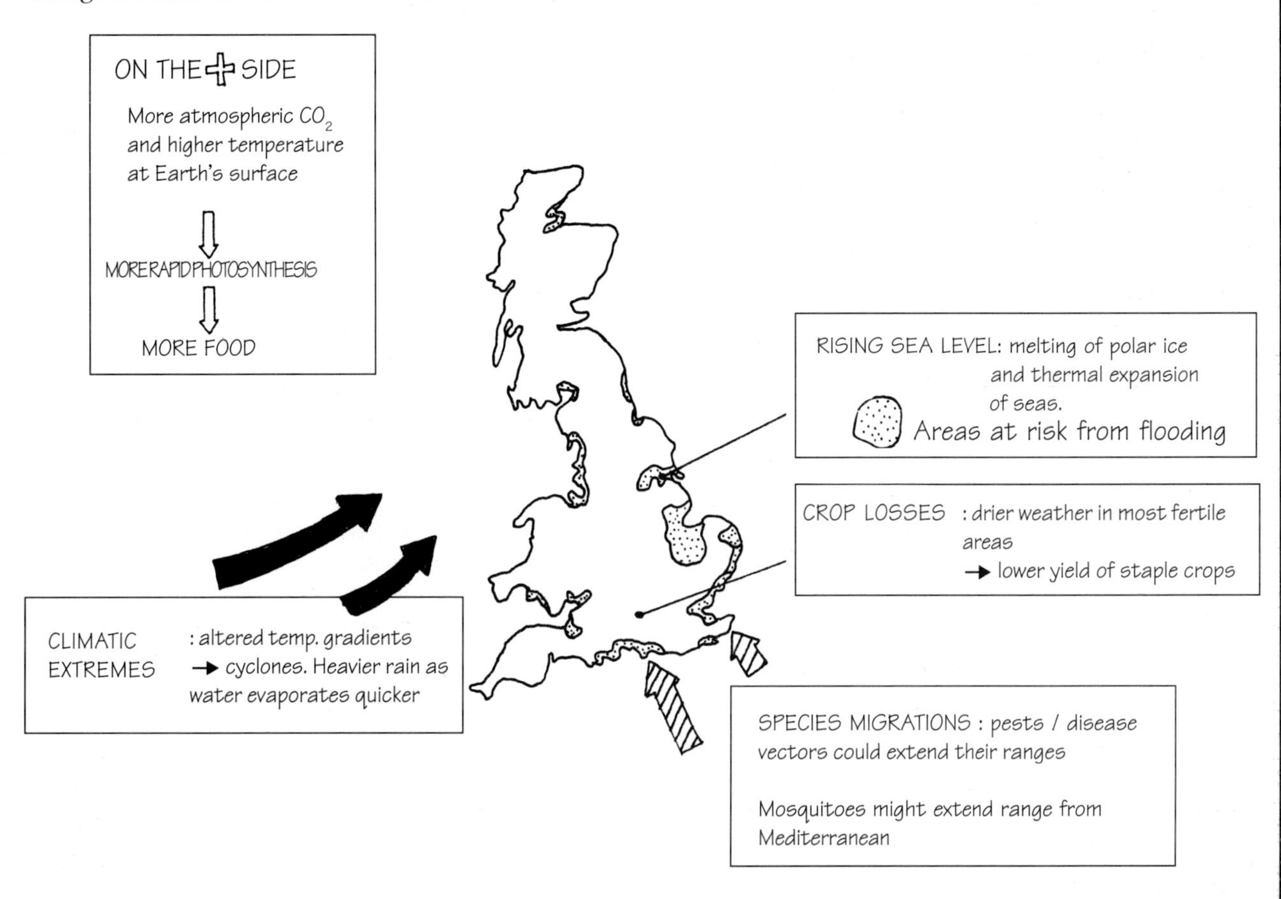

Solutions. The International Panel on Climate Change (IPCC) has concluded that global warming *is* taking place, and suggest two types of preventative policy:

1. **Reduction in emissions of greenhouse gases** : in Britain this seems likely to result from more efficient power generation (such as the new 'clean' power station at Drax in South Yorkshire) and simple conservation of energy measures such as loft insulation and double glazing. We might also examine alternative energy sources such as wind, wave, solar and hydroelectric power. Britain must also play a part in development of the Third World since an increase in fossil fuel usage there might offset any reductions in Britain and other European countries.

2. **Reafforestation** : at present the World is losing 24.5 million hectares of forest (1% of the total) per year - this generates carbon dioxide as brash is burned and reduces the carbon dioxide absorbing abilities of the terrestrial ecosystem. To significantly reduce atmospheric carbon dioxide concentrations we would need

   a. to plant much more timber
   b. to limit the use of timber as a fuel, instead using it as building material or as an alternative to oil as a source of chemicals

It has been estimated that the cost of controlling CO_2 emissions, that is preventing them rising further, would be in the order of $300 billion for EC countries but the alternatives to doing so - coastal flooding, agricultural changes, desertification, population movements and associated political instability may make this expenditure essential.

OZONE IN THE ATMOSPHERE IS ESSENTIAL FOR LIFE

(but too much in the wrong place can be harmful!)

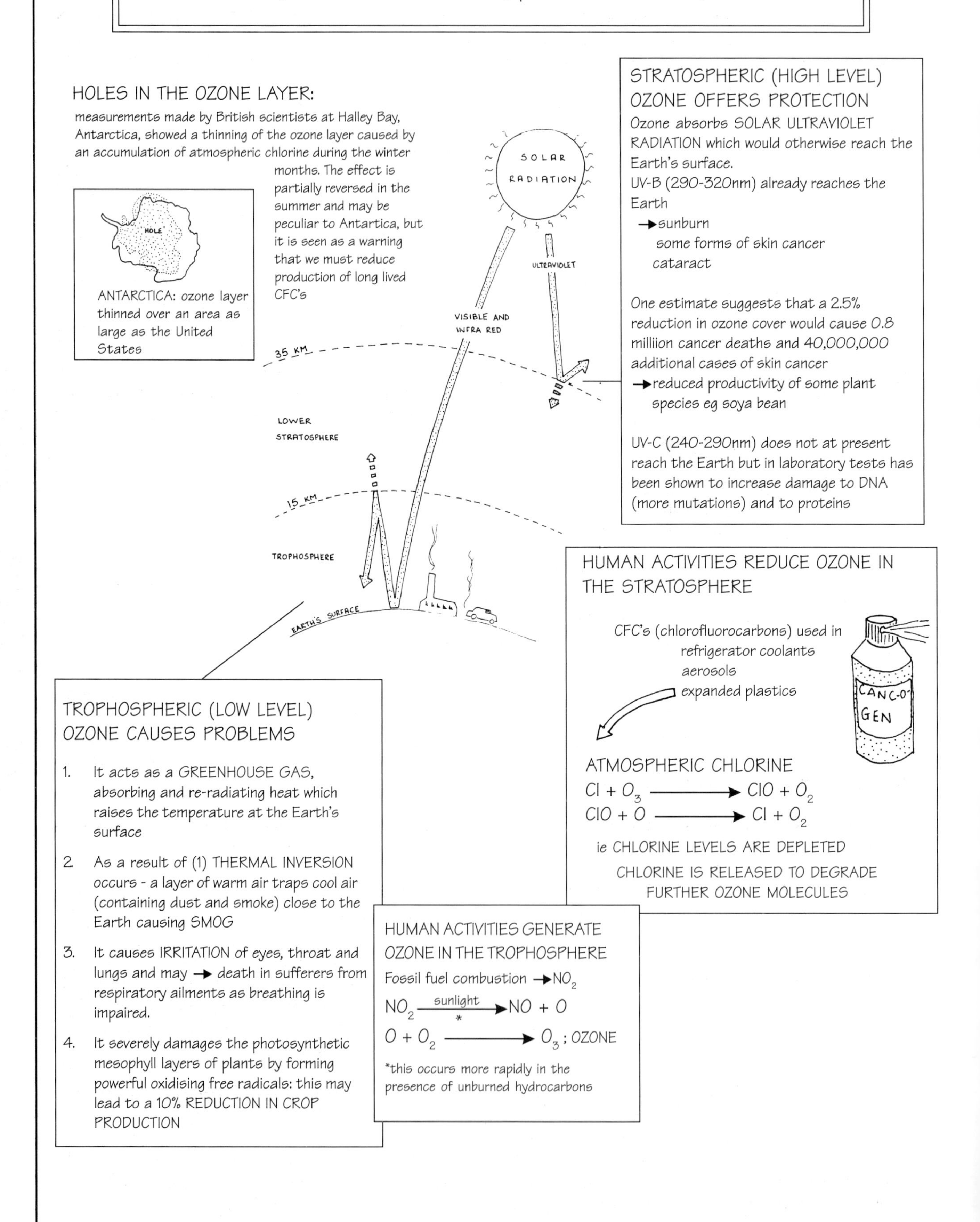

CFC's and the Ozone layer

Ozone is the most effective of the natural 'greenhouse gases' It is concentrated in the stratosphere where it also acts as a barrier to ultra-violet radiation from the Sun.

The problem : the ozone layer is being depleted by its conversion to molecular oxygen. This reaction is catalysed by chlorine and is most rapid at low temperatures. The chlorine is liberated from chlorofluorocarbons - $CFCl_3$ and CF_2Cl_2

$$2O_3 \xrightarrow[\text{chlorine, at low temperatures}]{} 3O_2$$

The possible thinning of the ozone layer presents a health hazard since the solar UV-B radiation is known to initiate and promote the development of skin cancers and cataracts.

The source : the CFC's are very inert molecules (which allows them to reach the stratosphere without being broken down) and are generated from a number of sources. They have formally been widely used as propellants in aerosols, refrigerants, components of air-conditioning systems and in the manufacture of expanded polystyrene packaging. Some chlorine is released directly into the stratosphere from the combustion of the ammonium perchlorate component of rocket fuels used in the launch of Space shuttles by the U.S.A.

Possible solutions : there has been a gradual reduction in the use of CFC's. They are effectively banned as propellants, very few new refrigeration systems use them and alternative packaging materials are being developed.

It is interesting to note that although *high-level* ozone is essential for life, *low level* ozone can be a serious health hazard. Low level ozone is that present in the air which we breathe - the World Health Organisation (WHO) recommends that atmospheric ozone concentrations should not exceed 75 - 100 parts per billion. Concentrations of this order are not uncommon in urban environments where photochemical smog (generated by the action of solar radiation on atmospheric pollutants) presents a real danger. Concentrations above WHO recommendations corrode buildings, metal surfaces and leaves of trees. Humans may suffer eye irritation and respiratory damage - asthmatics in particular may experience breathing difficulties.

Pollution of aquatic habitats: Eutrophication and the Biological Oxygen Demand

Freshwater pollution, of rivers and lakes, has been a major result of human activities. For hundreds of years water has been used as a seemingly limitless 'dump' for waste materials. Whilst floating crisp packets and condoms, and submerged skateboards and supermarket trollies probably do very little damage to the wildlife of aquatic habitats, there *are* two highly significant pollutants which have had a serious impact on aquatic ecosystems. These are **leached inorganic fertilisers** and **sewage**.

Nutrient enrichment of freshwater rivers and lakes is a well-known example of water pollution. The problem is summarised below:

POLLUTANT	SOURCE	PRINCIPAL PROBLEMS
Nitrate (NO_3^-)	Fertiliser run-off from agricultural land (leaching). Bacterial oxidation of raw sewage.	Eutrophication and increased B.O.D. of aquatic habitats. Blue-baby syndrome. Some evidence of increased incidence of stomach and tracheal cancer.
Phosphate (PO_4^{3-})	Phospholipid detergents in drainage water . Sewage and farmyard manure. Some leaching of phosphate fertilisers.	Eutrophication and increased B.O.D.
Sewage	Input from sewers. Inefficient sewage treatment	Eutrophication and increased B.O.D. Multiplication of pathogens.

Nitrates and phosphates : Fertilisers mean food

The source of nitrates and phosphates : Conventional agriculture cannot do without nitrogen and phosphorus fertilisers. Plants require a source of inorganic nitrogen and phosphorus for the synthesis of proteins, nucleic acids, membrane phospholipids, vitamins and hormones - they grow poorly (i.e. crop-growing areas are less productive) if the soil cannot provide these inorganic nutrients.

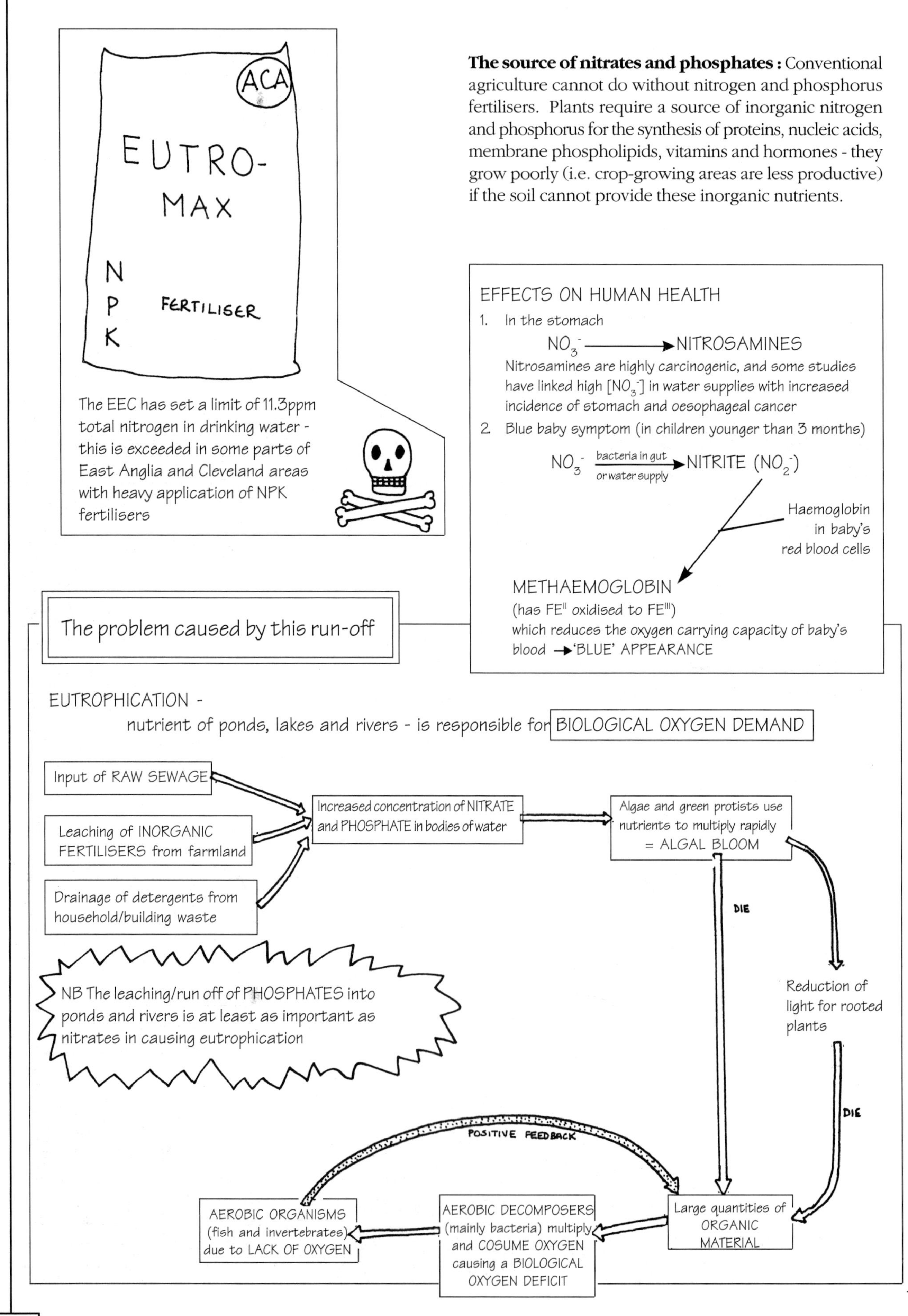

Farmers therefore supplement the soil with nitrogen- and phosphorus- containing compounds, but not all of the fertiliser they apply is absorbed by plant roots - some is washed from the soil by rainwater (the process of **leaching**) and runs off into local bodies of water. There is also a 'natural' run-off of nitrates and phosphates released by the decomposition of organic matter in the soil. Phosphates are also added to aquatic ecosystems by drainwater containing detergents, and run-off from mining and building operations.

The solutions are manifold, and depend upon the principal source of the nutrient.

a. **Changing agricultural practices** : fertilisers are expensive and farmers would appreciate that it is in their best interests to reduce leaching. Leaching is influenced by the specific crops grown, the climatic conditions and according to the season (see overleaf)

b. **Reduce the use of phosphate-containing detergents** : for example, a ban on the use of polyphosphates such as sodium tripolyphosphate as components of washing powders and other household cleaning agents would reduce the phosphate content of drainwater by between 30 and 50%.

EUTROPHICATION OF A SMALL POND

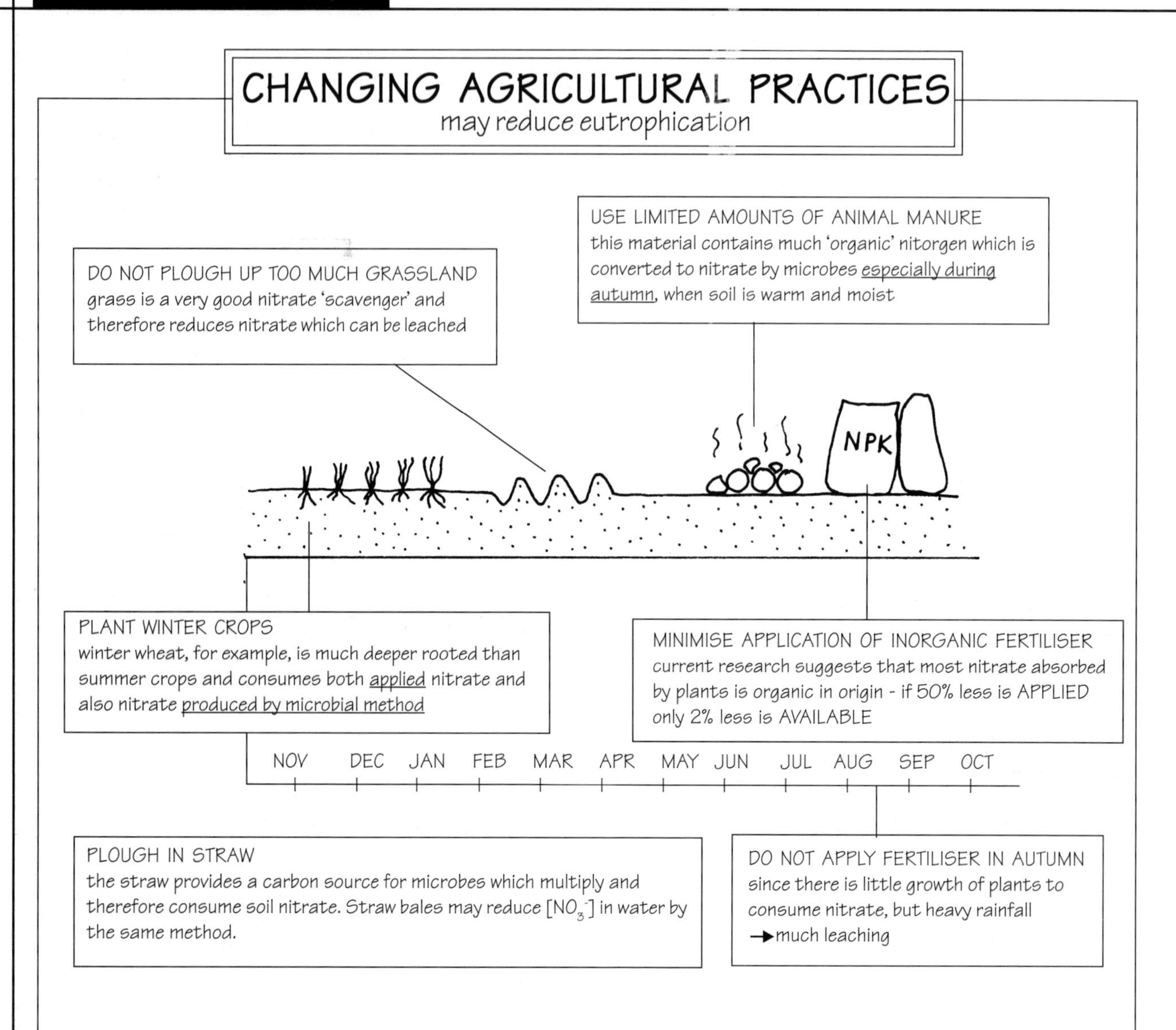

c. **Aeration of water** : may be a necessary short-term solution if the B.O.D. is too high, and only treats the *symptoms* of nutrient-enrichment. It involves bubbling oxygen under pressure into the lower layers of a body of water. Great care has to be taken to avoid mixing the nutrient-rich lower layers of the pond or lake with the well-illuminated upper layers, and to avoid increases in turbidity. Aeration is used commercially in fish farms, but is probably too expensive for larger-scale use.

d. **Treat sewage effectively** : this will reduce the input of nutrients into freshwater bodies to a level at which they can be decomposed harmlessly by the natural flora. The removal of phosphates from sewage water is very expensive - some water treatment plants precipitate phosphates from the water with aluminium or iron salts (this also clarifies the water by causing the flocculation of particulate matter). The principles of a water treatment plant are outlined on page 59.

Treatment of water with aluminium salts illustrates another important point - pollution treatment may transfer a problem! The Camelford water treatment plant in Cornwall used this method, but unfortunately, in 1988, the aluminium sulphate was administered to the wrong water tank, causing mass poisoning. Aluminium ions occur very widely in nature, but they have been shown to rise to toxic levels in areas subject to acid precipitation (p. 46). The range of effects of aluminium is described in the figure opposite.

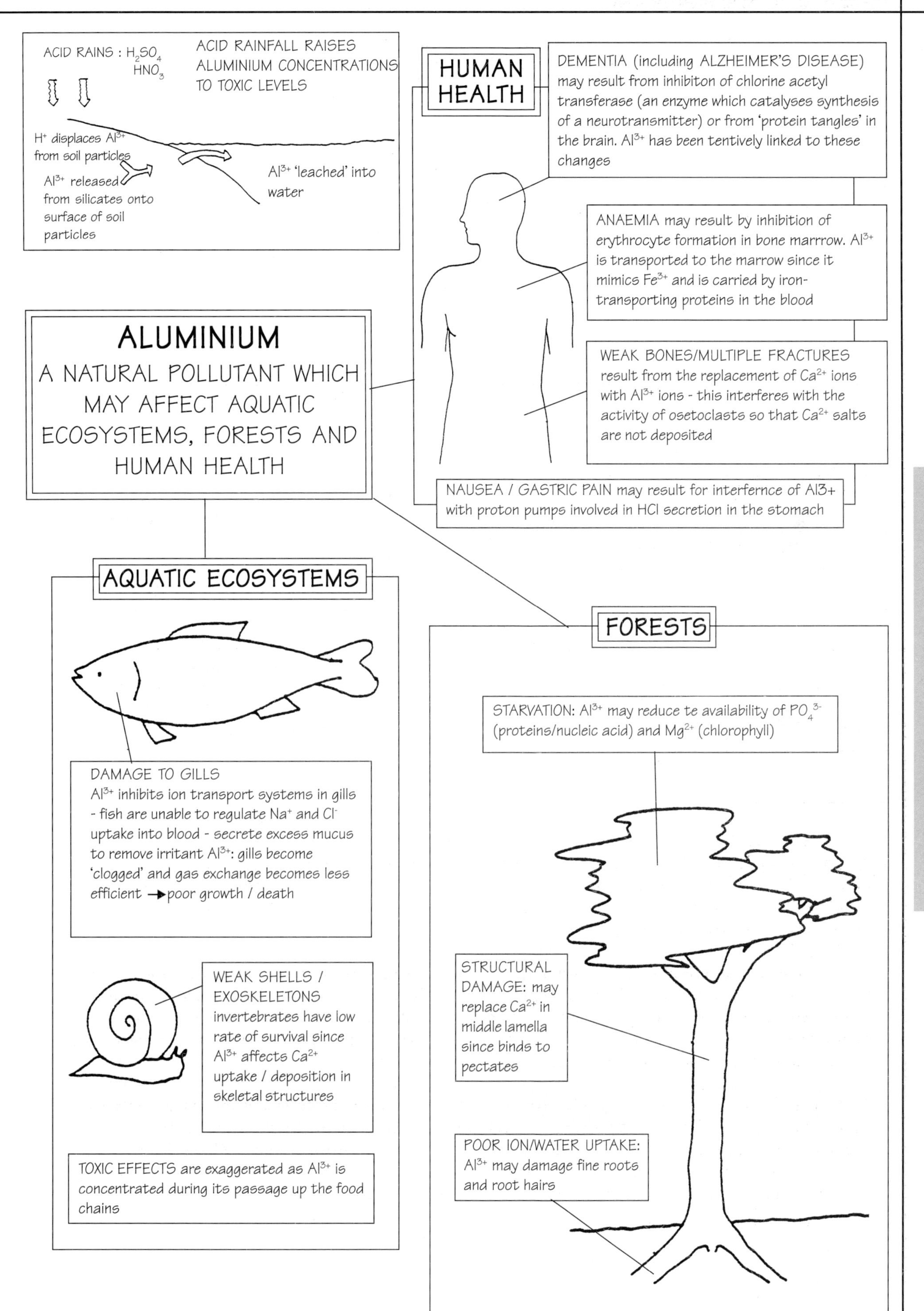
ACID RAINS : H_2SO_4 HNO_3
ACID RAINFALL RAISES ALUMINIUM CONCENTRATIONS TO TOXIC LEVELS
H^+ displaces Al^{3+} from soil particles
Al^{3+} released from silicates onto surface of soil particles
Al^{3+} 'leached' into water
ALUMINIUM
A NATURAL POLLUTANT WHICH MAY AFFECT AQUATIC ECOSYSTEMS, FORESTS AND HUMAN HEALTH
HUMAN HEALTH
DEMENTIA (including ALZHEIMER'S DISEASE) may result from inhibiton of chlorine acetyl transferase (an enzyme which catalyses synthesis of a neurotransmitter) or from 'protein tangles' in the brain. Al^{3+} has been tentively linked to these changes
ANAEMIA may result by inhibition of erythrocyte formation in bone marrrow. Al^{3+} is transported to the marrow since it mimics Fe^{3+} and is carried by iron-transporting proteins in the blood
WEAK BONES/MULTIPLE FRACTURES result from the replacement of Ca^{2+} ions with Al^{3+} ions - this interferes with the activity of osetoclasts so that Ca^{2+} salts are not deposited
NAUSEA / GASTRIC PAIN may result for interfernce of Al3+ with proton pumps involved in HCl secretion in the stomach
AQUATIC ECOSYSTEMS
DAMAGE TO GILLS
Al^{3+} inhibits ion transport systems in gills - fish are unable to regulate Na^+ and Cl^- uptake into blood - secrete excess mucus to remove irritant Al^{3+}: gills become 'clogged' and gas exchange becomes less efficient → poor growth / death
WEAK SHELLS / EXOSKELETONS invertebrates have low rate of survival since Al^{3+} affects Ca^{2+} uptake / deposition in skeletal structures
TOXIC EFFECTS are exaggerated as Al^{3+} is concentrated during its passage up the food chains
FORESTS
STARVATION: Al^{3+} may reduce te availability of PO_4^{3-} (proteins/nucleic acid) and Mg^{2+} (chlorophyll)
STRUCTURAL DAMAGE: may replace Ca^{2+} in middle lamella since binds to pectates
POOR ION/WATER UPTAKE: Al^{3+} may damage fine roots and root hairs

Analytical methods for monitoring pollution

These essentially fall conveniently into two groups:

1. Chemical monitoring, in which direct measurements of some **abiotic** component of the environment (oxygen concentration, for example) are made and compared with some notionally acceptable levels.

2. Biological monitoring, in which the numbers of certain **indicator species** are measured and then compared with those in a non-polluted habitat.

The principle of each of these is easily demonstrated by considering the effect of the release of some pollutant on a river ecosystem. Such a release may cause a marked eutrophication of the ecosystem (see p. 52) and notable changes in the flora and fauna (p. 58), and may be monitored by measuring the **biological oxygen demand** and the **Trent Biotic Index.**

BIOLOGICAL OXYGEN DEMAND is the mass of oxygen consumed by micro-organisms as the oxidatively decompose organic material. It is determined by measuring the oxygen concentration of one sample of water immediately after collection and of a second sample from the same source after incubation for 5 days. The BOD is then the difference in oxygen concentration between the two samples:

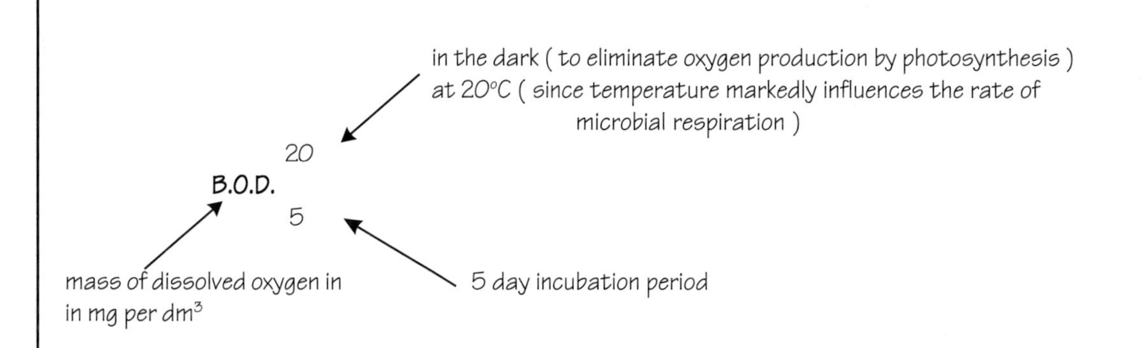

The oxygen concentration is most conveniently measured using an **oxygen electrode**

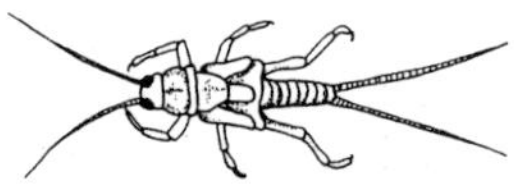

1. Stonefly nymph (up to 30mm)

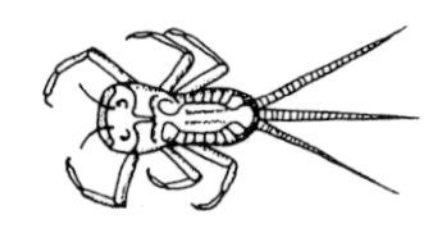

2. Flattened mayfly nymph (up to 16mm)

3. Caseless caddis fly larva (up to 26mm)

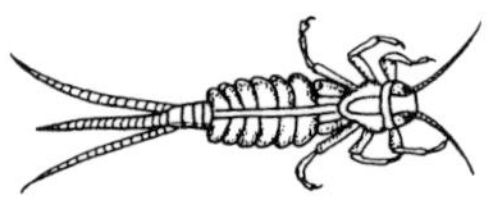

4. Swimming mayfly nymph e.g. *Baestis rhodanii* (up to 11mm)

5. Freshwater shrimp (up to 20mm)

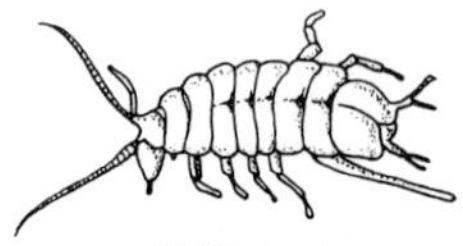

6. Water louse (up to 12mm)

TRENT BIOTIC INDEX operates, as do all biotic indices, on the assumption that animals of freshwater streams disappear following pollution by biodegradable organic compounds in the order shown opposite - thus stonefly larvae are the most sensitive (and therefore **indicator species** for non-polluted water) whilst oligochaetes such as *Tubifex* are the least sensitive (in fact the organisms are not displaying sensitivity to the organic pollutant, but to the depletion in oxygen concentration following its decomposition).

A sample of organisms is collected with a hand net and the organisms present in the sample are identified and the total number of groups is counted. To determine the biotic index of the sample site the table below is used as indicated:

1st DETERMINE THE NUMBER OF DIFFERENT GROUPS REPRESENTED IN THE SAMPLE. say 20-25

2ND WORK DOWN THIS COLOUMN, 'TICK OFF' EACH GROUP PRESENT IN THE SAMPLE eg a single stonefly nymph

Biogeographical region: Midlands, England		Total number of groups present									
		number of groups present									
		0-1	2-5	6-10	11-15	16-20	21-25	26-30	31-35	36-40	41-45
Plecoptera(Stonefly)	More than one species	-	7	8	9	10	11	12	13	14	15
nymphs present	One species only ✔	-	6	7	8	9	10	11	12	13	14
Epherneroptera (Mayfly)	More than one species*	-	6	7	8	9	10	11	12	13	14
nymphs	One species only*	-	5	6	7	8	9	10	11	12	13
Trichoptera (Caddis)	More than one species+	-	5	6	7	8	9	10	11	12	13
larvae present	One species onlyf	4	4	5	6	7	8	9	10	11	12
Gammarus present (Shrimp)	All above species absent	3	4	5	6	7	8	9	10	11	12
Asellus present (Louse)	All above species absent	2	3	4	5	6	7	8	9	10	11
Tubificid worms andi or Red Chironornid larvae present	All above species absent	1	2	3	4	5	6	7	8	9	10
All above types - absent	Some organisms such as Eristalis tenax not requiring dissolved oxygen may be present	- 0	1	2	-	-	-				

BIOTIC INDEX = 10

'Clean'streams would have an index close to **10** whilst progressively more polluted sources would have lower values, falling to **1 or 2** for a **heavily polluted** (and hence oxygen-deficient) stream.

Biotic indices have two key advantages over chemical monitoring systems.

1. it can detect **intermittent pollution** - a single fertiliser release might not be detected by chemical analyses once the fertiliser had been washed away but its effects on the fauna of the stream might still be detectable weeks or even months later.

2. it may act as a **biological signal** - routine chemical analysis of all known pollutants would be expensive and impractical, but a large change in biotic index could be seen as a reason to complete such testing since such a change might indicate that pollution is occurring.

Summary :

1. Pollution is a result of Human activities
2. Two well-documented areas of pollution are the atmosphere and freshwater.
3. A conservationist might need to identify a problem caused by pollution, determine the source of the pollutant and suggest viable remedies.
4. Significant atmospheric pollutants include carbon dioxide, sulphur dioxide, chlorofluorocarbons and ozone.
5. Important pollutants of freshwater habitats include nitrates, phosphates, raw sewage and some metals.
6. There are both chemical and biological methods available for measuring the 'health' of an ecosystem.

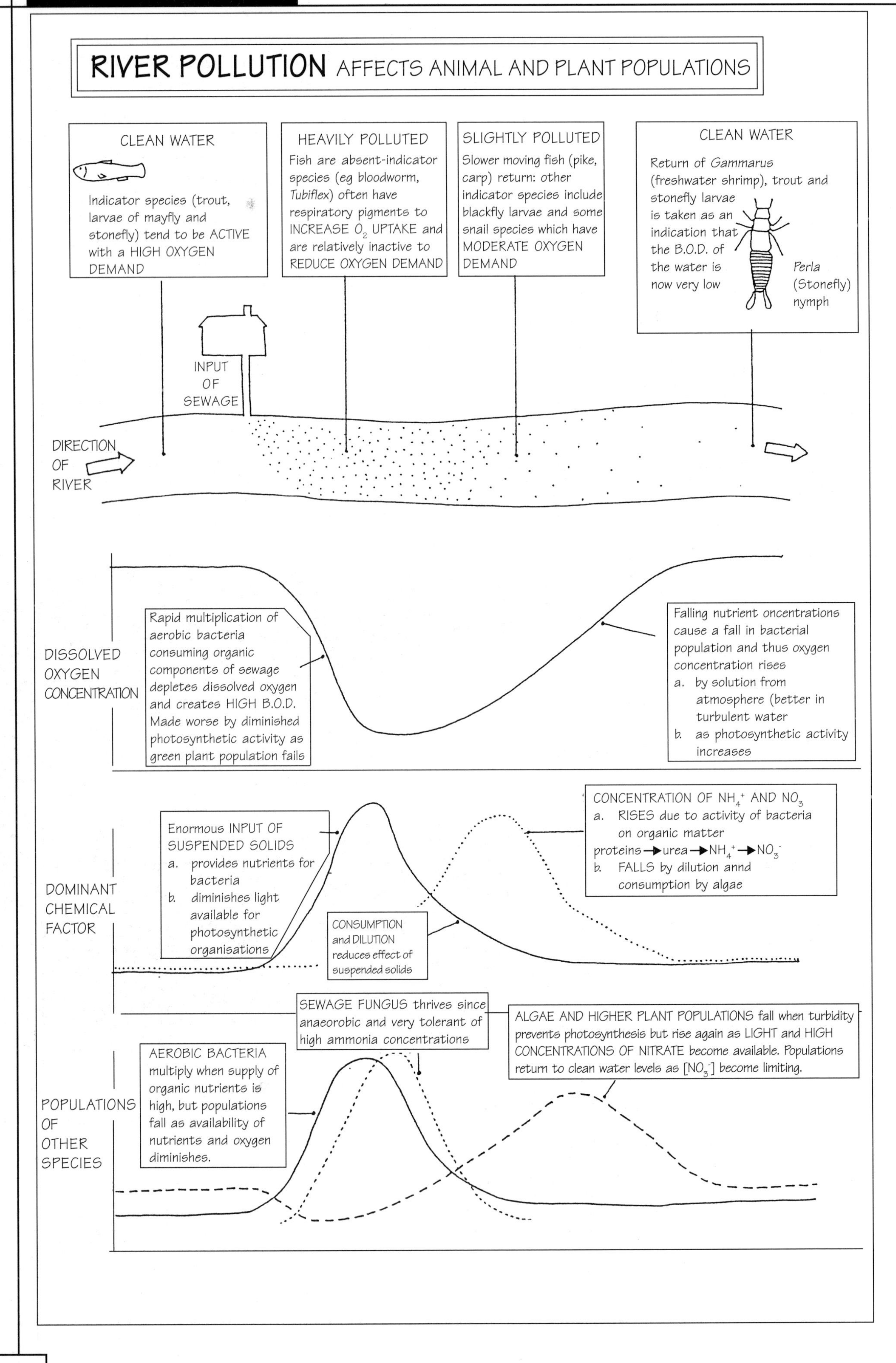
RIVER POLLUTION AFFECTS ANIMAL AND PLANT POPULATIONS
CLEAN WATER
Indicator species (trout, larvae of mayfly and stonefly) tend to be ACTIVE with a HIGH OXYGEN DEMAND
HEAVILY POLLUTED
Fish are absent-indicator species (eg bloodworm, Tubiflex) often have respiratory pigments to INCREASE O2 UPTAKE and are relatively inactive to REDUCE OXYGEN DEMAND
SLIGHTLY POLLUTED
Slower moving fish (pike, carp) return: other indicator species include blackfly larvae and some snail species which have MODERATE OXYGEN DEMAND
CLEAN WATER
Return of Gammarus (freshwater shrimp), trout and stonefly larvae is taken as an indication that the B.O.D. of the water is now very low
Perla (Stonefly) nymph
INPUT OF SEWAGE
DIRECTION OF RIVER
DISSOLVED OXYGEN CONCENTRATION
Rapid multiplication of aerobic bacteria consuming organic components of sewage depletes dissolved oxygen and creates HIGH B.O.D. Made worse by diminished photosynthetic activity as green plant population fails
Falling nutrient oncentrations cause a fall in bacterial population and thus oxygen concentration rises
a. by solution from atmosphere (better in turbulent water
b. as photosynthetic activity increases
DOMINANT CHEMICAL FACTOR
Enormous INPUT OF SUSPENDED SOLIDS
a. provides nutrients for bacteria
b. diminishes light available for photosynthetic organisations
CONSUMPTION and DILUTION reduces effect of suspended solids
CONCENTRATION OF NH4+ AND NO3
a. RISES due to activity of bacteria on organic matter
proteins → urea → NH4+ → NO3-
b. FALLS by dilution annd consumption by algae
POPULATIONS OF OTHER SPECIES
SEWAGE FUNGUS thrives since anaeorobic and very tolerant of high ammonia concentrations
AEROBIC BACTERIA multiply when supply of organic nutrients is high, but populations fall as availability of nutrients and oxygen diminishes.
ALGAE AND HIGHER PLANT POPULATIONS fall when turbidity prevents photosynthesis but rise again as LIGHT and HIGH CONCENTRATIONS OF NITRATE become available. Populations return to clean water levels as [NO3-] become limiting.

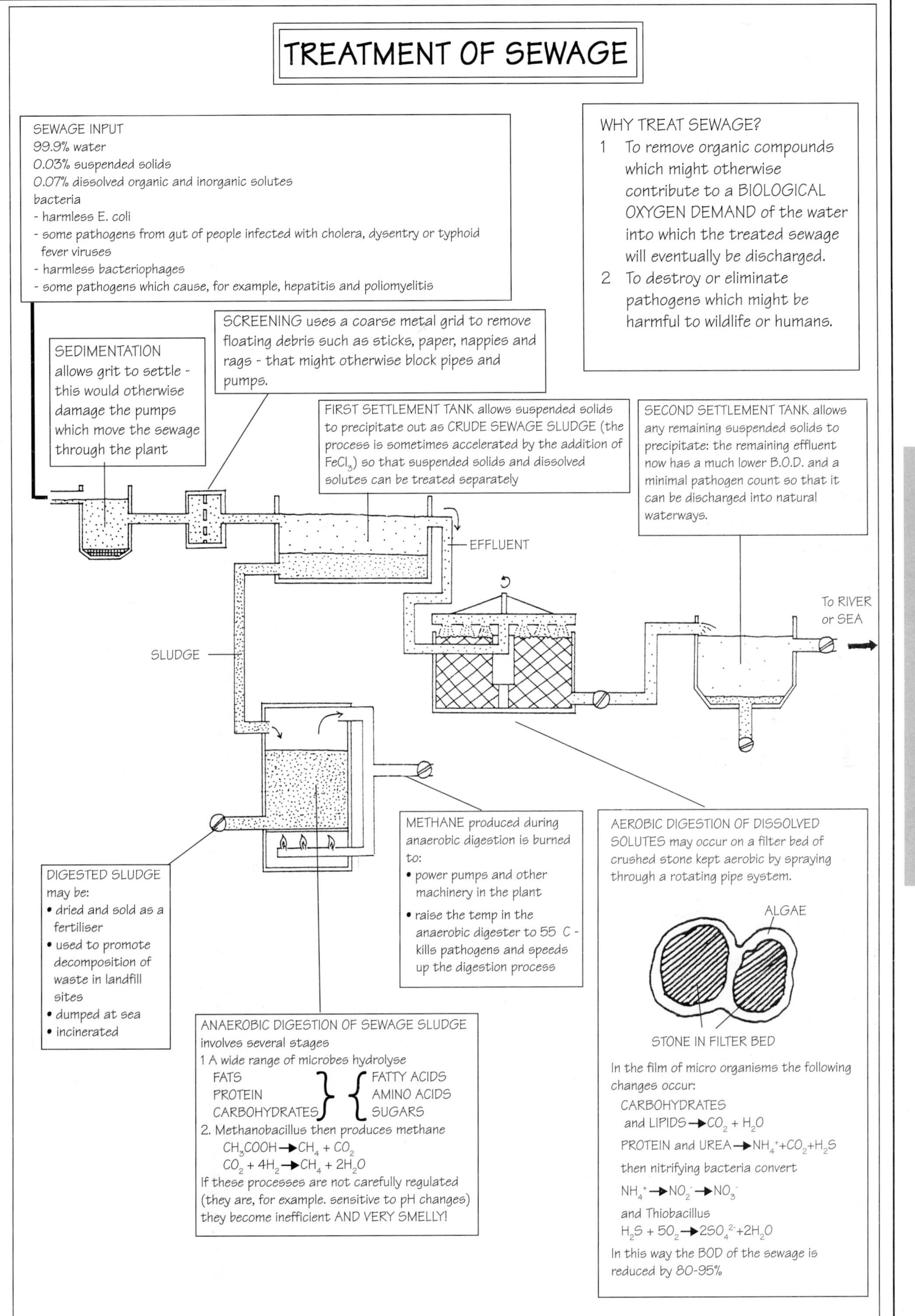

CONFLICTS WITH CONSERVATION

Agriculture & Conservation

Around the world, agriculture presents a serious threat to conservation of existing habitats. Although 75% of England is designated as farmland, only 2% of the UK population is involved in farming. In 1850, one farm worker produced enough food for about 4 people, now in advanced agricultural countries the same worker produces enough for 60 people. The enormous rise in productivity of land is due to many factors. These include :

- increased and more efficient use of machinery, use of pesticides to eliminate competitors for crop species
- increased use of inorganic fertilisers
- the tendency towards monoculture.

All of these can have negative effects on the environment.

Currently, there are many people who are very unhappy about agricultural surpluses within the EU and the cost of the Common Agricultural Policy (CAP), but in fact only a few specific products are in surplus - cereals, wine, beef and butter. We are not self-sufficient in food or timber. If we don't produce a surplus, where will we find food to send to third world countries in the event of famines and other disasters? Of course, politics often gets in the way of food aid, but without spare food we would not even be able to manage the current response. Most people would agree that the CAP needs very serious reforms, some of which are now taking place, but many would not want to scrap it. We could apply the same argument to the EU itself. After the Second World War, during which Britain had almost been starved into submission, successive governments encouraged farmers to maximise food production with subsidies as well as exhortation. Farmers in the EU and in Britain particularly have responded magnificently to that challenge, British farmers are the most efficient in the world. Unfortunately, very high efficiency usually also has some negative aspects and we are now asking whether these are acceptable. Part of the problem is that with only 2% of the UK population involved in farming, people understand less and less about what takes place on farms and ignorance often leads to prejudice.

The use of modern large farm machinery has resulted in increased field sizes and the removal of hedges. Pesticides have caused the reduction in population of many native wildflowers and some non-target insects and birds by direct toxicity or, more often, by removal of their food sources. High levels of applied fertilisers change flora dramatically and can result in excessive nitrate levels in rivers, leading to eutrophication. High yielding crop varieties tend to be more susceptible to disease and so require more fungicide treatments, particularly where crops are grown in near monoculture.

In this chapter we will look in detail at these effects in Great Britain; at hedge removal, drainage of wetlands for agriculture, overgrazing, pesticides and fertilisers.

In the UK commercial forestry has in the past also had a detrimental effect on some ecosystems and this will also be considered.

Hedge removal

A HEDGE (or hedgerow) is a row of bushes, shrubs or small trees, together with the herbaceous plants which grow beneath them - the author-naturalist Richard Mabey has described them as " linear coppice ". Hedge *removal* is a very emotive subject - for many it epitomises the damage to the countryside caused by modern farming, perhaps because it is the most easily visible change to the countryside this century (other than natural disasters like Dutch Elm Disease). The detractors of today's farmers cite the "prairies" of parts of Eastern England (e.g. Lincolnshire and Cambridgeshire) as the result of the greed of "Agribusiness".

It is important to realise that the farmed countryside has in the past continuously been refashioned. The speed of modern changes is, of course, greater, but that applies to all of modern life. Also, intensification of land use and the associated loss of hedgerows has not taken place evenly across the UK . Since cereals are now by far the major UK crop, changes are much greater where cereals can best be grown. The countryside of small fields and hedges that we regard as typically English is partially a recent invention dating from the 18-19th Centuries - in the middle of the 18th Century there were more hedgerow trees than there had ever been before or have been since.

Our hedgerows arise from two sources. A few are remnants of ancient woodland from which fields were cut in Saxon times but most are plantings to mark property and parish boundaries, and to fence in stock. In Tudor times the countryside had many large fields for sheep and open field strip farming, which was very inefficient. The arrival of cotton and the need to plant trees for shipbuilding led to a reduction in the number of sheep. The Enclosures Acts (1750-1850) and the earlier non-parliamentary enclosures of the 17th Century resulted in the planting of hedges as boundaries, and even more were planted to give smaller fields for rotation farming. . Before it was possible to date hedges it was thought that all hedges were the products of these enclosure Acts, but Oliver Rackham has been able to estimate that much enclosure went on well before it became a parliamentary obligation - one half of all the hedged and walled landscape of Britain dates back to between the Bronze Age and the seventeenth century. The invention of the seed drill by Jethro Tull in the early part of the 18th Century meant that a far greater area of land could be sown in a day than by hand sowing. As a result, the idea of hedge removal was discussed in the 1800's though little was actually done In the middle of the 19th Century about 1/10th of all land in Britain was "non-productive agriculturally" as hedges, roadside verges and ditches.

We do not know accurately how much hedgerow we have or how much has been lost because it has never been properly measured. It is estimated that the peak rate of removal meant that 8000 km (5000 miles) were lost per year between 1947 and 1963, although the rate of loss has declined somewhat since then, to about 3 200 km per year. In 1980 the probable remaining length of hedgerow in England was about 960,000km (600,000 miles)

Thus:

- an enormous length of hedgerow has been removed from the British countryside
- the rate of hedgerow removal has fallen considerably in recent years

We can explain this by considering two of the major functions of hedges, as parish, district and farm boundaries and as internal stock enclosures. The oldest, and biologically more valuable hedges tended to follow natural features and acted as boundaries, the newer, and less biologically diverse, hedges were often for internal stock control. It is these newer hedges which have largely been removed by the farmer, and many of the older ones remain relatively secure.

We can approximately estimate the age of a hedge by the number of woody species it contains. The more species, the older the hedge, with the proviso that some hedges were planted with mixed species. It is, however, very difficult to estimate the length of hedgerows or the number of trees they contained in the past. We also do not know the exact extent of hedges now. We have to make estimates from various sources.

Worked example:
The first 6 inch and 25 inch Ordnance Survey of 1845-1888 showed rather fewer trees than now but it did not record trees under 30 ft apart so would have under-recorded small trees (Rackham).

A 1951 Forestry Commission survey showed 56 million hedgerow and park trees of greater than 12 inches (30 cm) in girth. Of these, 17 million were saplings of 12-24 inches in girth and so were presumably planted from 1921-1936.

Although it is difficult to measure, we know that we have lost a lot of hedgerow in the last 50 years. The important questions are, how significant is this loss of habitat and how do we prevent further loss?

Value of the Hedgerow Habitat

We know that, roughly, we find only 1 extra woody species per 100 years of a hedge's age, so we can see how slowly plants colonise hedgerows. Only about 20 species of plants have a high proportion of their population in hedgerows and it is unlikely that their complete loss would make any species extinct although some would disappear in certain localities. In areas with little or no remaining natural woodland plant species that require settled or sheltered conditions are absolutely confined to mature hedges. Clearly the older a hedge, the more valuable it is likely to be to plant species.

Hedges are more important to animals. Of 28 British lowland mammals, 21 breed in hedges (14 commonly). 65 bird species (23 commonly) and 23 butterfly species (15 commonly) also breed in hedges. It has been suggested that in the case of birds loss of hedges results in smaller populations of relatively common woodland species rather than fewer species, but of course this might be equivalent to the extinction of species in localities which lack alternative 'woodland' habitat. Numbers of several species of birds and butterflies are decreasing in the UK for many reasons, and hedgerow removal can add to this problem.

Pollard et al (1974) said "We must conclude that while hedges are essential for the survival of many species of birds on many individual farms and in larger areas of countryside without woods, they are not essential for the survival of species in the country as a whole, either as providing breeding habitat or connecting corridors between suitable habitats." However, we must be careful not to look at such problems in too restricted a manner. We may say that the loss of a bird species from a

particular area is not important as there are plenty elsewhere, but if we continue to do that area by area we eventually end up with one isolated population with a reduced gene pool.

The value of hedges as "corridors" connecting areas of woodland is debatable. Many people believe that this a very important role for hedgerows but there is little firm evidence that it is significant for plants. It is probably quite significant for mobile mammal populations, but less significant for very territorial small birds. Hedges certainly help in linking small woodland areas each is individually too small support birds of prey. Much of the value of a hedge lies in the fauna supported by the herbaceous layer at its base - this can support enormous populations of invertebrates which are not only valuable as food sources to other animals but may be important predators of species which are potential pests to the crop grower. A major role of hedges lies in their visual contribution and in their amenity value. This is not insignificant and is certainly one reason why their removal has aroused such controversy.

To summarise so far:

- hedge loss is unevenly distributed - it mainly affects those parts of the country which have shifted from livestock to animal farming.
- loss of older hedges is of far greater significance to wildlife than loss of those hedges planted within the last 200 years.
- hedges provide significant wildlife habitats, and may link isolated islands of woodland.

Advantages and Disadvantages to the Farmer

The vast majority of hedges in the UK are farmer owned and so their future depends on farmers. The main disadvantages to farmers of hedgerows are that they make it more difficult to use big modern machinery and are expensive to maintain. Although removing hedges gives more land for farming, this is not a major gain. It is the turning time and turning area of equipment that is the important factor. By changing from 3.25 Ha fields to 20 Ha fields, row length can go from 200 metres to 500 metres and this saves 15% in working time.

Hedges are also costly to maintain properly. In the past when labour was cheap, hedges were cut back or layered by hand every 7-15 years. Nowadays, it would take a man about a fortnight to cut and lay a hedge that could be cut with a flail cutter in an hour at a cost of

£12. Unfortunately, flail cutters produce a different kind of hedge. It tends to be lower and saplings are very rarely allowed to grow into trees.

Hedges can also harbour pests and diseases damaging to crops but this is not a major problem. The Barberry (*Berberis vulgaris*) was once common in hedges but is now very rare as it has been removed because it is an alternative host to Black Rust (*Puccinia graminis*) a disease of wheat. Black Bean Aphids (*Aphis fabae*) that attack broad and field beans overwinter on Spindle Bushes (*Euonymus europaeus*). Some weeds which cause serious problems for the farmer can also flourish at the base of hedges, but there are techniques for dealing with them other than hedge removal. Hedges are often exposed to herbicide drift from crop spraying and hedge bottoms are intentionally sprayed to control couch grass (*Agropyron repens*). This results in their tending to contain only coarse, herbicide resistant species such as Cow Parsley (*Anthriscus sylvestris*), Cleavers (*Galium aparine*) and Sterile Brome (*Bromus sterilis*): the last two being serious weeds of agriculture.

The main advantage of hedges in the past was to control and shelter stock. Fences are initially more expensive than hedges and hedges will last much longer, but their maintenance costs can be very high. Grants are available to farmers for the capital costs of new fencing but were not available for the maintenance of hedges until recent EU grants. In areas where animals are no longer kept, particularly in the East of England, there is no farming need for hedges. They provide very little shelter for crops, as protection from wind is limited to 16-24 metres from a 2 metre hedge. Even a 6 metre high hedge would require fields to be no bigger than 2.25 Ha in size to gain the benefit. There is some suggestion that the sheltered air behind hedges encourages deposition of fungal spores and pest insects on crops. The only economic advantage of hedges to the arable farmer is as cover for game. Hedges may also contain predatory birds and insects, which may form natural controls of some pest species. The raised banks on which many boundary hedges stand form an ideal habitat for many of the insect species which play a crucial role in the pollination of cultivated flowering crops, particularly clover and fruit trees.

The Future

Conservationists are asking farmers to continue to farm in traditional ways that in many cases do not make commercial sense. There is no doubt that, in some areas, hedges have been grubbed out for no other reason than that the farmer thinks it looks more tidy and efficient. However, in wholly arable areas of the country, hedges have little economic value in farming other than as game cover. Merely stopping farmers from removing hedges is not enough as badly maintained hedges are not ecologically very useful. RSPB studies in the 1970's showed that the average quality of remaining hedgerows was declining. A high proportion of them were too low, narrow and intensively managed to be of much use as wildlife habitat. Where hedges still have a part to play, traditional methods of hedge cutting should be promoted. Closely cropped machine-cut hedges have much less wildlife value and neglected hedges become bare at the bottom as the trees grow. It is almost certainly better where hedges are not required, to try to maintain a small portion of well managed hedges especially the older, more floristically diverse ones and to encourage the planting of small areas of new woodland which provide game cover and habitat for other creatures, are more convenient for the farmer to manage and have amenity value. We also have to remember that for conservation to really work, it is not enough to merely preserve some parts of an old ecosystem, because for any such system to survive in the long term, it needs new growth, new blood. Newly planted woodlands or hedges are needed as well as the maintenance of old ones. As a result of public pressure, farmers are now planting more new hedges than they have for some time for game and for amenity value, while the rate of hedgerow removal is decreasing. Recent changes in the CAP are also likely to help in this direction. If we wish to keep our remaining hedgerows and we should certainly want to keep the older and well maintained ones, we must ensure that Government policy (EU set-aside and UK MAFF) promotes farming that is in tune with the environment as well as efficient.

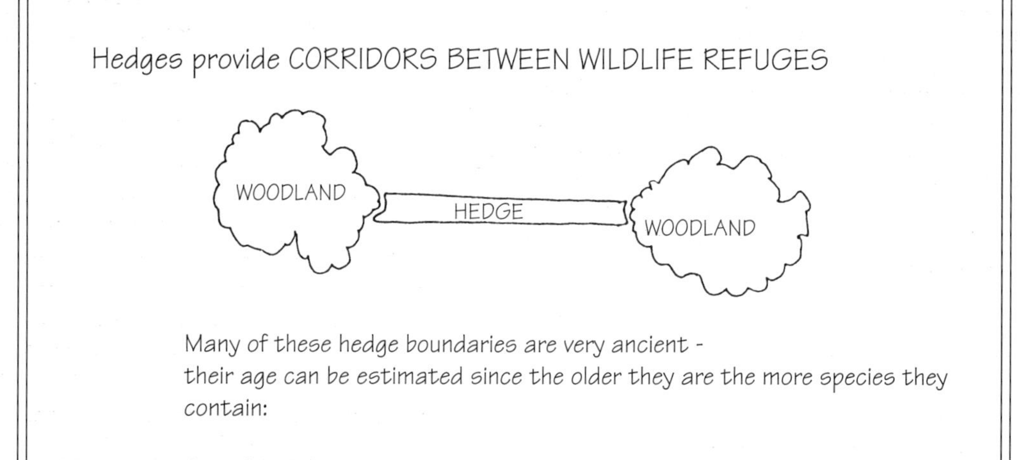

One in 5 hedgerows to be protected

By Charles Clover, Environment Editor

SIX years after promising legislation to protect hedgerows, the Government is expected to announce proposals later this month to protect a fifth of all hedges in England and Wales.

The proposals will make it illegal for farmers and landowners to remove a hedge without notifying the local authority. But they will still be allowed to rip it out, provided that the hedge is not ancient or of historical significance and does not contain rare species.

Pressure has been building for protection to be given to hedges since a survey showed that, despite many new ones being planted since the 1980s, there was a net loss of more than 10,000 miles of hedgerow a year between 1990 and 1993.

Environmentalists are highly critical of the criteria for deciding which hedges should be protected — a draft of which has been seen by *The Daily Telegraph*.

Conservationists describe the proposals as "minimalist" and say they omit any protection for hedges in scenic landscapes, such as national parks and areas of outstanding natural beauty.

Under proposals drawn up by the Agricultural Development and Advisory Service (ADAS), a hedge qualifies for protection if it is:

□ An ecclesiastical parish boundary — many of these date back to the Saxon period.
□ Part of an archaeological feature, for instance a hedge which lies along the rampart of a fort.
□ The documented boundary of a pre-1600 estate or manor.
□ Part of a documented field system which pre-dates the parliamentary enclosures between 1750 and 1850.
□ Part of a parliamentary enclosure hedgerow that is "outstanding in the country".
□ Directly associated with a nationally-important historic event or person, or has a cultural connection of national importance.
□ Contains rare species listed in the Wildlife and Countryside Act.
□ Contains seven or more native woody species in a 30-metre length. This requirement is reduced to six in the North of England.
□ A hedge along a road.

The proposals are expected to go for public consultation this month and become regulations by July.

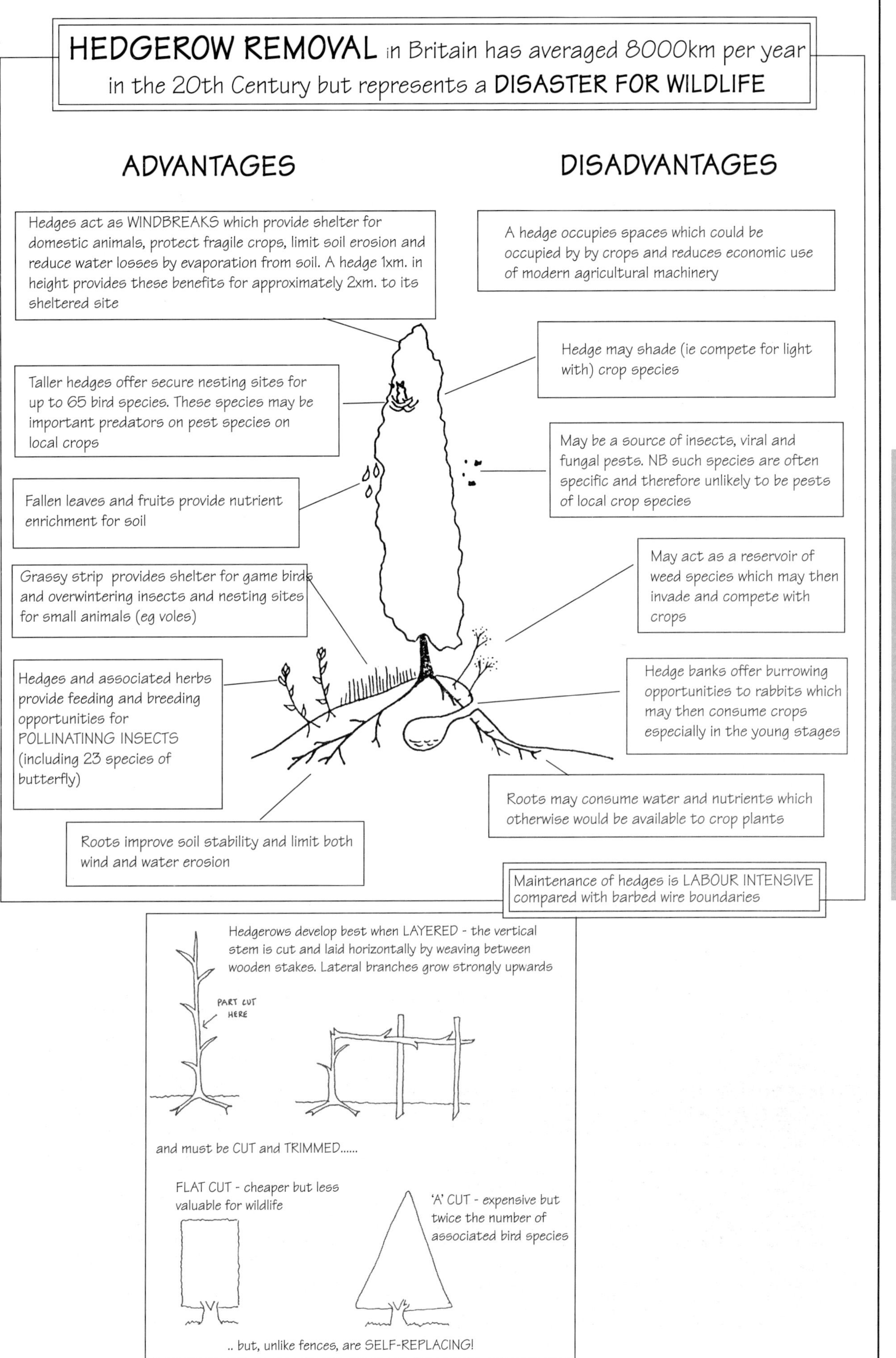
HEDGEROW REMOVAL in Britain has averaged 8000km per year in the 20th Century but represents a DISASTER FOR WILDLIFE
ADVANTAGES
DISADVANTAGES
Hedges act as WINDBREAKS which provide shelter for domestic animals, protect fragile crops, limit soil erosion and reduce water losses by evaporation from soil. A hedge 1xm. in height provides these benefits for approximately 2xm. to its sheltered site
Taller hedges offer secure nesting sites for up to 65 bird species. These species may be important predators on pest species on local crops
Fallen leaves and fruits provide nutrient enrichment for soil
Grassy strip provides shelter for game birds and overwintering insects and nesting sites for small animals (eg voles)
Hedges and associated herbs provide feeding and breeding opportunities for POLLINATINNG INSECTS (including 23 species of butterfly)
Roots improve soil stability and limit both wind and water erosion
A hedge occupies spaces which could be occupied by by crops and reduces economic use of modern agricultural machinery
Hedge may shade (ie compete for light with) crop species
May be a source of insects, viral and fungal pests. NB such species are often specific and therefore unlikely to be pests of local crop species
May act as a reservoir of weed species which may then invade and compete with crops
Hedge banks offer burrowing opportunities to rabbits which may then consume crops especially in the young stages
Roots may consume water and nutrients which otherwise would be available to crop plants
Maintenance of hedges is LABOUR INTENSIVE compared with barbed wire boundaries
Hedgerows develop best when LAYERED - the vertical stem is cut and laid horizontally by weaving between wooden stakes. Lateral branches grow strongly upwards
PART CUT HERE
and must be CUT and TRIMMED......
FLAT CUT - cheaper but less valuable for wildlife
'A' CUT - expensive but twice the number of associated bird species
.. but, unlike fences, are SELF-REPLACING!

Drainage of Wetlands

Wetlands are amongst the world's most threatened ecosystems. Wetland drainage rivals deforestation as the most damaging alteration to our environment. Man has long attempted to control water flows from the times of the Sumeriands and Egyptians when the best arable land was that regularly flooded by the Tigris/Euphrates and the Nile. We also want to control rivers and wetlands for the purposes of safety, water supply, hydro-electricity, industry and leisure.

Although rice can flourish in places where regular flooding brings nutrients and helps control weeds, other cereals require drier conditions and hence drainage. In parts of Britain, farmland is drained in the winter and irrigated in the summer. Because these drained soils are so fertile, natural wetlands are prime sites for agricultural expansion. Of course, wetlands are also lost for the other reasons as stated above such as flood prevention; control of mosquitoes and hence malaria; ports on estuaries; peat removal for fuel and horticulture and reservoirs.

River straightening, drainage and removal of tree cover can result in greater run-off of rainfall so that flow in rivers is more erratic leading to floods downstream. Peat cutting can also make this worse as where present it acts like a sponge, giving a buffering effect. The risk of flooding in the UK has been tackled in the past by raising river banks but this may not be the best answer. The disastrous flooding of the Mississippi in the USA in 1993 happened upstream of all the raised banks (levees). In 1953 a high tide in the North Sea coupled with gale force Northerly winds caused floods over large areas of Eastern England and the Low Countries. River walls in London would probably have been adequate if there had not been such extensive flooding of estuarine farmland. The farmland was not greatly damaged but a number of people died. As a result, a great length of new sea wall was built on the Essex and Suffolk coast, the enormously expensive Thames Barrier was constructed and the banks of the Thames were raised downstream from London. The sea walls are now crumbling and are probably at the end of their useful life. The cost of replacing them, made worse by the steady sinking of South Eastern England is prohibitive and the Government is now considering the re-establishment of salt marshes subject to regular flooding with much lower defences behind them.

Estuarine marshes are made from soil washed down by rivers and then deposited where the river slows down, meanders and floods. Embankment stops this deposition, so that the soil is instead carried to the sea where it requires dredging from ports or deposits in the river bed blocking flow and raising the river level, so that higher banks are required. If land is drained and the water pumped to a river, the drained land often sinks, especially if it is peaty and if at the same time, the river level rises, the draining becomes more and more of an uphill task (literally). The draining of the Fens and Romney Marsh for agriculture were carried out because of the inherent fertility of the soils. Once they were drained, embankments were built which stopped further flooding and deposition of alluvial silt. Fertilisers now have to be applied, which because of the high water table, result in eutrophication

As much as 70% of the dry weather flow of some British rivers is effluent. Rivers are also a very convenient source of domestic water. Abstraction of water from rivers and aquifers has resulted in some rivers ceasing to flow in summer months. In the drought summer of 1976, the River Darent in Kent ceased to flow along long stretches. It is the only crayfish river in Kent and populations have still not recovered.

Wetland Species

Drainage of wetlands has resulted in the loss of Crane, Stork and Spoonbill from the list of British birds. Drainage in Saxon times may have been responsible for the loss of the beaver from England. Surprisingly, the otter has survived better in Britain than in many European countries, although it is still a threatened species despite some recent improvement. Smaller species have not been so hard hit because they can survive in smaller areas such as remaining ponds. However, even these require a surrounding habitat that is not extensively farmed (e.g. salt marsh grazing). Such grazing is also important for duck, geese and waders. Reservoirs and reclaimed quarries and pits have compensated a little for these losses. The use of many reservoirs for leisure pursuits (other than birdwatching) reduces their value to wildlife.

Wetland ecosystems around the world have much in common. In marshes, rivers and lakes, for example, the common reed (*Phragmites communis*) is extremely widespread. They can be divided into open water systems (rivers, lakes) and semi-terrestrial (marshes, fens, bogs). Open waters are subject to infilling with silt and colonisation by vegetation and small ponds and lakes can eventually become semi-terrestrial. Wetlands include the most and least productive ecosystems in the world. Where nutrients are brought in continuously and water is moving and oxygenated, wetlands support luxuriant foliage and a large range of animals. In semi-terrestrial systems where flow is much reduced with very low nutrient levels and the area permanently waterlogged causing near anaerobic conditions, breakdown of organic matter is very slow so nutrients are not recycled. These conditions give rise to infertile systems of low productivity such as peat bogs and tundra.

The wetlands of Britain are of two types. In the North and West, higher rainfall and cooler summers mean that there is excess water all year. In such conditions, peat moors and bogs can form above the water table. These systems are acid and of low fertility. In the South and East, there is a moisture deficit for at least some part of the summer and here wetlands occur where river flow is reduced in low-lying flat country. The peat systems are most at risk from peat extraction or afforestation in the case of the flow country of Scotland. The wetlands of the South and East have the most value for farming and have been and are being drained for this purpose.

In the last 30 years or so, about 100,000 Ha a year in England and Wales have been drained for farming. The Ministry of Agriculture gives grants of about £50 million a year for the purpose. Such work can only succeed if local water authorities and Internal Drainage Boards undertake pumping schemes and other water regulation measures. They probably spend about the same amount again as MAFF. Until recently this has been done without regard to the environmental costs.

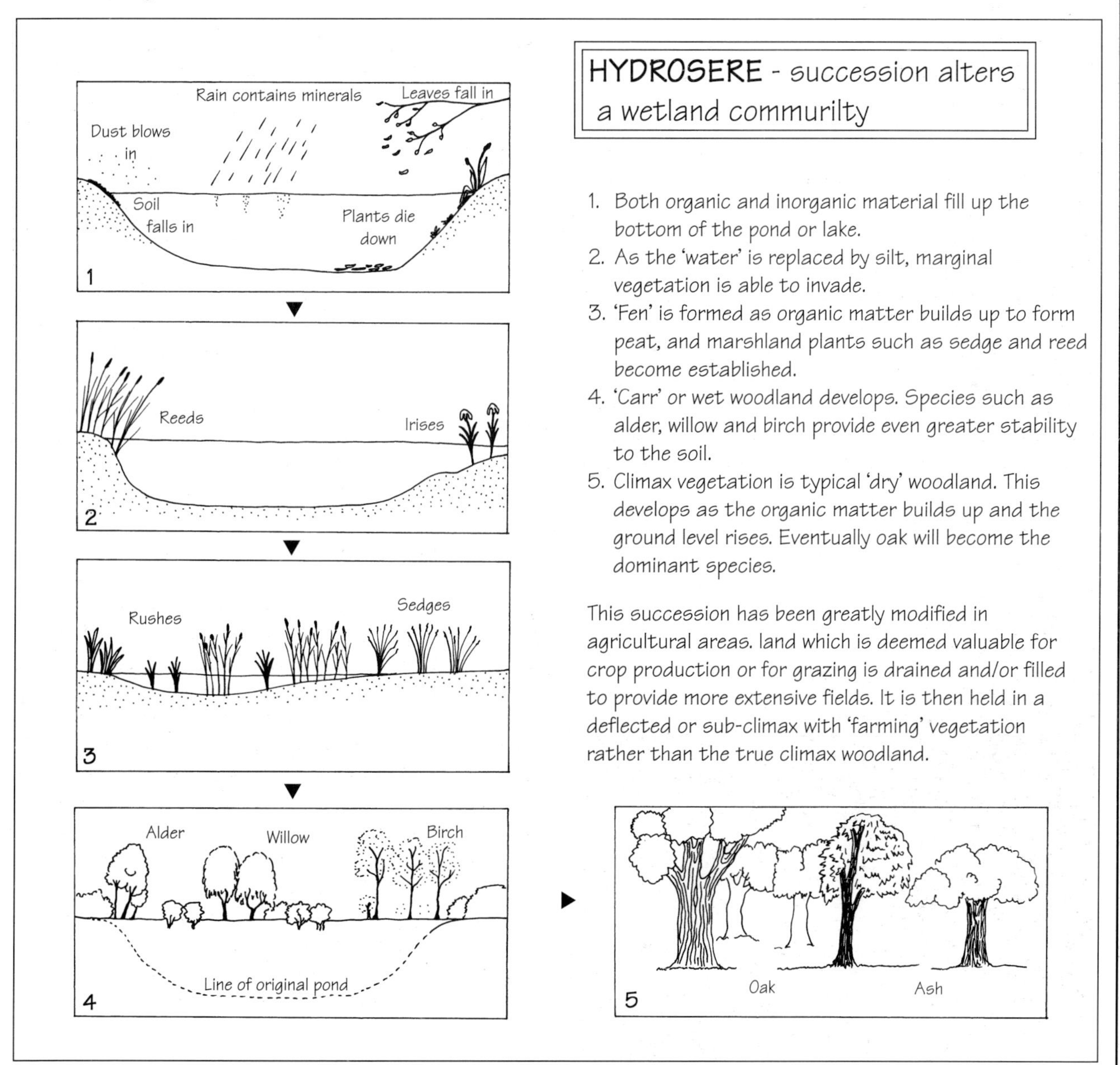

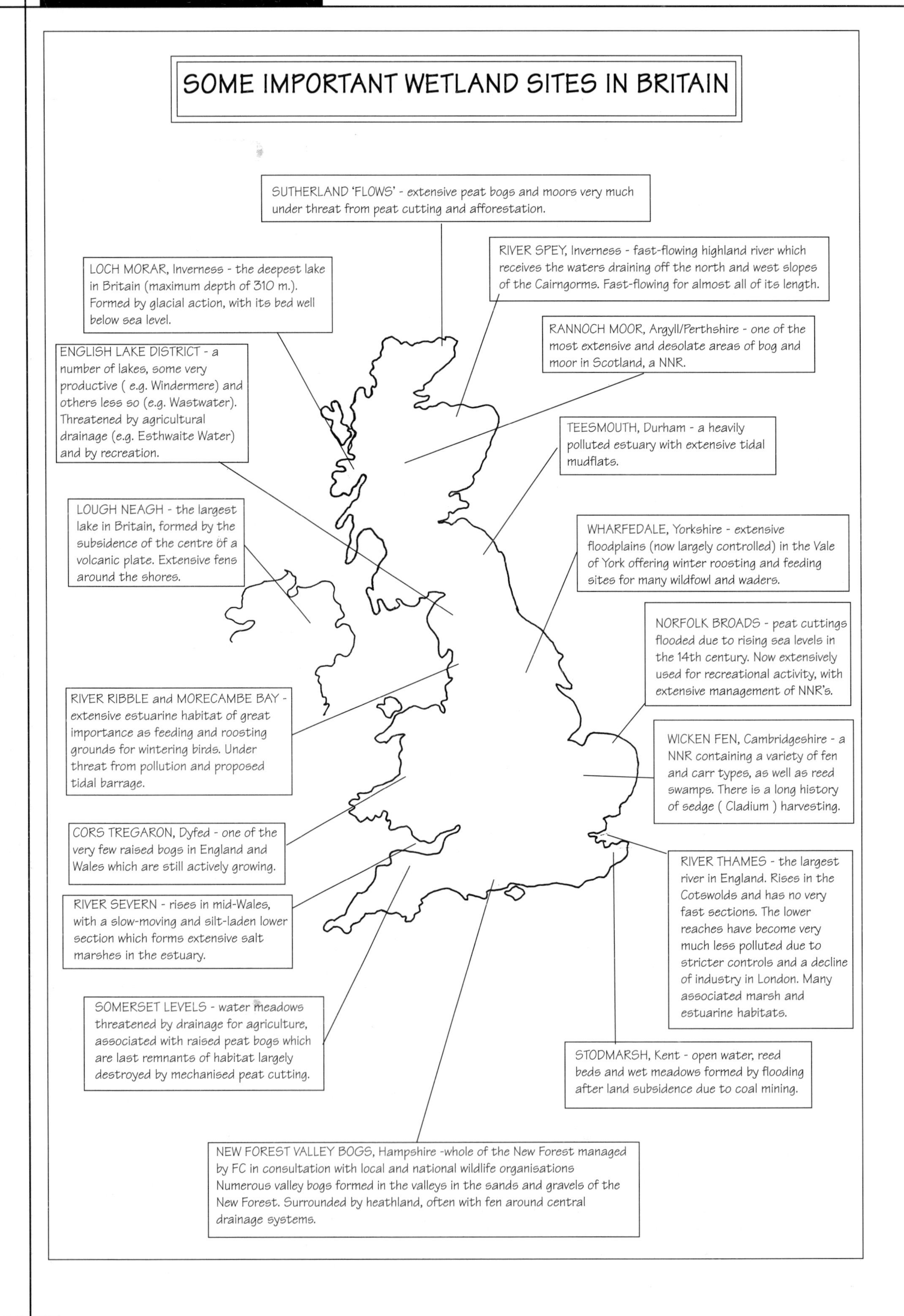
SOME IMPORTANT WETLAND SITES IN BRITAIN
SUTHERLAND 'FLOWS' - extensive peat bogs and moors very much under threat from peat cutting and afforestation.
LOCH MORAR, Inverness - the deepest lake in Britain (maximum depth of 310 m.). Formed by glacial action, with its bed well below sea level.
RIVER SPEY, Inverness - fast-flowing highland river which receives the waters draining off the north and west slopes of the Cairngorms. Fast-flowing for almost all of its length.
RANNOCH MOOR, Argyll/Perthshire - one of the most extensive and desolate areas of bog and moor in Scotland, a NNR.
ENGLISH LAKE DISTRICT - a number of lakes, some very productive (e.g. Windermere) and others less so (e.g. Wastwater). Threatened by agricultural drainage (e.g. Esthwaite Water) and by recreation.
TEESMOUTH, Durham - a heavily polluted estuary with extensive tidal mudflats.
LOUGH NEAGH - the largest lake in Britain, formed by the subsidence of the centre of a volcanic plate. Extensive fens around the shores.
WHARFEDALE, Yorkshire - extensive floodplains (now largely controlled) in the Vale of York offering winter roosting and feeding sites for many wildfowl and waders.
NORFOLK BROADS - peat cuttings flooded due to rising sea levels in the 14th century. Now extensively used for recreational activity, with extensive management of NNR's.
RIVER RIBBLE and MORECAMBE BAY - extensive estuarine habitat of great importance as feeding and roosting grounds for wintering birds. Under threat from pollution and proposed tidal barrage.
WICKEN FEN, Cambridgeshire - a NNR containing a variety of fen and carr types, as well as reed swamps. There is a long history of sedge (Cladium) harvesting.
CORS TREGARON, Dyfed - one of the very few raised bogs in England and Wales which are still actively growing.
RIVER THAMES - the largest river in England. Rises in the Cotswolds and has no very fast sections. The lower reaches have become very much less polluted due to stricter controls and a decline of industry in London. Many associated marsh and estuarine habitats.
RIVER SEVERN - rises in mid-Wales, with a slow-moving and silt-laden lower section which forms extensive salt marshes in the estuary.
SOMERSET LEVELS - water meadows threatened by drainage for agriculture, associated with raised peat bogs which are last remnants of habitat largely destroyed by mechanised peat cutting.
STODMARSH, Kent - open water, reed beds and wet meadows formed by flooding after land subsidence due to coal mining.
NEW FOREST VALLEY BOGS, Hampshire -whole of the New Forest managed by FC in consultation with local and national wildlife organisations Numerous valley bogs formed in the valleys in the sands and gravels of the New Forest. Surrounded by heathland, often with fen around central drainage systems.

Pesticides

For the vast majority of farmers in Britain, pesticides are an essential tool. Pesticides include herbicides (weedkillers), fungicides (for controlling diseases of crops), insecticides and acaricides (to control insect and mite pests of crops and animals), molluscicides (slugs and snails) rodenticides (rats and mice) and other smaller categories such as plant growth regulators and desiccants (to assist harvest). It has been estimated by the World Health Organisation (WHO) that, around the world, about 30-40% of all crops grown are lost to pests in one of the categories above. In the UK, the Home Grown Cereals Authority has shown in trials that from 1988-1990, application of fungicides to wheat caused an average yield increase of 20% (range 16-23%) while in 1991/92 season (a bad fungal year) yield improvement was 27-28%.

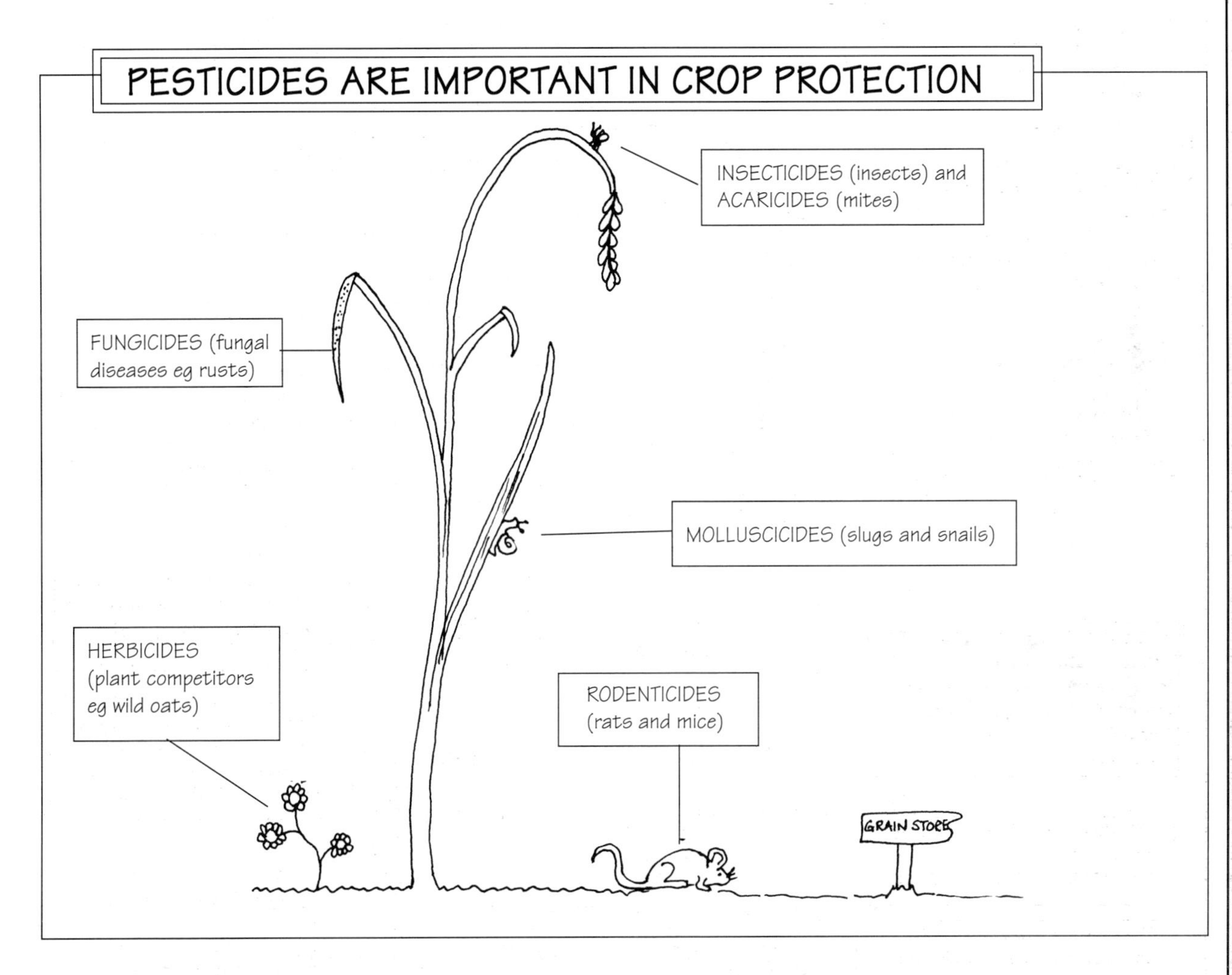

The first modern pesticides were developed just after the war and initially consisted of three classes of chemical. The organochlorine insecticides of which DDT is the best known, organophosphate insecticides and derivatives of phenoxy-acetic acid. The latter are mimics of auxins and control broad-leaved weeds and grasses. They are still commonly used as selective herbicides in cereals and in lawn weedkillers. Several inorganic chemicals had been used as pesticides before this time: sulphur and various copper salts such as Bordeaux Mixture as fungicides, arsenic salts as insecticides and herbicides.

It is unfortunate that the term "organic" has been appropriated for a particular type of farming and gardening which does not allow the use of modern pesticides. Many "organic" growers will, however, happily use sulphur or copper salts as fungicides. To the chemist, organic means containing carbon and so all modern pesticides are organic chemicals while sulphur and copper salts are inorganic (do not contain carbon).

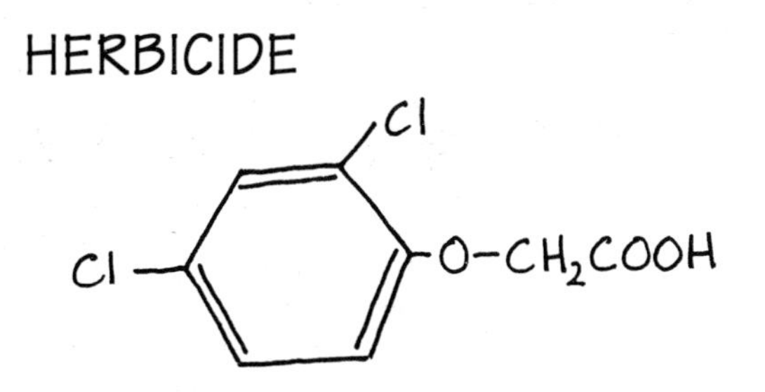

2,4•D (2,4 dichlorophenoxyethanoic acid)

DDT and other organochlorines, particularly Aldrin and Dieldrin came into widespread use in the UK in the 50's and early 60's. There were large scale deaths of seed eating and other birds and some mammals especially in East Anglia. These included pigeons, pheasants, rooks and predators such as raptors and foxes. The population of sparrowhawks declined dramatically. In Scotland, the numbers of Golden Eagles were greatly reduced. In 1963, the UK population of Peregrine Falcon had dropped by 44% from the 700 breeding pairs of 1939. Elsewhere it fared even worse: the USA population dropping by 85%.

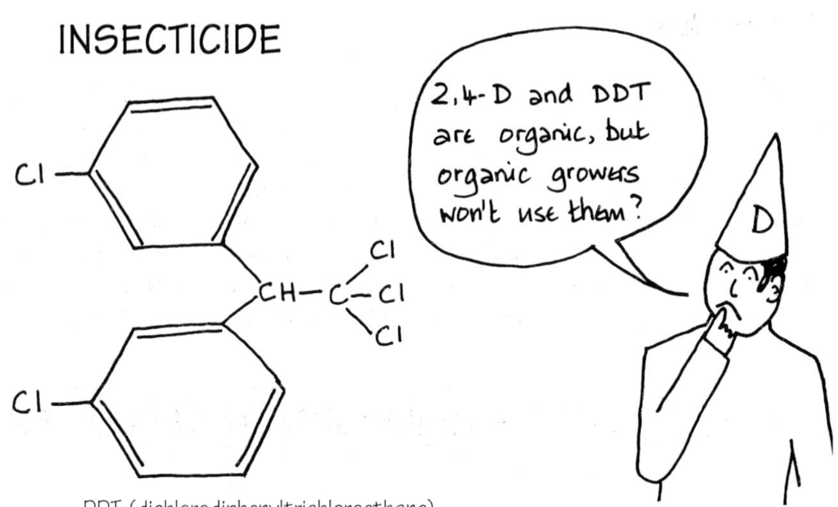

DDT (dichlorodiphenyltrichloroethane)

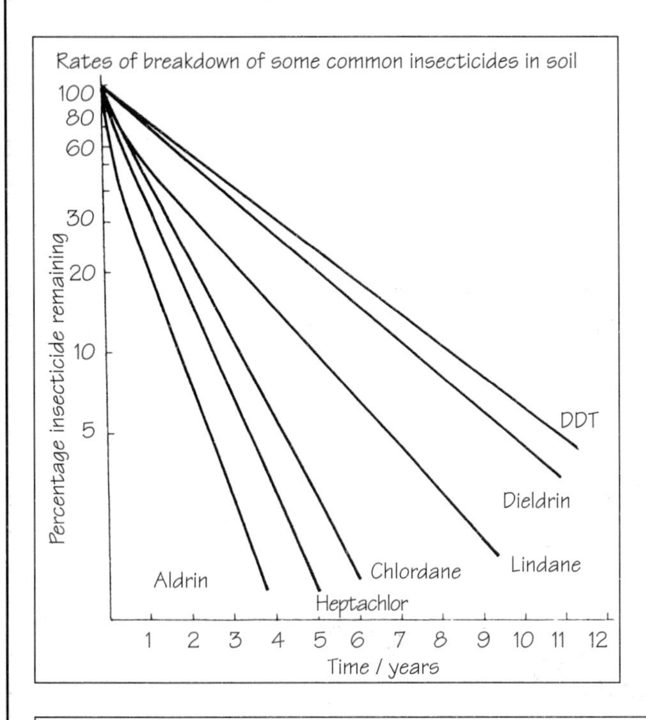

Work by the Nature Conservancy showed (Newton 1974, Ratcliffe 1972) that Dieldrin cereal seed dressings and Aldrin sheep dips were to blame. One of the particular problems of the Organochlorines was that they were very persistent in the environment and because of this slow breakdown, they accumulated in the food chain, causing deaths of predators and, in the case of birds, further population reductions due to thinning of eggshells. Rachel Carson's famous book "Silent Spring" (1962) has had a great influence on the public's perception of pesticides, but the organochlorine problem was tackled in the UK by a voluntary agreement in 1961 to restrict the use of Aldrin and Dieldrin arid to only treat cereal seed with Dieldrin for autumn sowing when it was less of a hazard as there were many other sources of food for birds at that time. The use of these persistent organochlorines was greatly restricted through the 60's and 70's leaving a very small number of minor uses in the 80's and they are now completely banned.

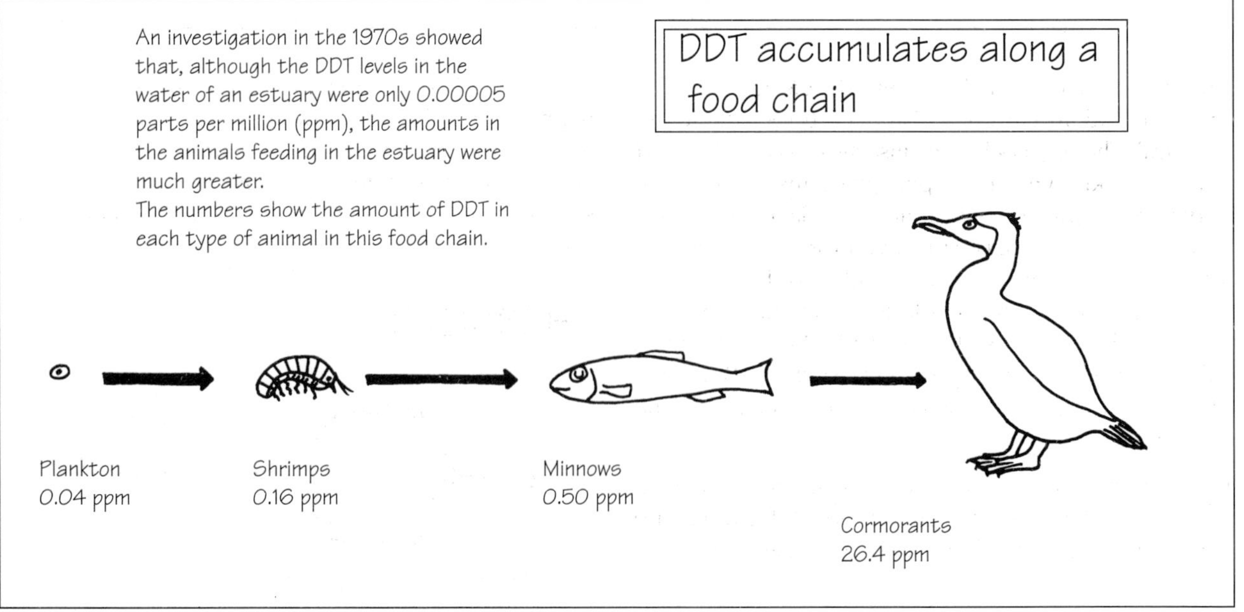

After these problems the registration and use of pesticides has come under tighter and tighter legal controls, resulting in the UK in the Control of Pesticide Regulations (COPR - 1986) enacted under the Food and Environment Protection Act (FEPA). All pesticides in the UK have to be approved for use by MAFF and an enormous quantity of data has to be generated on their efficacy and safety to users, consumers of the food, wildlife and the environment. As a result of this, pesticides are the most well-studied of any chemicals (natural or man-made) in the environment. All European states are now moving towards harmonisation of pesticide regulations within the E.U.

Why use Pesticides?

Some people believe that all pesticides are dangerous and farmers should stop using them because they damage the environment and residues can be left in foods and may be toxic. A small percentage (6%) of UK crops are grown "organically", that is without the use of pesticides at all or with the minimal use of certain "natural" pesticides. A few people claim that organic food tastes better, but all tests carried out show no detectable difference. Those who buy organic food do so more often because of their fear of residues or worries about environmental effects. It is important that consumers have a choice. In the same way that some people prefer their food to be "additive" free, i.e. not containing artificial colours or preservatives, so they want pesticide free food. It seems obvious that no-one would want to eat pesticide residues, but pesticides make food cheap and blemish free, so we have to make a choice. In the past, food was produced without use of pesticides and so it should be possible to do so again. It is, however, not possible to turn back the clock. The world population has been and is continuing to rise rapidly but we have most of the land on which food can be grown already under production. To increase food output we only have two choices: we can farm more land, which means destroying forests or draining wetlands (see earlier) or using marginal land with resulting desertification or erosion or we produce more per unit of land.

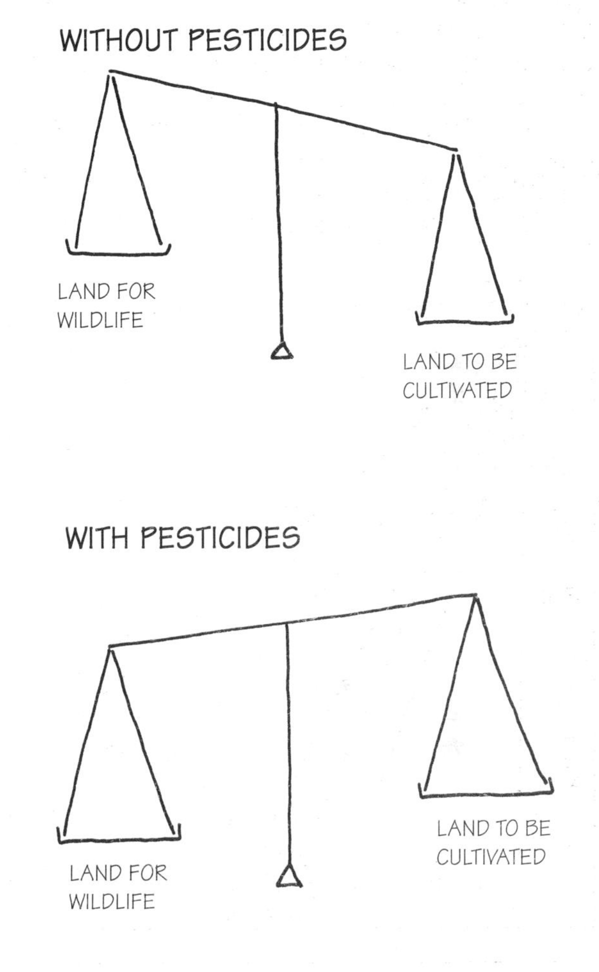

Even if all pesticides were banned, we would still be able to produce food much more efficiently than in the past because of modern machinery and crop varieties, but we would be able to produce a lot less than we do now. This may not matter for cereal crops which are in surplus in the EU, but would cause problems in the case of other foodstuffs.

Pesticides

The main reason for the public buying and being encouraged to buy "organic" food is that it has not been treated with pesticides. The general perception of pesticides is that they are very toxic, are extremely damaging to the environment and are used excessively and carelessly by farmers. Much of the language used by those who would have them banned is highly emotive. Crops are "drenched" in pesticides; they are "poisoning the countryside"; they leave "toxic" residues in our food; they are "carcinogenic" (cancer causing). If this is the case, it would certainly be sensible to reduce and if possible, stop the use of pesticides. It will be useful to examine each of these points in turn.

1) Pesticides are overused : The use of pesticides in the UK certainly increased during the 1960's and '70's. This is because this was the period of the highest rate of introduction of new molecules. The requirements for registration of pesticides are now so great that it takes about 10 years from synthesis of a new chemical to its first sales. The data necessary for approval of a product cost about £50-70 million to generate. This means that only extremely large multi-national companies can afford it and that far fewer new chemicals are now registered each year than in the 60's and 70's. The newer molecules are much more active and specific than before. The result is that quantities of pesticide used in developed countries is decreasing. In the UK, annual pesticide tonnage has fallen by 32.2% over the 8 years from 1983 to 1991. The advent of set-aside (see p. 111) is causing usage to fall still further.

New pesticides are discovered in four ways.

- Natural pesticides, for example pyrethrin insecticide from flowers of the chrysanthemum family is extracted and used as it is or chemically modified.
- Chemicals are randomly synthesised and tested to see if they have biological activity.
- An essential biochemical pathway in a pest e.g. the synthesis of chitin in insects, is identified and molecules synthesised and tested to see if they can block it.
- Chemical derivatives of an existing pesticide are made and tested to see if they have improved or slightly different activity.

Because of the huge complexity of biological systems method, the last has the highest success rate for Agrochemical companies. Hence many pesticides fall into certain chemical categories, such as the early products, the organochlorines, the organophosphates and the phenoxy acid derivatives. More modern such chemical groups are the ureas (herbicides), triazines (herbicides), synthetic pyrethroids (insecticides based on pyrethrin) and triazole (fungicides).

2) Why pesticides can't solve all pest problems
Another factor in the reduction of pesticide usage is Integrated Pest Management (IPM). In the sixties and seventies, such was the success of pesticides, that many farmers thought that all pest problems could be solved by them. But then problems started to arise caused by pesticide resistance, pest resurgence and new pest selection.

a) Resistant Pests
In any large population of organisms there will be genetic diversity. Many pesticides have a specific site of action on one enzyme in the pest. A small percentage of individuals in a population may have variants of that enzyme such that the pesticide is not as effective, or is totally ineffective against it. Equally, all organisms have means of chemically altering toxic chemicals so that they can be made harmless. The doses of applied pesticide must be sufficient to overcome that system. Some individual pests may have an altered detoxifying system or a faster one that renders them resistant. In the absence of a pesticide, these genetic differences may be neutral i.e. they do not affect the individuals "fitness" to survive or they may even be a disadvantage i.e. an altered enzyme in a crucial pathway may make the individual smaller or slower growing. The neutral mutation would result in a constant (but possibly small) percentage of the population carrying the gene, while

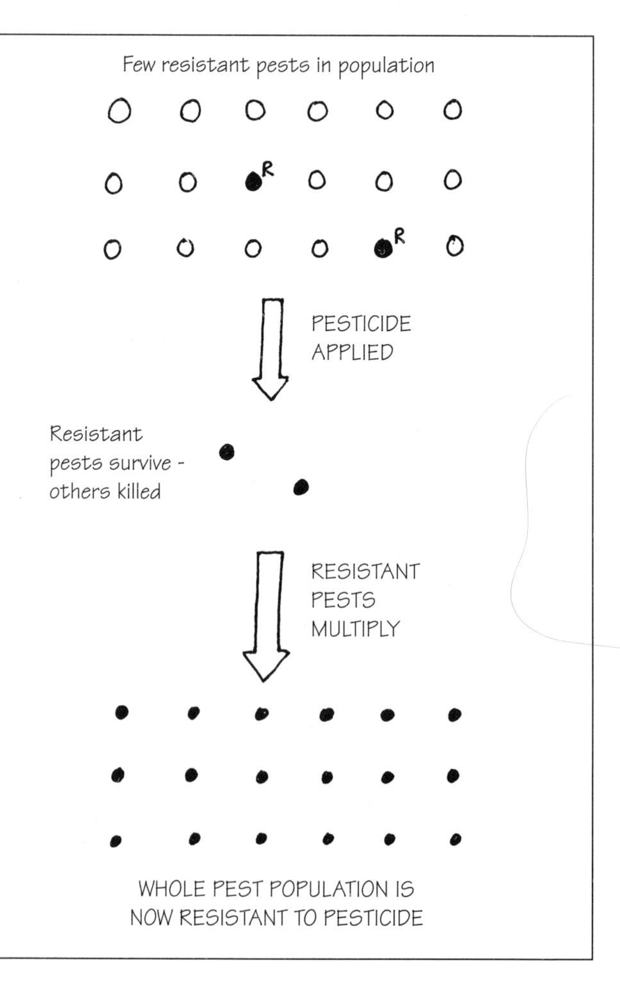

the disadvantageous mutation would give a reducing percentage of the population with the gene as the "fitter" individuals survive better. However, if we apply a pesticide that wipes out the "normal" gene population, the small percentage with the altered gene has a chance to thrive. The next time we apply the pesticide, progeny from the individuals with altered genes will form a larger proportion of the population and that proportion will increase with each application until we have a totally resistant pest. As many pesticides belong to distinct chemical families and therefore have the same mode of action, the chances of resistance developing are higher.

Resistance is a greater problem in pests that reproduce rapidly as the genes conferring resistance are spread more quickly.

b) Pest resurgence

Many pest species are capable of extremely rapid increases in numbers - these increases are prevented by the action of the natural predators of the pests. Pesticides may kill not only pests but also their predators - if the predators are slow to increase in number, the predators may reproduce unchecked!

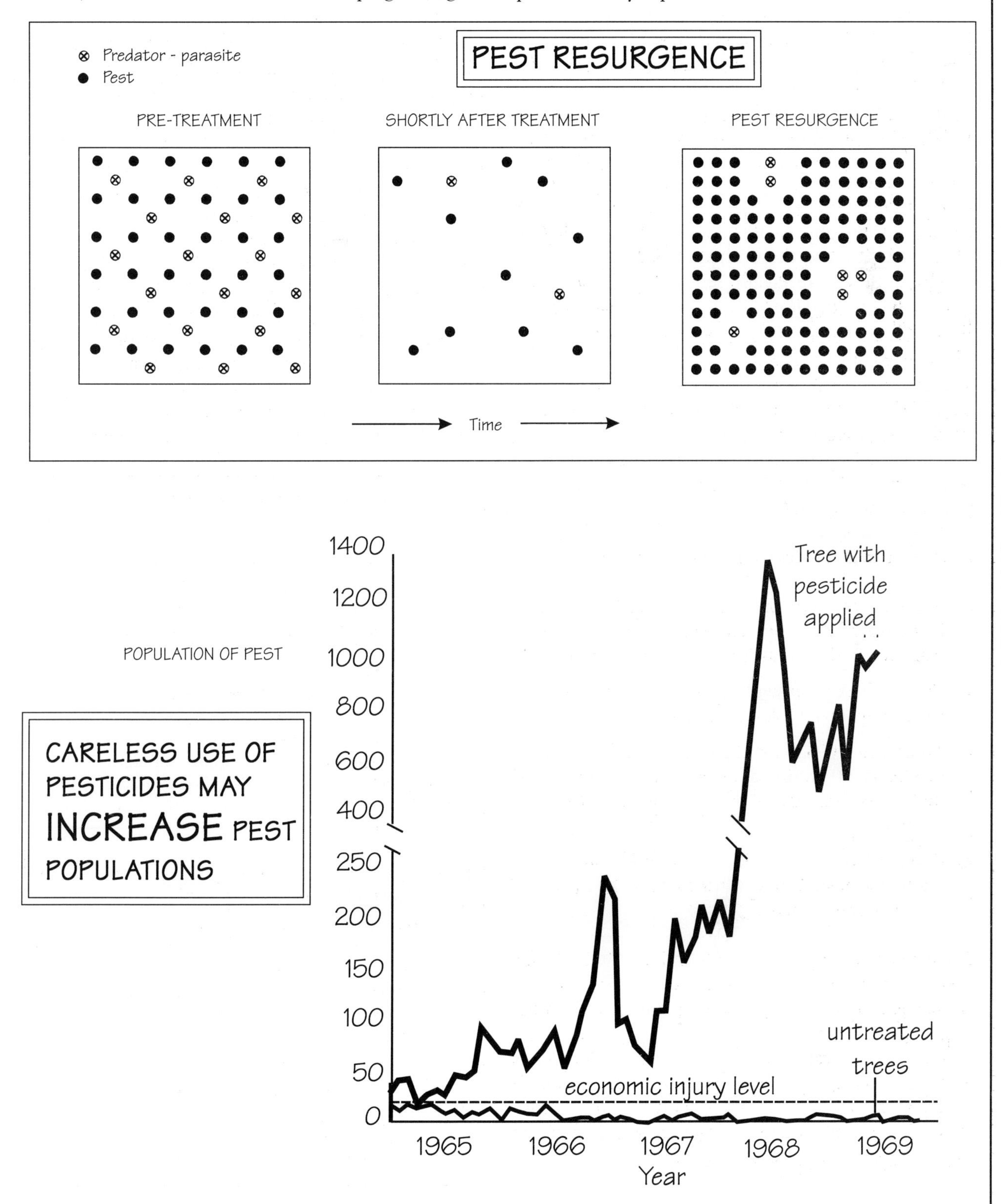

c) New Pest Selection

In any ecosystem, there are dominant plants or animals. If by some means you remove the dominant organisms, others have a chance to thrive. If a farmer grows wheat and has a lot of broad-leaved weeds (dicotyledons) there are a number of very effective herbicides he can use to remove them. However it is much more difficult to remove grass weeds (monocotyledons) because the wheat is itself a grass and to achieve a selective kill of one grass in others is more difficult than to kill dicots in monocots or vice versa. If cereals are grown intensively, year after year, the weed grasses can become more of a problem as their "weed competition" has been removed. Such is the case with sterile brome (*Bromus sterilis*) and latterly other bromus spp. in cereals.

In the case of insecticides and acaricides in particular, many of the current products are very broad spectrum and so can kill predators as well as pests. Spider mites (*Panonychus ulmi*) in orchards have become resistant to organophosphorus insecticides and acaricides. Moreover, because these chemicals are very broad spectrum, they have greatly reduced the populations of natural mite predators (invertebrates). Fruit growers have now generally stopped using such products as they are no longer effective.

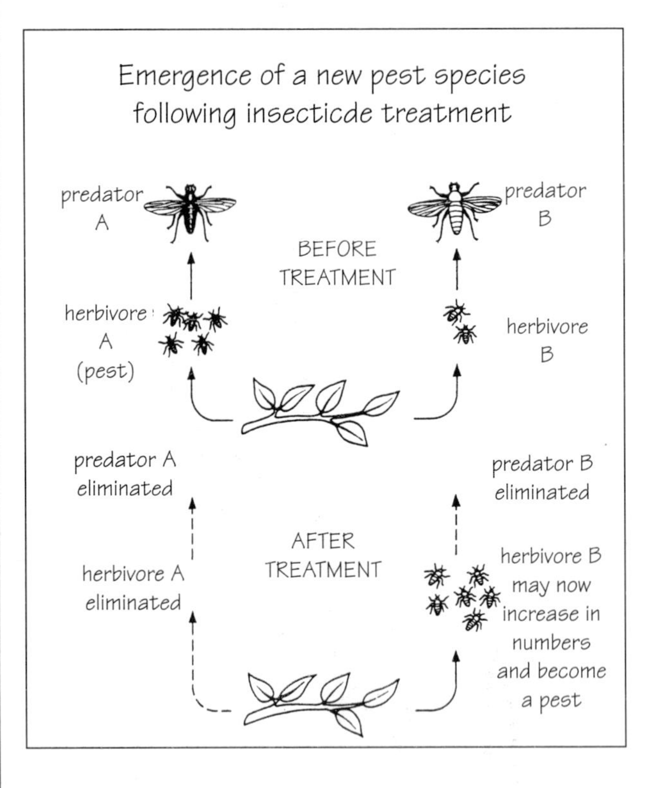

3) I.P.M. (Integrated Pest Management)

Farmers and growers have come to see that pesticides cannot cure all the problems and that all methods available should be used. This is Integrated Pest Management. There are many methods of keeping pests under control that do not involve pesticides, such as manipulating sowing and harvest dates to avoid pest

*** Sowing and harvest dates.**

Oilseed rape can be sown in the autumn or the spring. Autumn sowing has the advantage of higher yields (due to early growth in the spring) and earlier flowering. The earlier flowering means that the crop is less at risk from Pollen beetles (*Meligethes* spp.) which usually require an insecticide spray on Spring Rape. However, autumn sown rape can be vary badly damaged (often to the point of crop loss) in some parts of the country by pigeons. Autumn sown crops can also be attacked by Cabbage stem flea beetle (*Psylliodes chrysocephala*) which is not a problem in spring sown crops. If the autumn is extremely wet (such as 1992) farmers may have no choice but to leave sowing to the spring. Carrot fly (*Psila rosae*) is a very serious pest of carrots, celery, parsnips and parsley. It has two generations a year, the main periods of crop damage being June/July and October/January. Sowing in June can avoid damage by the first generation. Equally, early harvest of spring sown crops can avoid damage by the second generation. Carrots left in the ground to be lifted fresh during the winter are liable to be damaged. Soil insecticides, applied at planting are effective against the early generation but do not persist long enough to control the second.

*** Resistant varieties**

Plant breeders are always trying to breed resistance to various plant diseases into plants. For some diseases this can be very effective, but others are more intractable. Canker (Phoma lingam) of oilseed rape has reduced greatly in importance over the last 10 years due to new resistant varieties. Resistance to insects also occurs in the wild but has been much more difficult to use. A potato variety bred a few years ago was resistant to aphids but after years of development it had to be scrapped when it was found to contain toxic levels (to humans) of solanine (an alkaloid). All potatoes contain solanine but at a low enough level to be safe. Genetic engineering can now allow the gene for the insecticidal toxin produced by *Bacillus thuringiensis* to be transferred to and expressed in cotton plants. Trials of such plants are already underway. Whether such developments are good or bad needs to be discussed in public in more detail than to date.

*** Crop rotation**

Farmers have always practised crop rotation but the range of crops in the rotation is generally smaller nowadays than formerly, because of the specialisation of land use for maximum yields. Crop rotation reduces the build up of certain pests and diseases and because of the selectivity of herbicides also allows better control of grass weeds in oilseed rape than cereals and better control of broad-leaved weeds in cereals than oilseed rape for example. New UK crops such as sunflowers and linseed and set-aside (once the rules are sorted out) may widen the opportunities for crop rotation.

TECHNIQUES OF INTEGRATED PEST MANAGEMENT (IPM)

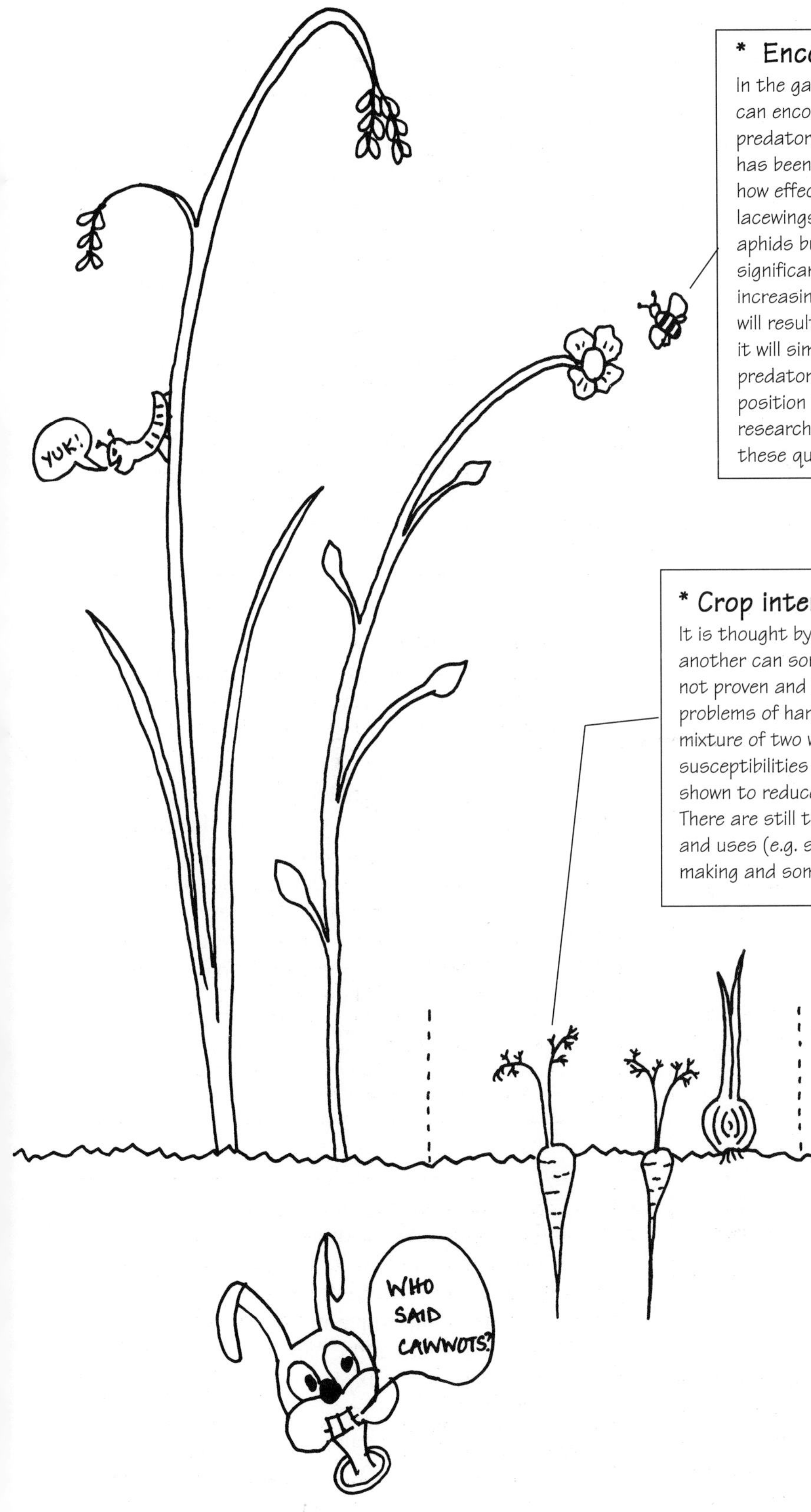

*** Encouraging predators**

In the garden, flowers growing near vegetables can encourage hover flies, some of which are predators of aphids. However, very little work has been done on what are the best flowers and how effective the predation is. Ladybirds, lacewings and spiders are also predators of aphids but we do not know the relative significance of them. We do not know if increasing hover fly or other predator numbers will result in better control of aphids or whether it will simply result in increased predation of the predators. We do not know where the equilibrium position lies. Work is under way at a number of research institutes to try to answer some of these questions.

*** Crop interplanting**

It is thought by some that interplanting one crop with another can sometimes reduce pest problems. This is not proven and in any case would present tremendous problems of harvest for farmers. However, planting a mixture of two wheat varieties with different susceptibilities to various cereal diseases has been shown to reduce the spread of fungal disease in a crop. There are still the problems of different harvest dates and uses (e.g. some wheat is good for bread or biscuit making and some only for animal feed) to overcome.

*** Physical barriers.**

In the garden, cabbages can be protected from cabbage root fly by putting collars around the neck of young plants as the fly lays its eggs in the soil on or very close to the plant neck. If eggs were laid too far away (even a couple of inches) the larvae would not be able to damage the plant . Fine netting about 2 ft high around small blocks of carrots will prevent carrot fly damage as the fly is very small and flies close to the ground. There are no physical prevention methods used in agriculture because of the scale of commercial growing.

peaks, encouraging predators, physical barriers, crop rotation, crop interplanting and resistant crop varieties. Gardeners use most of these, although some are impractical for field scale use. Organic farmers use many of them, but some farmers have forgotten about them or ignored them while pesticides were so successful.

Some of these techniques are already widely used and have been for some time but others require further research work.

A combination of all these methods plus the use of timely and specific pesticides is likely to provide the best results in the future. Methods of managing pest resistance are also being used. All farmers now understand the need to vary the types of pesticide used so that chemicals with different modes of action are alternated to avoid selection of a particular resistant population. Although in general we would like to use very specific pesticides to reduce damage to non-target organisms, in the case of fungicides, broad spectrum, multi-site compounds sometimes provide the best means of controlling resistance. Older fungicides like sulphur and copper salts and new ones like chlorothalonil do not kill fungi by blocking one enzyme on a particular pathway, but inhibit various metabolic pathways. The chances of resistance arising to these is much lower as a number of separate gene mutations would need to have taken place in one or more individual organisms.

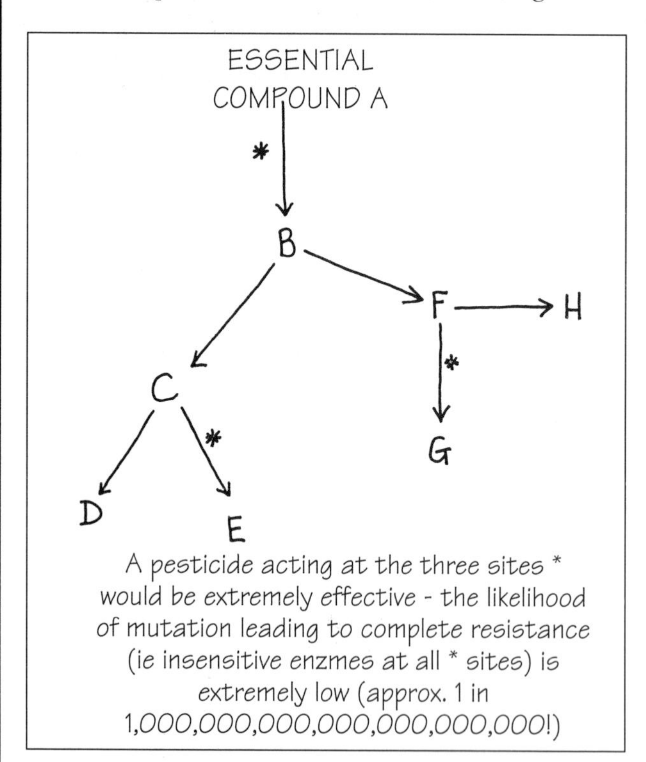

A pesticide acting at the three sites * would be extremely effective - the likelihood of mutation leading to complete resistance (ie insensitive enzmes at all * sites) is extremely low (approx. 1 in 1,000,000,000,000,000,000,000!)

There is no doubt that, in the past, pesticides have been overused but with the increase in cost of pesticide development and the reductions in farmer subsidies, pesticides are relatively expensive and farmers cannot afford to waste any.

4) Pesticides are poisoning the countryside

Again, while this was certainly true in the past with the organochlorines, the lessons were learnt from that disaster and the situation is improving rapidly. As described above, because many insecticides are broad spectrum, they have tended to reduce predator as well as pest populations. The major culprits were the organochlorines (now phased out) and the organophosphorus (OP) compounds. The latter have survived in use much longer because they are very rapidly broken down in the environment and so do not bio-accumulate. Birds and foxes are found which have died from OP poisoning, but in most cases this is due to deliberate, illegal poisoning. It is almost certain that some vertebrate predators die each year from consuming insects killed by pesticides, but the numbers are very small and there are certainly not the large population reductions as there were with Aldrin and Dieldrin. It is likely that there have been population reductions in non-target invertebrates including potential pest predators but it is difficult to quantify. This general reduction in insect populations must, of course, have an effect on the populations of insect eating birds and other animals. OP's (and a class of chemicals called carbamates which are chemically unrelated to OP's but act on the same enzyme system) are mostly very toxic to bees and there have certainly been serious bee poisoning incidents in the past and tighter controls have been placed on the use of such sprays when crops are in flower. OP's are being used less and less as many pests are resistant and more specific, less toxic products come onto the market. However, a new class of broad spectrum insecticides, the synthetic pyrethroids are increasing in use. Naturally occurring pyrethrum is a very broad spectrum insecticide which is effective in very low doses and has very low mammalian toxicity. However, it is very rapidly broken down in sunlight. It is used extensively in household insecticides and garden insecticides with a very short harvest interval. It is not effective for agricultural use. Chemical derivatives of pyrethrum have been developed which have the same broad spectrum and high activity but which are resistant to photo-chemical degradation.

The effects of farming and pesticides in particular are most visible in the case of wildflowers. We bemoan the fact that we do not see the old flowers of cereal fields any more; poppies, cornflowers, corncockles, corn marigolds, pheasant's eye, pansies etc., and this is because the countryside is "drenched" in pesticides so that nothing natural will grow any more. This is not, however, the case. It is true that most cereal crops do not contain any significant numbers of these flowers but they often contain wild oats, blackgrass, sterile brome and cleavers for example, because these are more difficult to kill with current herbicides than the wildflowers. Any farming alters the local ecology, no matter how sympathetically it is done. The "organic" gardener may use no pesticides, but she or he pulls up "weeds" and picks caterpillars off her or his lettuces.

MONITORING EFFECTS OF PESTICIDES ON THE ENVIRONMENT:
THE ICI ENVIRONMENTAL SCIENCES DEPARTMENT

BIRDS AND MAMMALS

If there is any evidence from laboratory studies that vertebrates may be affected by the use of pesticides, field experiments are carried out by Environmental Sciences.

Fieldwork on birds requires large experimental areas of at least 25 ha (55 acres) per plot. Work on birds is particularly necessary when chemical seed dressings are involved. Seed treatments are a particularly efficient way of protecting the seed and the young plant in that the chemical is placed just where it is needed. Problems can nevertheless arise if seed-eating birds feed on the treated seed.

Effects of agrochemicals on birds are assessed by plotting the numbers of occupied territories before and after sowing treated seed, or applying the chemical another way. Most birds are highly territorial during the breeding season, the breeding pairs coming together and defending their territories from others of the same species. A competent bird observer can follow a regular route around the experimental and untreated areas and plot on a map the position of each bird seen or heard. This is repeated for several weeks at intervals of a day or two and the territory outlines plotted.

Any dead birds are analysed for residues to determine if their death was due to the chemical or to natural causes.

Work on small mammals, such as mice and voles, is done on similar large areas, using trapping and marking techniques to measure the populations.

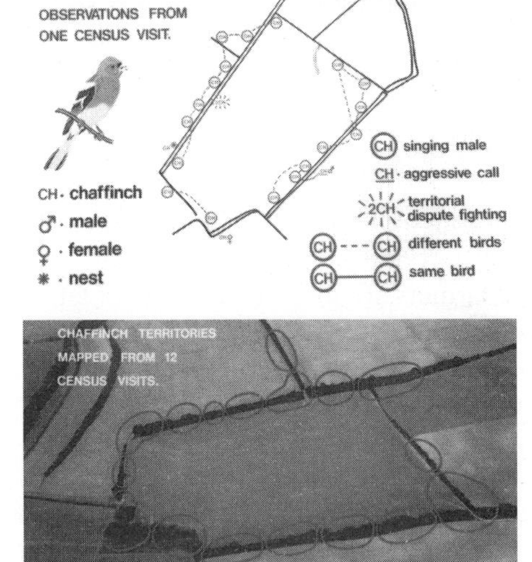

HONEY BEES

THE honey bee is an important pollinator of some crops as well as a producer of honey: thus the possible effects of pesficides, particularly insecticides, need to be assessed. This involves laboratory work to measure the oral and contact toxicity of the chemical to bees, followed by field work, if necessary, to check that it can be used safely by farmers, growers and gardeners or to establish the special practical usage instructions that may be needed for this safe use.

For field experiments three 5 ha plots of a suitable flowering crop, such as oilseed rape, are selected, the plots being several kilometres apart so that bees will not fly between them. Hives of bees are placed close to each plot and the plots are sprayed from the air, this being the form of application which is usually most damaging to bees. One plot is sprayed with the test chemical: one is a control plot which is unsprayed: while the third plot is a control which is sprayed with a chemical known to be damaging to bees.

When bees are poisoned in the field they usually fly back to the hive where they die and their bodies are carried out and discarded by the worker bees. The bodies of the dead bees are collected in trays and counted. The chemical control plot is important, as a high kill in it indicates that the bees were actively foraging and were at risk at the time the spray was applied. More subtle effects, such as on foraging behaviour, are also studied and the health of the hive is monitored.

"Weeds" are just plants growing where we don't want them. Pesticides will alter the flora more than mechanical or hand weeding, but fortunately most plants are more resilient than we might think. The few plants of agricultural land that are endangered species in the UK, such as Pheasant's eye and Shepherd's needle have become rare more through loss of habitat than application of pesticides.

When land is taken out of farming and left untouched, such as in conservation headlands (Chapter 3) and set-aside (Chapter 7) it does not become covered in nice wildflowers but in "weed" grasses and coarse perennials such as docks and thistles, because it is so fertile and generally, wildflower communities do better on soils of low fertility.

It is certainly the case that, in the past, the use of some pesticides has been excessive, not generally on the crops themselves but more on headlands, hedge bottoms and sterile strips around fields. Gradually this is changing and most farmers are more aware now of farming with minimal wildlife disturbance. The introduction of set-aside should give greater opportunities for habitat improvement if properly managed by MAFF.

Aerial spraying of pesticides gives rise to many complaints where the spray drifts from its intended target. Tighter controls have been applied by recent legislation, which should reduce problems, but many people question whether in a windy country like the UK, where crops and housing intermingle so much, aerial spraying of pesticides should be allowed at all.

d) Pesticides are toxic and carcinogenic

Pesticides vary in chemical complexity from an element, Sulphur to very complicated organic molecules of large molecular weight. Some are natural, such as pyrethrum, derris (an extract from the roots of a tropical tree), nicotine (from tobacco) and neem extract (from the neem tree of India). Some are derivatives of natural materials, but most are synthetic chemicals. There is an assumption among those with no knowledge of chemistry, that "chemicals" are nasty and harmful and "natural" things are good and safe. This is nonsense. All substances, natural or otherwise, are element or compounds: all are chemicals. The only distinction one can make is that some are known to be naturally occurring and some have, so far, only been synthesised. I say "so far" because our knowledge of chemicals in plants, fungi and bacteria is very rudimentary. One of the economic arguments for preserving rainforests (see Chapter 9) is that they contain an enormous diversity of plants, many of which have not been identified or catalogued and have never been studied. Many of these plants may well contain chemicals for use as pharmaceuticals as we know that native tribes have used many such remedies in the past. Some chemicals that we regard as synthetic may well exist somewhere in plants.

There is absolutely no reason to assume that naturally occurring chemicals are any safer than synthetic ones. We know that many natural compounds are carcinogenic or highly toxic. No chemical can ever be proven to be completely safe. As long ago as the 15th century Paraclese said "Everything is a poison, nothing is a poison. It is the dose that makes the poison." Two paracetamol tablets cure a headache and are completely safe. Even if we take 8 every day for 3 days they are completely safe, but if we signifcantly exceed the daily dose , paracetamol is usually fatal. Vitamin A is essential for humans, without it we die. Yet if we consume too much it can kill us. We cannot possibly cover all the circumstances in which a chemical could occur or all the chemicals it could be mixed with or all the genetic variation in the populace. What we can show, with extensive testing, is that there is no significant risk. This is the aim of the enormous amount of toxicological data submitted to register each pesticide.

We are not happy with the phrase "no significant risk". We would like to be assured that there is no risk at all or we want pesticides banned. Unfortunately, we cannot live risk free. Even if we accept that, we say "O.K., but why add extra unnecessary risks". The answer is that they are not unnecessary. We have available to us in the Western world today the biggest range of cheap, wholesome food that we have ever had, and that is the result of modern agriculture including pesticides. We know that certain diseases are diet related. If we do not eat enough roughage, we appear to be at greater risk of colon cancer; if we eat too much saturated fat we are at greater risk of heart disease and so on. Greater variety in diet generally leads to better health.

The toxicity of pesticides, like any other range of chemicals, varies enormously. Generally, the most toxic (to mammals) are insecticides, the least toxic, herbicides and the others in the middle. Organophosphorus and carbamate insecticides are the most toxic of those currently used. Both these chemical types act by inhibiting a particular enzyme called cholinesterase. In all animals including insects and mites, transmission of messages along nerves requires a chemical messenger. When a message is transmitted down a nerve cell and it comes to the junction with the next cell, the transmitter is released, crosses the gap (the synapse) and causes the next nerve cell to "fire" and so on down to the muscle. One of the most common such messengers is acetylcholine. An enzyme in the synapse (cholinesterase) breaks the messenger down very rapidly to acetate (ethanoate) and choline. So that the nerve is ready to fire again immediately if required. OP's and carbamates block the action of the enzyme so that the acetylcholine is not broken down and nerve transmission is blocked.

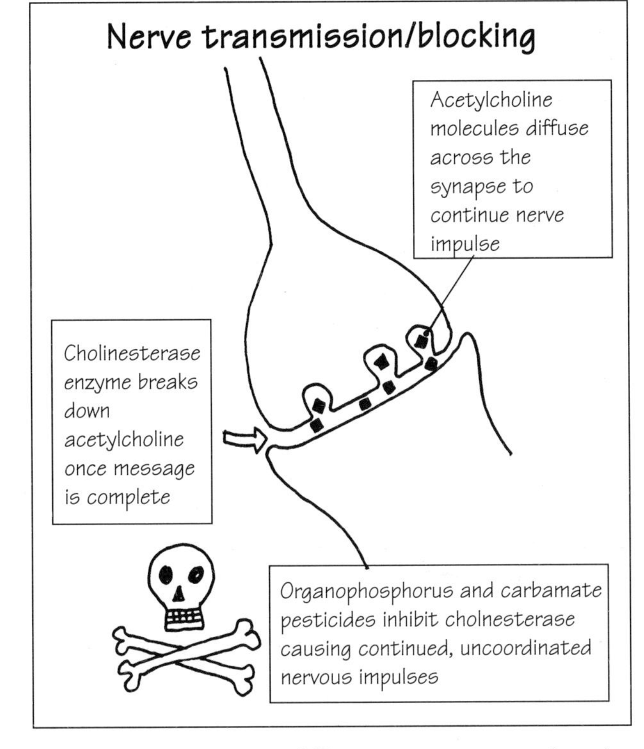

The enzyme varies in different organisms and so by chemical modification, specificity can be altered. Some materials are very broad spectrum and toxic to insects (including bees) and mites and animals. These are being replaced by better materials. Some are broad spectrum but of low toxicity to mammals and so can be used in pet flea collars or even in a shampoo for head lice (malathion). One carbamate is so specific, that it kills aphids but not ladybirds or bees (pirimicarb).

As with any generality, the statement above that insecticides are the most toxic and herbicides the least toxic pesticides has many exceptions. Paraquat is notoriously a toxic herbicide, but it is very safe in use. It only has contact action on plants, and is absorbed by the soil on contact, so has no residual activity. The dreadful poisoning incidents reported in the press are due to suicide attempts or accidental poisonings due to the liquid being decanted from the original pack and stored in unmarked containers. This is illegal under the Control of Pesticide Regulations (COPR). Equally, a naturally occurring insecticide BT is, as far as anyone can tell (see above), completely non-toxic to animals. A naturally occurring bacterium, *Bacillus thuringiensis*, which infects insects produces a toxin which kills its host. BT is grown in fermentation vats and the toxin and bacterial spores are harvested and bottled. The product is diluted and sprayed onto crops.

Those prejudiced against synthetic chemicals will say that of course BT is safe, it's natural! Nicotine is a naturally occurring insecticide but it is extremely toxic. Ricin is a chemical produced by Castor Oil plants. It is one of the most toxic, quick acting poisons known. It is believed that a Bulgarian defector, Georgi Markov was killed by secret police agents in London in the 1970's by being jabbed in the leg by a sharp umbrella point containing ricin.

People are very worried by residues of pesticides in food and the fact that they may be carcinogenic. What must be realised is that no approved pesticide is a proven human carcinogen. When it is said that a chemical is a suspect carcinogen' it means that in certain tests both in vivo and in vitro, it shows properties that could make it a carcinogen. The doses used for these tests are much higher than could ever be eaten by any consumer. They have to be high to obtain a statistically meaningful result. If a pesticide shows such properties, and many don't, it is a suspect or possible carcinogen. The residues of it that are allowed in food must be, by law, one hundredth or even one thousandth of the No Effect Level (NOEL) determined from tests on animals. We cannot avoid carcinogens in our environment. We breathe them in and eat them, natural and synthetic every day. Radon in the air is carcinogenic, as is other people's cigarette smoke. Well done toast and overcooked beefburgers contain carcinogens. Sunlight is carcinogenic if you get sunburnt. The point is, as stated above, dose makes the poison. We have defence and repair mechanisms in the body which work very well providing they are not swamped by high levels of a poison or carcinogen.

Dr. Bruce Ames is a very eminent American scientist. He developed a test, carried out in a Petri Dish, to determine whether a chemical was a mutagen or not. A mutagen can alter the genetic code of organisms and thus may be carcinogenic. This test is accepted as a worldwide standard. He tested a number of pesticides and other synthetic chemicals and found that on average, about half of them were mutagens. He was very worried by this and for a while was a vociferous campaigner for the banning of pesticides and food additives. Then one day he wondered whether any naturally occurring chemicals were also mutagens. He started testing some. He found to his amazement that about half the natural chemicals he tested were indeed mutagens and has calculated that our diet contains 10,000 times more natural pesticide than man-made pesticide residues. He realised that the mere fact that we consume mutagens does not mean that they will give us cancer.

We have innate repair systems which are very effective. Mushrooms, specially raw are highly carcinogenic and peanut butter is even worse as it contains one of the most potent carcinogens known; an aflatoxin produced by a fungus that grows on stored peanuts. One cup of coffee contains more carcinogens that a year's dietary intake of pesticide residues. One hundred cups of coffee contain a lethal dose of caffeine. No-one as far as I know, is calling for the banning of mushrooms, coffee and peanuts. We must realise that no human activity is without risk, including eating "organic" food. What matters is that risks are minimised and that any risk is outweighed by a benefit. Many drugs can have serious side effects but, if we are ill, we take them because we can see the benefit. The risks of pesticides are very small indeed, if there are any, but the benefits in terms of good quality, cheap, plentiful food are enormous.

e) Residues

A large part of the high investment and long time taken to register a new pesticide is due to the extensive safety testing required. Thorough toxicological testing includes acute toxicity, irritancy, carcinogenicity, teratogenicity (whether it can cause birth defects), embryo toxicity, two year feeding studies, no-effect level and fate and breakdown in mammals and plants and the soil. Residue levels in harvested crops are also determined. From this latter data, regulatory bodies are able to set a maximum residue level (MRL). The MRL does not in itself have any toxicological significance. It is merely used for monitoring of food. If the pesticide is being used properly at the right timing and dose, the MRL should not be exceeded. If in random food samples MRL's were found to be exceeded, regulatory authorities would require the registration holder to carry out further trials to determine why. The no-effect level for a pesticide is found from two year feeding studies in rats (and sometimes other animals). This is the amount of pesticide that can be administered daily in an animal's food without there being any noticeable effect on the animal. This gives the ADI or acceptable daily intake. For a pesticide to be approved, its MRL or MRLs if it is used on more than one crop, must be sufficiently low that the general population's possible daily intake of that pesticide is much smaller than the ADI. In fact, the maximum consumption of the pesticide residue is usually one hundredth or less of the acceptable daily intake. Monitoring of residues in food in 1991 showed that no residues at all were found in 72% of samples; 26% had residues below the MRL; and the 2% of samples with residues above the MRL were well below the levels of the ADI. Monitoring is deliberately targeted at those foodstuffs in which pesticide residues are most likely to be found.

GENETICALLY ENGINEERED CROPS

Crops approved for cultivation or import to the US
(as of September 1996)

Herbicide-tolerant oilseed rape
Virus resistant squash
Delayed ripening tomato
Insect-protected maize
Increased laurate oilseed rape
Herbicide-tolerant soyabeans
Insect-protected potatoes

Products EU approved

Herbicide-resistant tobacco
Herbicide-resistant soyabeans

Pending EU approval

Insect-protected maize
Herbicide-resisant maize
Herbicide-tolerant oilseed rape
Hybrid oilseed rape

Products in research

Diease resistant wheat
High-solids potatoes
Higher sugar strawberries
Plants that produce naturally coloured cotton fibres
Plants that produce biodegradable plastic polymers for packaging and industrial use.

RESISTANCE TO PESTS AND HERBICIDES

a gene is inserted into the plant which enables it to make INSECTICAL CRYSTAL PROTEIN (ICP) which affects the gut of caterpillars so that they cannot feed and eventually die.

the crop plant has a gene transferred into it which makes it resistant to herbicides. The field of growing crop can then be sprayed with the herbicide which will selectively kill the 'weeds' since they do not possess the 'resistance' gene.

TRANSFERRING GENES WITH *Agrobacterium tumefaciens*

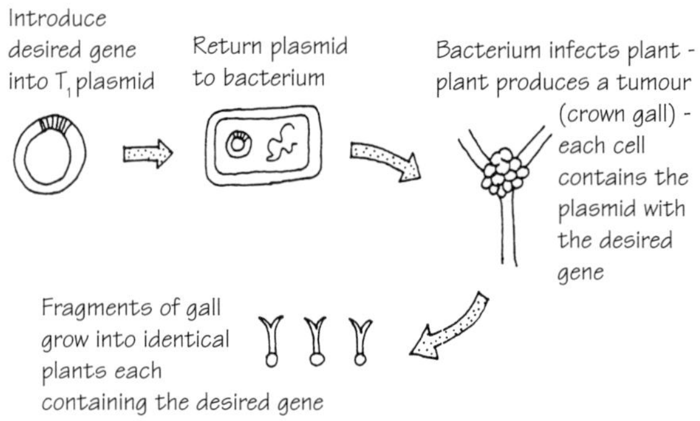

Introduce desired gene into T_i plasmid

Return plasmid to bacterium

Bacterium infects plant - plant produces a tumour (crown gall) - each cell contains the plasmid with the desired gene

Fragments of gall grow into identical plants each containing the desired gene

GENE TRANSFER CAN PROMOTE DESIRABLE CHARACTERISTICS

GENE TRANSFER IS ALSO IMPORTANT IN ANIMALS

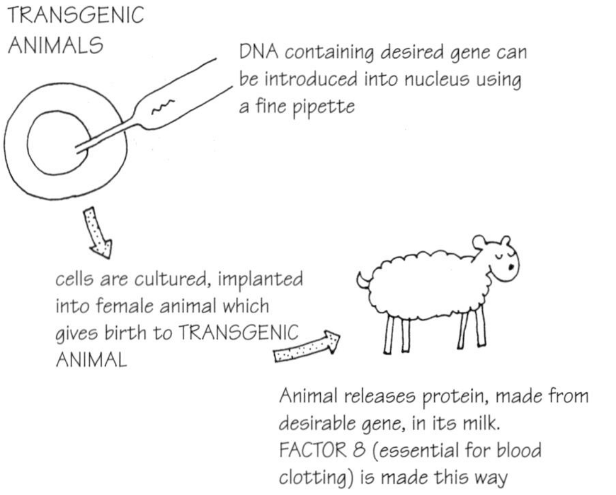

TRANSGENIC ANIMALS

DNA containing desired gene can be introduced into nucleus using a fine pipette

cells are cultured, implanted into female animal which gives birth to TRANSGENIC ANIMAL

Animal releases protein, made from desirable gene, in its milk. FACTOR 8 (essential for blood clotting) is made this way

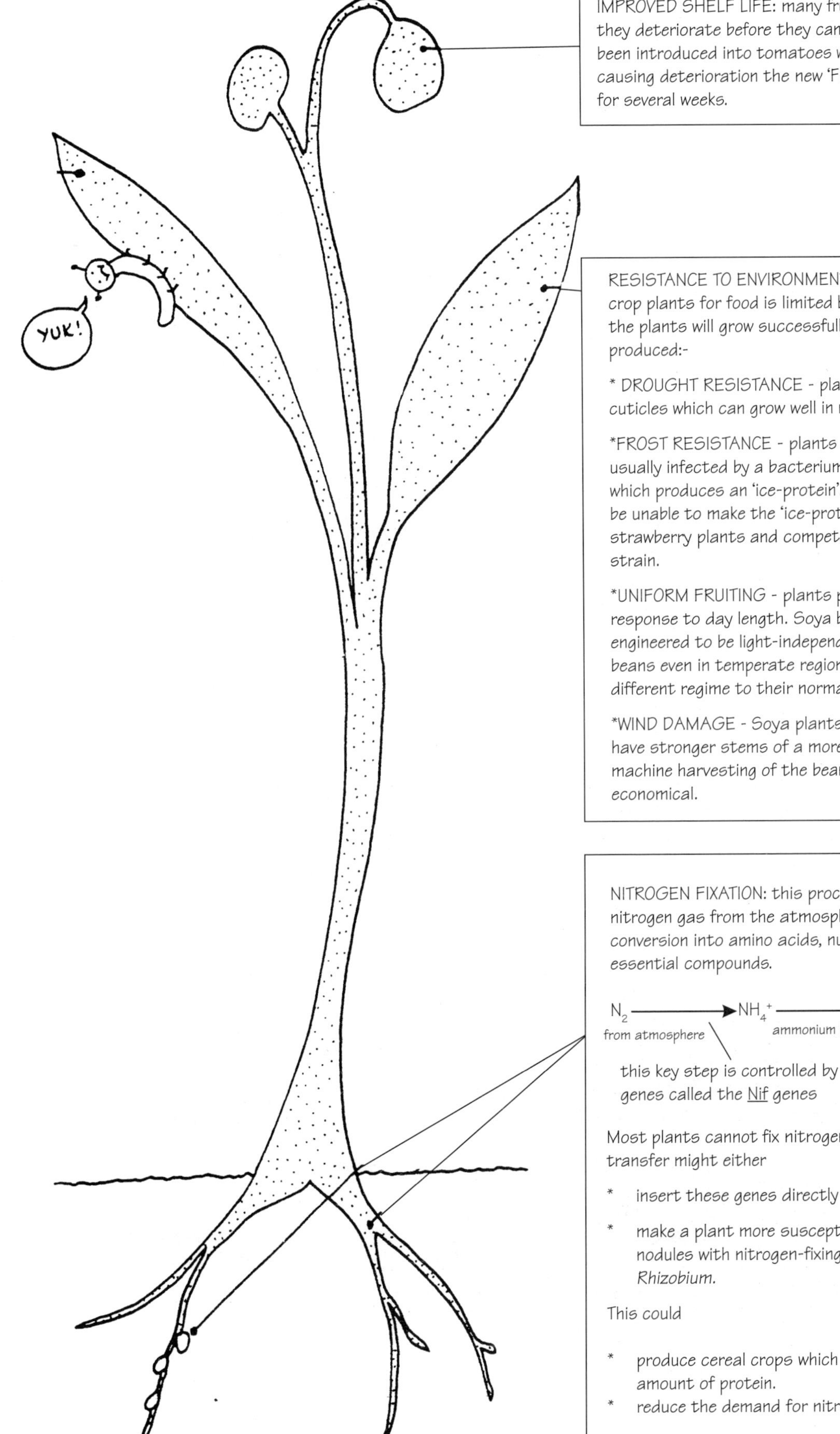

IMPROVED SHELF LIFE: many fruits are wasted because they deteriorate before they can be sold/eaten. A gene has been introduced into tomatoes which inhibits the enzymes causing deterioration the new 'FLAVR-SAVR' tomatoes last for several weeks.

RESISTANCE TO ENVIRONMENTAL CONDITIONS: the use of crop plants for food is limited by the conditions in which the plants will grow successfully. Gene transfer has produced:-

* DROUGHT RESISTANCE - plants with thicker, more waxy cuticles which can grow well in more arid areas.

*FROST RESISTANCE - plants damaged by frost are usually infected by a bacteriumn *Pseudomonas syringae* which produces an 'ice-protein'. A bacterium engineered to be unable to make the 'ice-protein' is sprayed onto strawberry plants and competes with the damage causing strain.

*UNIFORM FRUITING - plants produce flowers and fruits in response to day length. Soya bean plants have been engineered to be light-independent and so can produce beans even in temperate regions of the world with a different regime to their normal habitat.

*WIND DAMAGE - Soya plants have been engineered to have stronger stems of a more uniform height which makes machine harvesting of the beans more efficient and economical.

NITROGEN FIXATION: this process involves the reduction of nitrogen gas from the atmosphere into a form suitable for conversion into amino acids, nucleotides and other essential compounds.

N_2 ⟶ NH_4^+ ⟶ amino acids and other compounds

from atmosphere; ammonium ions

this key step is controlled by enzymes coded for by 12 genes called the Nif genes

Most plants cannot fix nitrogen but it is hoped that genes transfer might either

* insert these genes directly into a plant
* make a plant more susceptible to the formation of root nodules with nitrogen-fixing bacteria of the genus *Rhizobium*.

This could

* produce cereal crops which also manufacture large amount of protein.
* reduce the demand for nitrogenous fertilisers.

Eye boy's $4m award sparks fungicide fears

by Julie Smyth and Steve Ball

A COMMON garden chemical allegedly linked to 140 cases of British babies born without eyes was last night at the centre of new safety fears after a court in the United States ordered its manufacturer to pay $4m in damages.

The test case will lead to a flood of similar actions by British families who say exposure to the chemical when their children were in the womb was the reason they have no eyes. Last night their lawyers were in the United States preparing their cases.

The chemical involved is Benlate, the trade name for the fungicide benomyl. Gardeners use it to kill grey mould on strawberries and raspberries, while farmers spray it on cereals and oilseed rape fields.

The six-person jury in Florida county court ordered Dupont, the American chemical giant, to pay $4m to seven-year-old John Castilla Jr. His mother, Donna Castilla, claimed she was exposed to Benlate when she walked next to a fruit farm near her home in Palm Beach.

Dupont immediately announced it was appealing. "The verdict is a defeat for sound science. We believe the jury has been swayed by emotion rather than fact and we will vigorously defend the product," said Mike Upstone, a manager for Dupont UK.

Last night the Ministry of Agriculture said it would be seeking a full report on the judgment from the Miami court but insisted there was no cause for concern.

"Provided the normal safeguards are followed it is safe. We would not sanction a chemical for domestic use if there was this risk."

The Advisory Committee on Pesticides, an independent committee, reviewed the chemical two years ago and gave it the all-clear; it could find no connection between the eye condition and use of the spray, said a spokesman.

Up to seven alleged clusters of the eye condition, known as anophthalmia, have been identified in Britain — Lincolnshire, South Yorkshire, Surrey, Shropshire, West Sussex, Fife and east central Scotland.

Peter Attenborough, 36, of Newburgh, Fife, whose six-year-old son Jonathan suffers from microphthalmia and coloboma, other structural eye defects, said the implications of the judgment were massive, with dozens of British families expected to lodge claims in the American courts.

"We are ecstatic. It has been something we have been trying to prove for three years," said Attenborough, who called on the government to withdraw the use of the fungicide.

PESTICIDES ARE ESSENTIAL...

... but research into toxicity and methods of application is vital

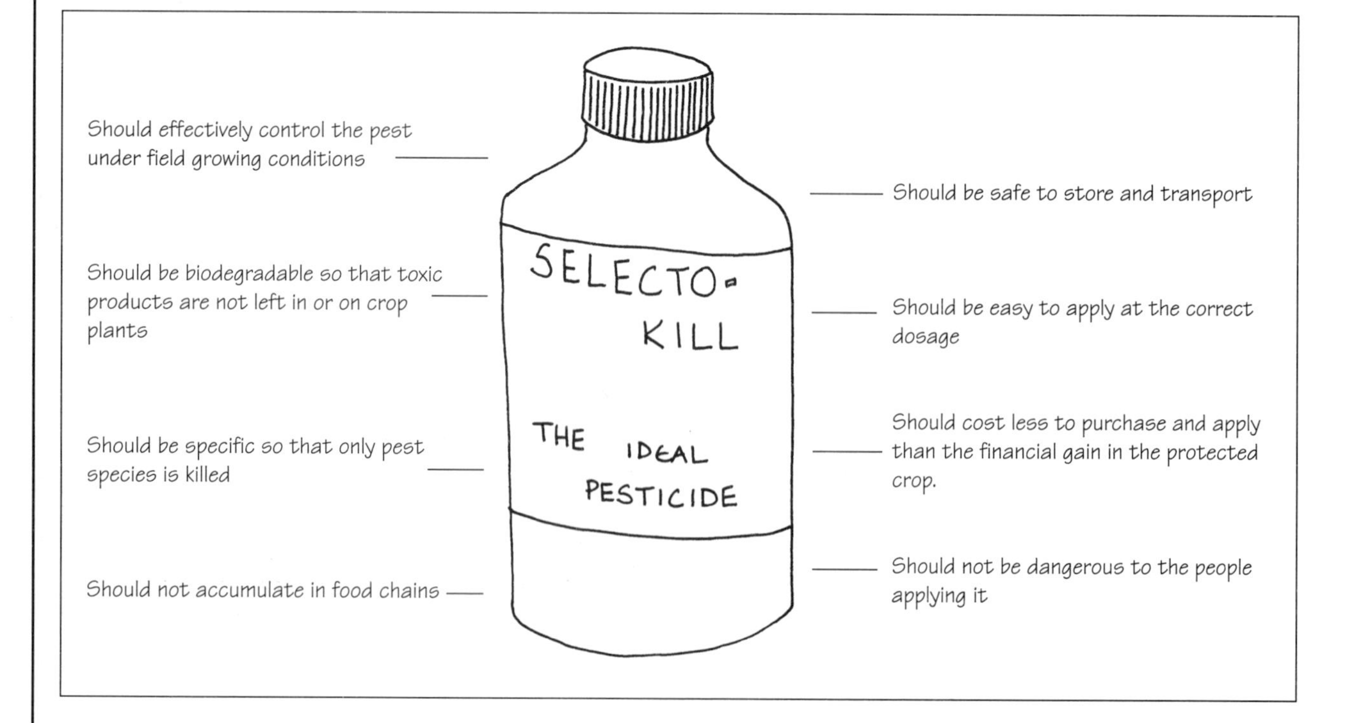

Pesticides and Fertilisers v Organic Farming

Organic Farming

In the last two centuries in Britain up until the Second World War, farming meant a mixture of animals and crops. Cattle and pigs were kept and fed on grass and root crops grown on farms and their manure was used as the fertiliser for crops such as cereals grown for human consumption. The cattle provided milk and meat and the pigs meat. Latterly, in some cases, some naturally occurring fertilisers, such as rock phosphate or guano (seabird droppings) were used, but generally there was a closed or nearly closed system on farms with little or no external inputs. From the ecological point of view, this is an ideal system. It is managing an ecosystem for profit (see Chapter 2), even if it is not truly a natural one. This is what most organic farmers try to do today, although, because of specialisation in farming nowadays, many have to bring manure onto farms from neighbouring farms because they do not keep enough animals themselves. This doesn't alter the basic principle of the old mixed farming system. This must be the ideal way to farm in Western Europe and would be very effective from the conservation point of view.

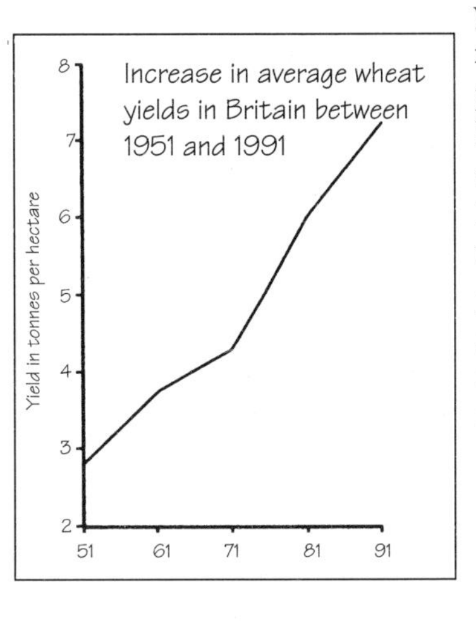

Why did farmers change from this system? The answer is that, while it is a very efficient use of limited resources, it does not maximise production and this is what farmers were asked to do. Other than on specialist farms, such as those growing vegetables or fruit or hops, cereals have always been the main UK crops. Wheat, Barley, Oats and Rye are widely grown across Western Europe. They require different conditions but are all suited to our climate and soils. Wheat is the most important in the UK and the best soils and climate for it are in the Eastern half of England. With the advent of new high yielding varieties, large farm machinery, cheap fertilisers and pesticides, the best farmers on the best land could consistently achieve a yield of 10 tonnes per Hectare compared with about 2 tonnes 20 years ago. This potential and the presence of a guaranteed market has resulted in specialisation. Most arable farmers grow cereals at some stage of their rotation but the best cereal land grows mostly cereals, the best potato land, potatoes, the best sugar-beet land, sugar beet and so on. The East of England is mainly arable farming and the West mainly mixed (cattle and crops) or sheep on the higher land. If most or all of England went back to mixed farming, we would have to import much more of our food.

INTENSIVE FARMING

BIG BENEFIT

Time (minutes) taken by the average industrial male worker to earn money to buy these foods

	Early 1950's	Mid 1980's
Eggs (size 4 per dozen)	91.2	14.3
Pork (per lb)	43.0	15.4
Bread (white 1lb loaf)	5.4	3.5
Chicken (frozen per lb)	58.7	9.4
Cheddar Cheese (per lb)	32.9	17.7

Cheaper food

(Source- National Farmers' Union)

but

POSSIBLE PROBLEMS

SPECIALISATION
farmers may grow only a single crop, or keep only one type of animal

WASTE DISPOSAL
straw from cereal growers and slurry from livestock units

POLLUTION
nitrate and phosphate fertilisers; pesticides

DISEASE
rapid spread of infections in monocultures

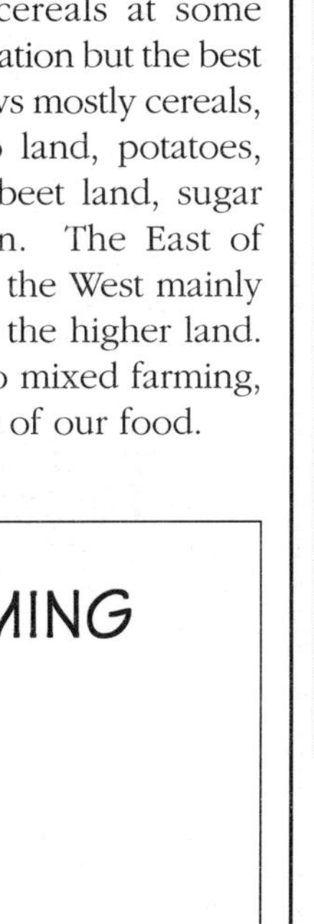

It is certainly true that most people in Britain today are not happy with many aspects of modern farming, but it is quite possible to greatly improve the environment on farms without drastic bans or Luddite movements. Conservation of some hedges, plus planting and maintenance of farm woodland and some or all of the measures outlined on p. 92 can greatly improve the situation. From the organic farmers' point of view that would still leave two major problems; inorganic fertilisers and pesticides.

Organic and Inorganic Fertilisers

Plants need a range of elements to be able to grow. The major nutrients are Nitrogen (N), Phosphorous (P) and Potassium (K - the chemical notation for Potassium). Sulphur is also very important but it is present in many soils at a sufficient level and until recently was supplemented in industrial countries by very high levels of atmospheric Sulphur Dioxide (see p 45).

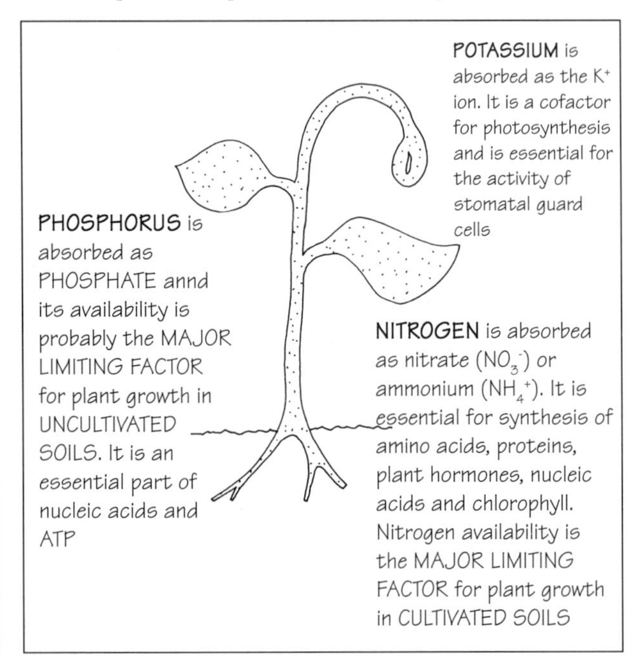

Then there is a number of micronutrients which are necessary in differing amounts for healthy plant growth. These include iron, calcium, sodium, magnesium, manganese, copper, boron, zinc, molybdenum and selenium.

For crops to grow well, sufficient NPK must be added regularly. This can be done by addition of organic or inorganic fertilisers. Both types of fertiliser provide exactly the same nutrients to the soil or plants but it is the immediate availibility to plants that is different.

Inorganic fertilisers contain nitrogen in the form of ammonium salts, nitrates or urea (which is strictly an organic compound but is synthesised), potassium as soluble salts and phosphorus as soluble and insoluble salts. The nitrogen comes from the atmosphere, fixed by a chemical process (Haber process), the potassium salts are mined and the phosphorus comes from crushed phosphate rock which is treated with sulphuric acid to liberate phosphoric acid.

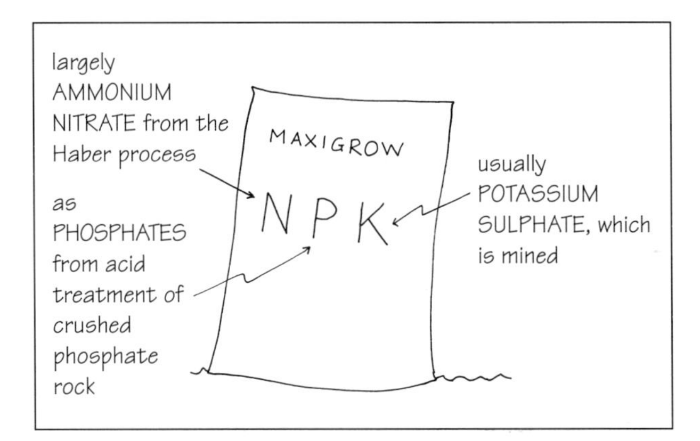

Organic fertilisers are animal manure, including birds (guano or chicken manure), are processed from dead animals (fish, blood and bone or hoof and horn), are green manures (plants which grow rapidly and fix NPK efficiently and are then dug into the ground); are derived from plants (seaweed meal) or are naturally occurring minerals processed as little as possible (crushed phosphate rock).

Both types of fertiliser give NPK to the crop but because much of the nitrogen, potassium and phosphorus in organic fertilisers is locked up in organic (carbon containing) compounds, it has to be released by soil micro-organisms before it can be taken up by the crop. Some organic growers term this "feeding the soil not the crop". Organic matter is also built up in the soil. This improves its structure, giving better winter drainage and summer water holding capacity. Organic fertiliser is thus a slow release or controlled release material. The NPK in organic fertilisers is much more quickly available to plants but, unless specially treated, is not slow release. This means that farmers need to make "split dose" applications of inorganic fertiliser (in 2 or 3 parts through the season) to a crop whereas manures are applied only once per crop, before the crop is sown.

In fertilisers,
potassium content is always expressed as K_2O
and phosphorus as P_2O_5

Farmyard manure, being natural in origin, varies considerably. Farmers not growing organically still sometimes use manures if they are available locally and this sometimes includes sewage sludge. Their large bulk makes transport over any great distance totally uneconomic. Even where these farmers use manures, they would supplement them with inorganic products. It is this low concentration of NPK in manures that makes their use in high yield modern systems unviable.

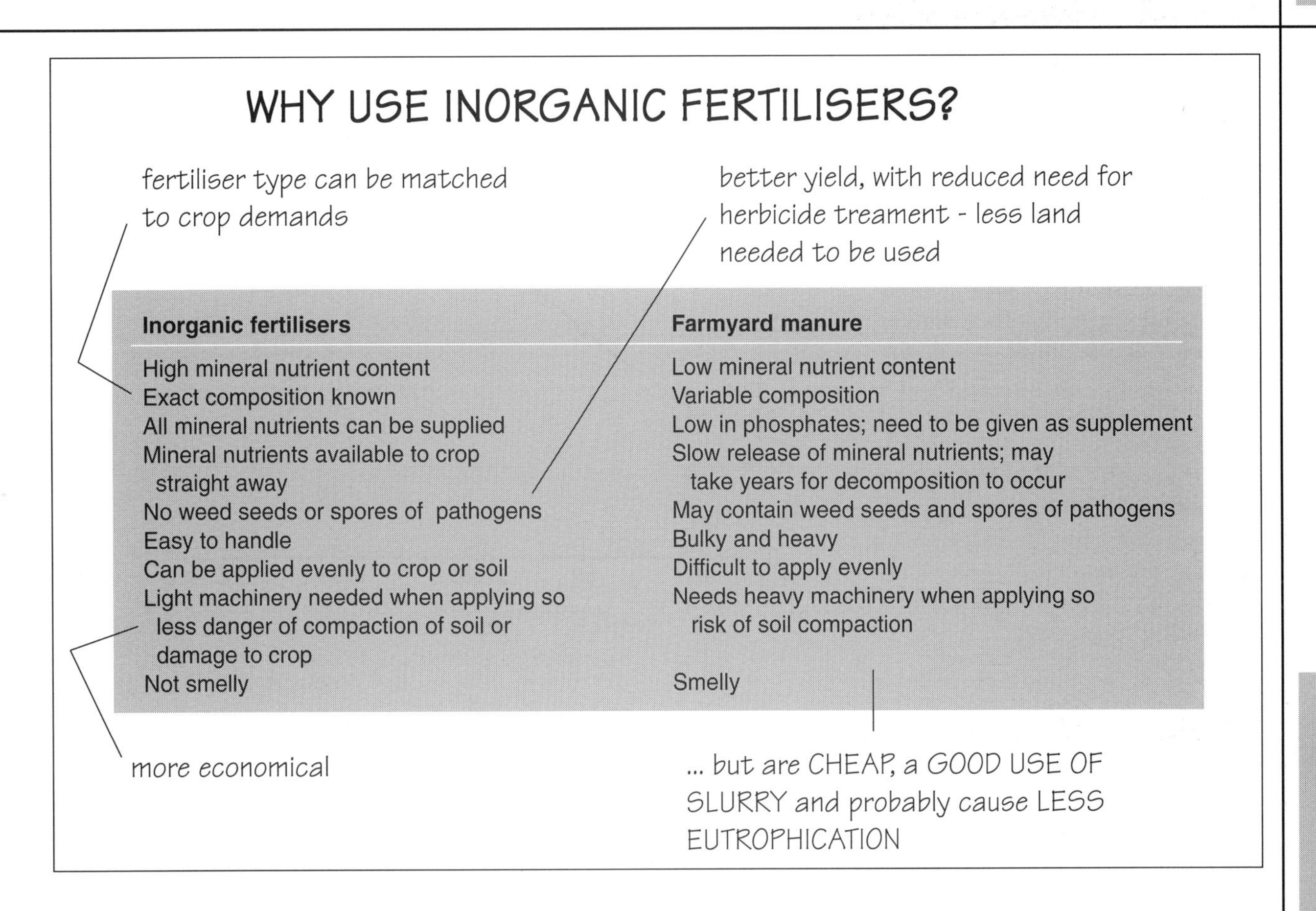

Inorganic fertilisers are highly concentrated, containing very little other than NPK. They contain the following materials:

Compound	%N	%K_2O	%P_2O_5	%S
urea	46			
ammonium nitrate	35			
ammonium sulphate	21			24
mono-ammonium phosphate (MAP)	12		61	
di-ammonium phosphate (DAP)	21		53	
potassium sulphate		54		18
farm yard manure (fym)	0.2	0.4	0.2	

It has been suggested that these high rates of applied fertilisers are responsible for the current problems of nitrate pollution (see p52) but this is not yet clear. Nitrate leaching from bare ground in the winter may also be a factor. However, restrictions on nitrogen fertiliser usage are being considered in several countries. Some organic growers also suggest that not using bulky organic manures will result in reductions of soil organic matter content, but again, work at Boxworth experimental farm suggests that this is not happening, presumably because the increase in plant density and in intensive systems leads to greater soil residues.

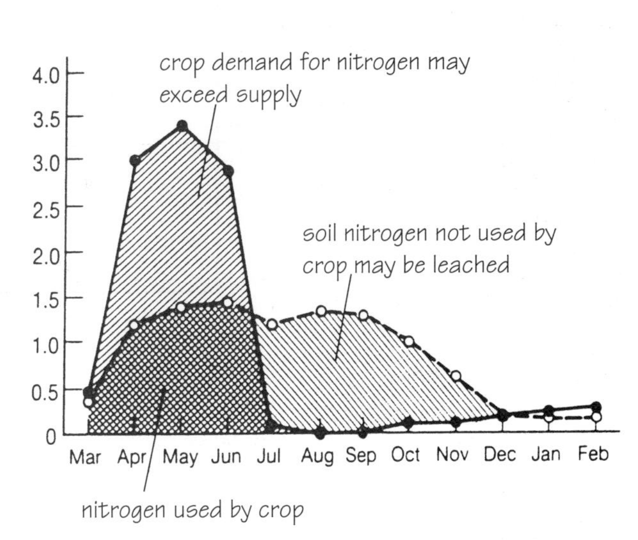

Without modern concentrated fertilisers, the current high yields cannot be obtained, but with the aim of the present CAP reforms being to reduce production, moves towards lower input farming are being taken in some areas. Long Ashton Research Station near Bristol, along with other similar institutes across Europe is in the forefront of such work with its LIFE project (Less Intensive Farming and the Environment). It may be possible using all the modern methods of farming but keeping fertiliser and pesticide usage to an absolute minimum to achieve yields at least approaching current levels and farm profitability.

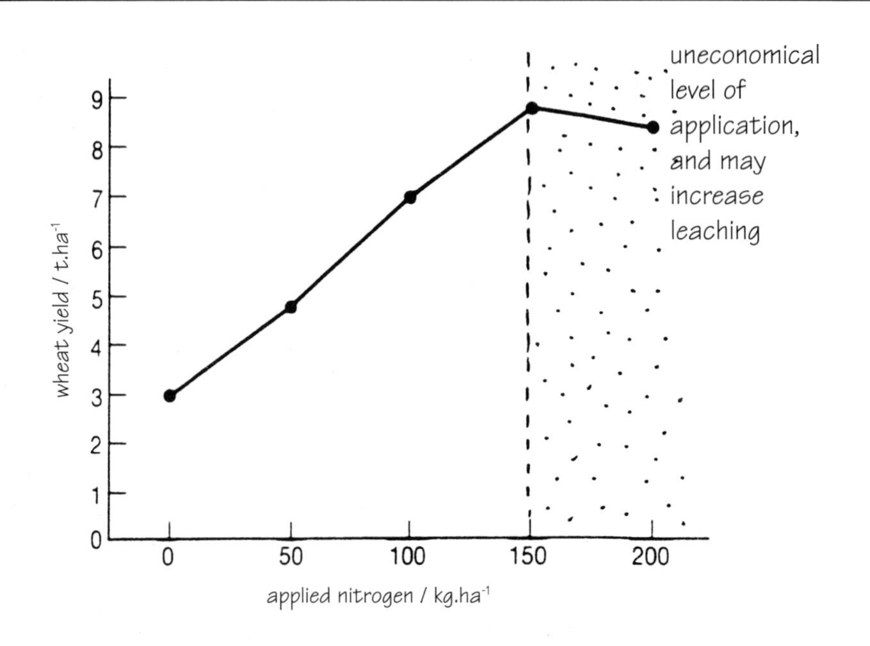

Biological Pest Control

More effort is being devoted nowadays by pesticide companies to developing pesticides of natural origin. These can be of two types; naturally occurring chemicals such as nicotine, pyrethrum, Derris, Neem or *Bacillus thuringiensis* toxin, and actual predatory organisms. *Bacillus thuringiensis* has no known mammalian toxicity and very high selectivity. Different strains of the bacterium, which occur naturally, control most Lepidoptera (BT var. *kurstaki*), mosquitoes (var. *israelensis*), wax moth, which is a pest of bee hives (var. *aizawa*) and certain coleoptera especially Colorado Beetle, a pest of potatoes (var. *tenebrionensis*).

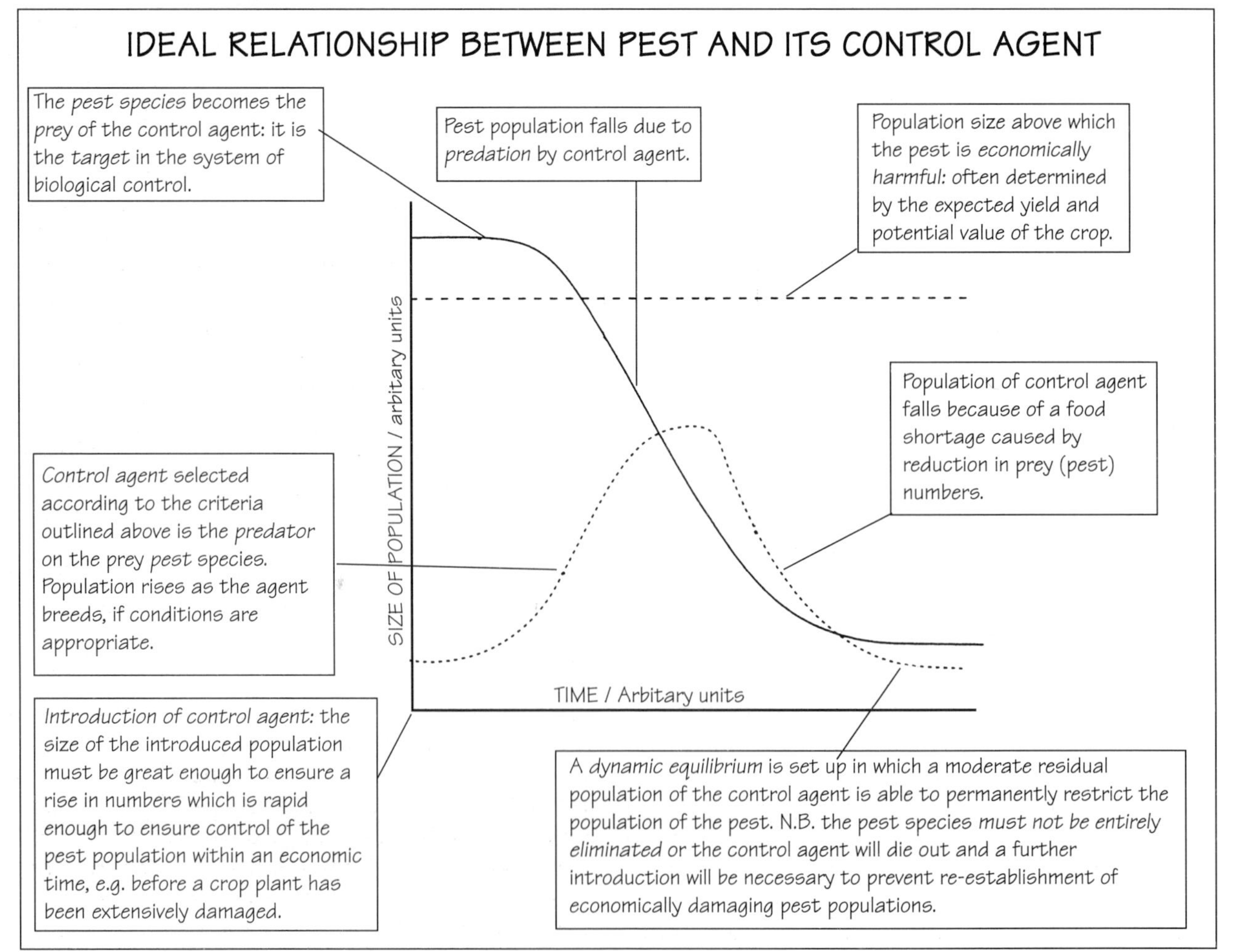

Naturally occurring predator organisms are often very specific, are not toxic and leave no residues in food, although their careless use can be much more of a problem than pesticides. The release of predatory organisms into an environment in which they are not normally found (non indigenous) can be disastrous. There have been examples of this in the past, both intentional and unwitting. Release of cats and rats from ships onto islands where predators did not previously exist was the cause of the extinction of the Dodo on Mauritius and the near extinction of the Kakapo in New Zealand (both Dodo and Kakapo being flightless birds nesting on the ground in the absence of natural predators). In Australia, Cane toads were introduced to control insect pests in sugar cane. The toads are now a bigger pest than the insects.

One has to be very careful in releasing living organisms. If a pesticide turns out to be dangerous to wildlife (e.g. Aldrin, Dieldrin) then swift action to ban its use will result in recovery of the threatened animals even it is takes some time due to residues remaining in the food chain. But, if an introduced organism is found to cause problems, stopping its use does not solve the problem as it continues to breed in the wild. It is essential that extensive work is done to make sure, before use, that the predator will not "escape" and cause problems.

TYPICAL BIOLOGICAL CONTROL PROGRAMME

1. Identify the pest and trace its origins, i.e. where did it come from?
2. Investigate original site of pest and identify natural enemies of the pest.
3. Test the potential control agent under careful quarantine to ensure
   a. that it is specific (does not prey on other species)
   b. will not change its prey species and become a pest itself
   c. has a life cycle which will allow it to develop a population large enough to act as an economic control.
4. Mass culture of the control agent.
5. Development of the most effective distribution/release method for the control agent.

Probably the best way of ensuring this is to use indigenous predators that have not been selected or modified in any way, the only interference being concentration in a particular area. As a trite example, one could collect ladybirds from various plants in the garden and put them on roses to eat the aphids there. The next stage on would be to breed ladybirds indoors and release them onto garden plants.

This would not in fact work as the ladybirds would not stay where they were placed and would probably fly into next door's garden instead. Work has been done on nematodes (microscopic worms) that infect soil pests. There is already a product on the market for greenhouse use that controls vine weevil (*Otiorhynchus sulcatus*) larvae in the soil of pot plants and another one which may be available soon for control of slugs.

Another way of ensuring the safe release of predators is to use non-indigenous organisms that cannot survive frost. A number of biological controls are used in commercial greenhouses for control of summer pests. Many of these are now also available to amateur gardeners. The main ones are; *Phytoseiulus persimilis*, a predatory mite that eats the sap sucking pest red spider mite (*Tetranychus urticae*) and *Encarsia formosa*, a minute wasp which lays its eggs in the scales (larvae) of whitefly (*Trialeurodes vaporariorum*). There are other specific predators for aphids (*aphidoletus*), mealybugs, Western flower thrips and woolly aphids. The predators die off in the winter because it is too cold and because their food sources disappear. This sort of control is particularly suitable for greenhouses as they are controlled environments and even winged predators tend to stay where they have been placed. *Phytoseiulus persimilis* has also in the last two years been used outside the greenhouse in field crops to control spider mites in strawberries. Other organisms are in the development stage such as fungi to control weeds and aphids.

Providing that great care is taken not to release predatory organisms that can create future problems, this is a very promising area for future development because the predators can be very specific and integrate well into IPM systems. The difficulty is that unless *all* important arthropod pests of a crop can be controlled with predators, the farmer may not be able to use them to control any pest. Because many insecticides/acaricides are not very specific the use of a pesticide against one pest you may well kill the predators that have been introduced to control other pests. In France, after a rapid rise in the use of biocontrol agents under glass from 1979 to 1990, usage has dropped by 6.8% since 1991. This is because relatively new pests, Western flower thrips (*Frankliniella occidentalis*) and *Bemesia tabaci* are now spreading and two others; an aphid (*Aphis gossypii*) and a leaf-*miner (Liriomysa huidobrensis)* are increasing. Once growers have to spray against these, they cannot use predators for other pests. Work is already underway to find new predators and, particularly in the case of the thrips, looks promising, so the downturn should only be temporary.

Pheromones

Pheromones are volatile chemicals that many insects use to communicate over large distances. There are various types of pheromone but the two types most worked on and already yielding useful pest control results are alarm and sex pheromones. Sex pheromones are released by females to attract males. Some are very specific mixtures of optically active molecules that are very difficult to synthesise. Extraction from insects for field use is impossible because of the tiny quantities emitted. Others, however can be copied synthetically. Synthetic pheromones can be used in at least three ways to help control pests.

a) Release of sufficient pheromone in an area where females are present can swamp the male detection system, so that few males manage to find females to mate.

b) Pheromone traps - sticky paper traps that gradually release pheromone over a period - can be placed near certain crops and inspected regularly. When the grower starts to find males in the trap, he knows that the crop needs spraying. Equally, of course, if none are found, a pesticide spray can be avoided. This technique is used in the UK to determine the optimum time for spraying, if necessary, against pea moth (*Cydia nigricana*) in peas.

c) For small scale use e.g. in gardens, pheromone traps can be used which contain some device for killing the moths. This can be for example, a water trap or a pesticide. If enough traps are used, most male moths can be caught and so no mating or egg-laying takes place. A trap is sold in the UK for control of codling moth (*Cydia pomonella*) in apples. In a sheltered garden, one trap is sufficient for up to 5 trees in an area up to 100 metre radius, so it can be seen how far away a tiny amount of pheromone can be detected.

Recent work in Holland suggests that aphids on lettuces can be controlled with as little as one tenth of the normal amount of insecticide (a carbamate or organophosphorus material - see above) if it is applied with the aphid alarm pheromone ((e)-beta-farnesene). Aphids usually congregate at the heart of lettuces and so are difficult to get at. The farnesene makes them disperse rapidly away from the hearts, thus picking up insecticide.

Pheromones are a very interesting area of research for IPM but it is very difficult to extract and identify picograms (10^{-9} g) or even femtograms (10^{-12} g) of pheromone and then often even harder to synthesise it in the right optical isomers and proportions in a mixture. Success so far has come with those pheromones which are single chemicals, not mixtures.

Pesticides are necessary to our Agriculture. Organic growing is very risky as in some years pest epidemics can occur (and used to) and you cannot control them. This may be acceptable if what is grown is a luxury item (as organic food is now) but it is very serious if the nation's food supply is at risk. As an example, the Irish Potato Famine in which so many people died was caused by a fungus, Potato Blight (*Phytopthera infestans*). There is still no treatment "organic" farmers can use which controls this disease adequately.

The conclusion to be drawn from the above is that while pesticides can be dangerous and cause serious environmental problems (they have done so in the past), with current legislation and environmental awareness, careful monitoring and continued development of Integrated Pest Management, they may be precision tools not bludgeons in the future.

The late Prof. Kenneth Treharne, Director of the AFRC Institute of Arable crops research said in 1989 "it is now two generations since the public faced the spectre of food shortages, so there is some complacency and lack of awareness of the considerable difficulties faced by farmers today.

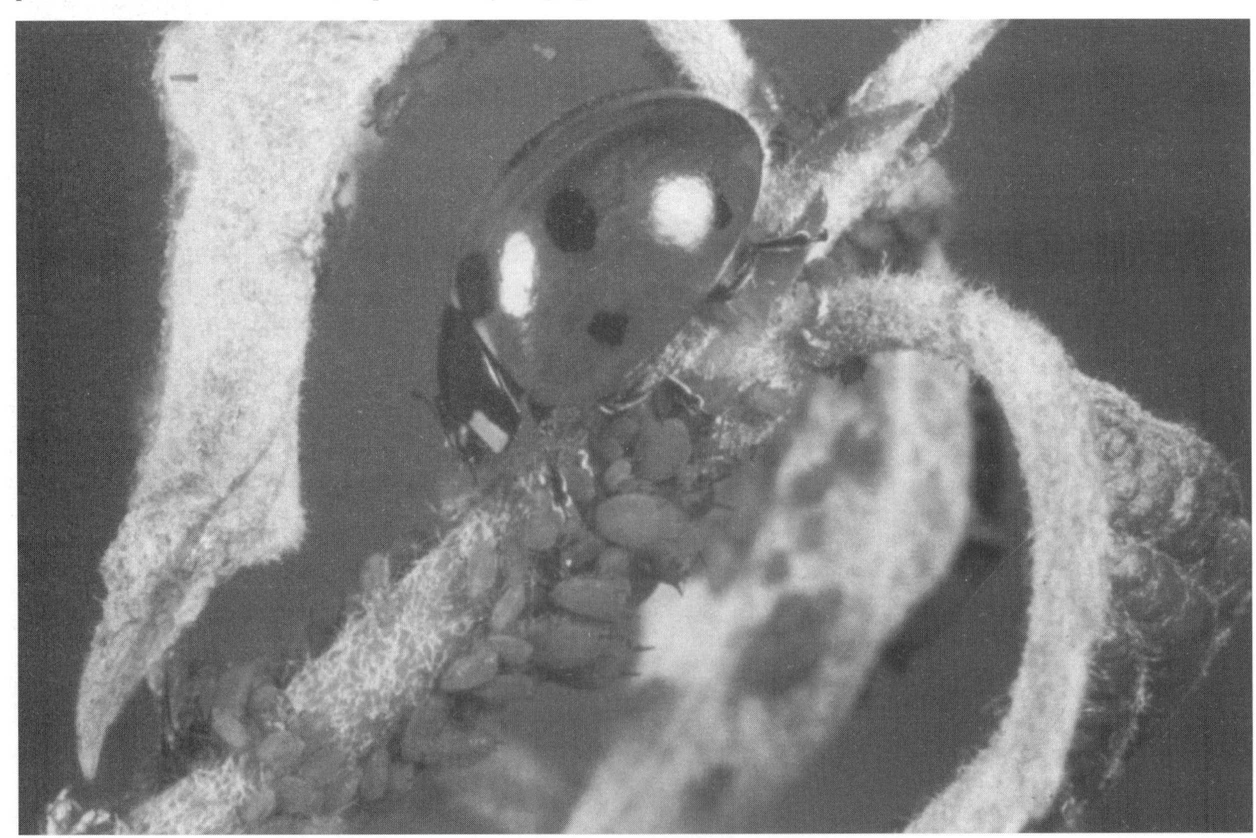

The Farming and Wildlife Advisory Group

The Farming and Wildlife Advisory Group has existed for more than 25 years with the stated aim:

> *"...to give the best possible advice to those who use the land commercially, helping them to work in ways which combine caring for the environment with running sustainable businesses".*

FWAG emphasises that there is no essential conflict between the demands of the environment and economics, and seeks to demonstrate that farmers working in harmony with nature can produce real environmental gain *and* economic betterment in both the short and the long term.

FWAG has initiated the new LANDWISE programme...

The Landwise programme offers the farmer:

- a detailed REVIEW which studies past, present and planned farm activities with a detailed examination of priority areas
- a PLAN which highlights important wildlife habitats and makes appropriate management suggestions

The plan comes with a unique series of CABCARDS which enable farm workers to implement management plans with greatest environmental sensitivity

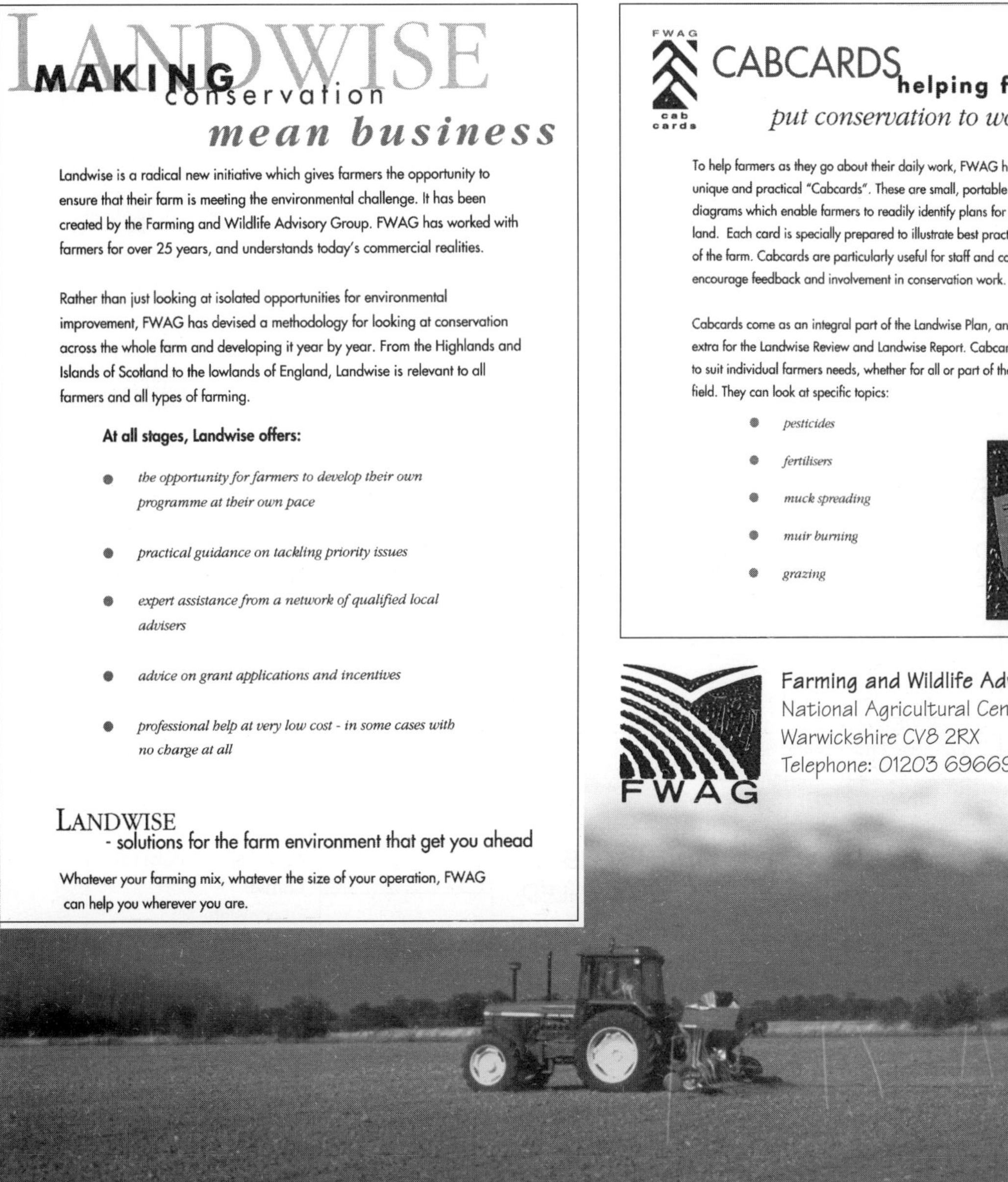

FWAG

cab cards

CABCARDS helping farmers

put conservation to work

To help farmers as they go about their daily work, FWAG has developed unique and practical "Cabcards". These are small, portable and weatherproof diagrams which enable farmers to readily identify plans for specific areas of land. Each card is specially prepared to illustrate best practice for each part of the farm. Cabcards are particularly useful for staff and contractors as they encourage feedback and involvement in conservation work.

Cabcards come as an integral part of the Landwise Plan, and as an optional extra for the Landwise Review and Landwise Report. Cabcards are available to suit individual farmers needs, whether for all or part of the farm, or field by field. They can look at specific topics:

- *pesticides*
- *fertilisers*
- *muck spreading*
- *muir burning*
- *grazing*

FWAG

Farming and Wildlife Advisory Group
National Agricultural Centre, Stonleigh,
Warwickshire CV8 2RX
Telephone: 01203 696699

FWAG has also been instrumental in setting up WHOLE FARM CONSERVATION initiatives. The group has pointed out

- every piece of land is important, both environmentally and commercially - planning for conservation across the whole farm will optimise land use for both purposes
- traditionally conservation projects such as pond creation or tree planting have been operated in isolation, and one may even have been unhelpful to the other

and has suggested that the interplay between all farm activities, and the knock-on effect of each on the others should be considered when conservation and commercial plans are laid.

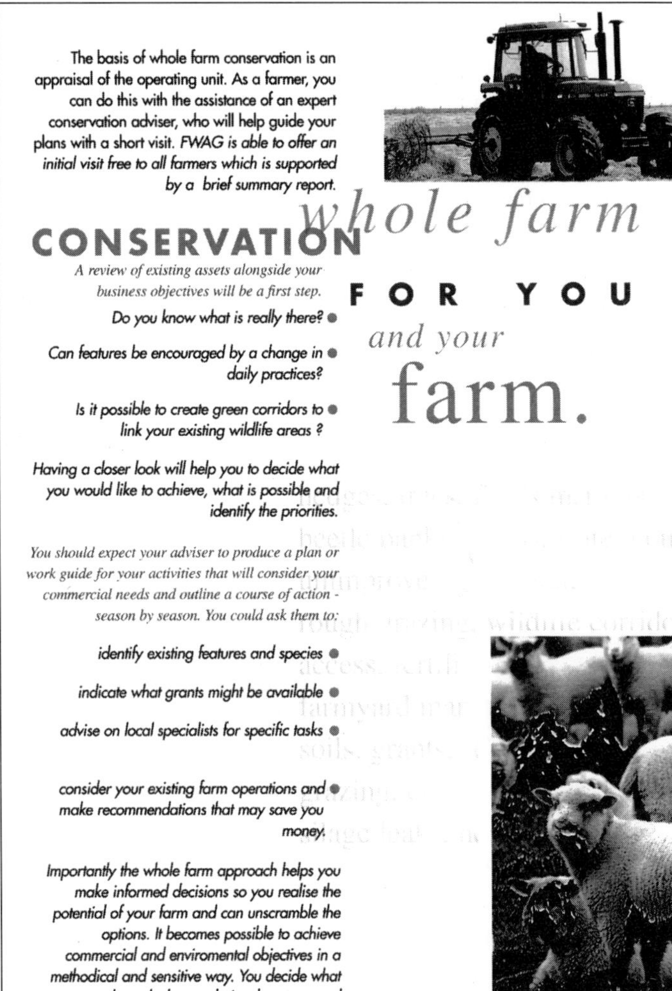

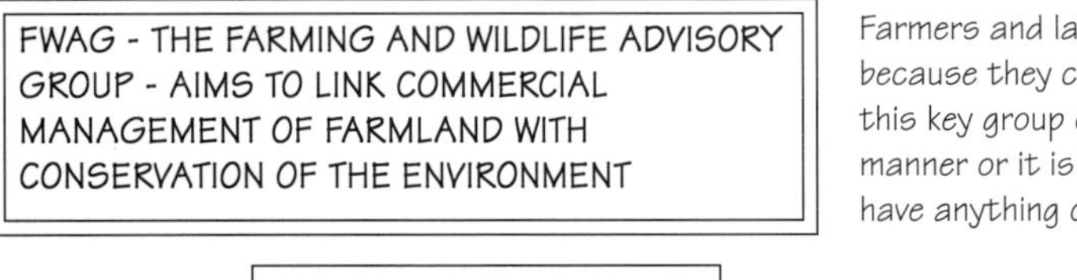

FWAG - THE FARMING AND WILDLIFE ADVISORY GROUP - AIMS TO LINK COMMERCIAL MANAGEMENT OF FARMLAND WITH CONSERVATION OF THE ENVIRONMENT

Farmers and landowners hold the key to effective conservation because they control 80% of the UK land area. It is vital that this key group operates in an environmentally sympathetic manner or it is unlikely that other conservation initiatives can have anything other than a minimal or local effect.

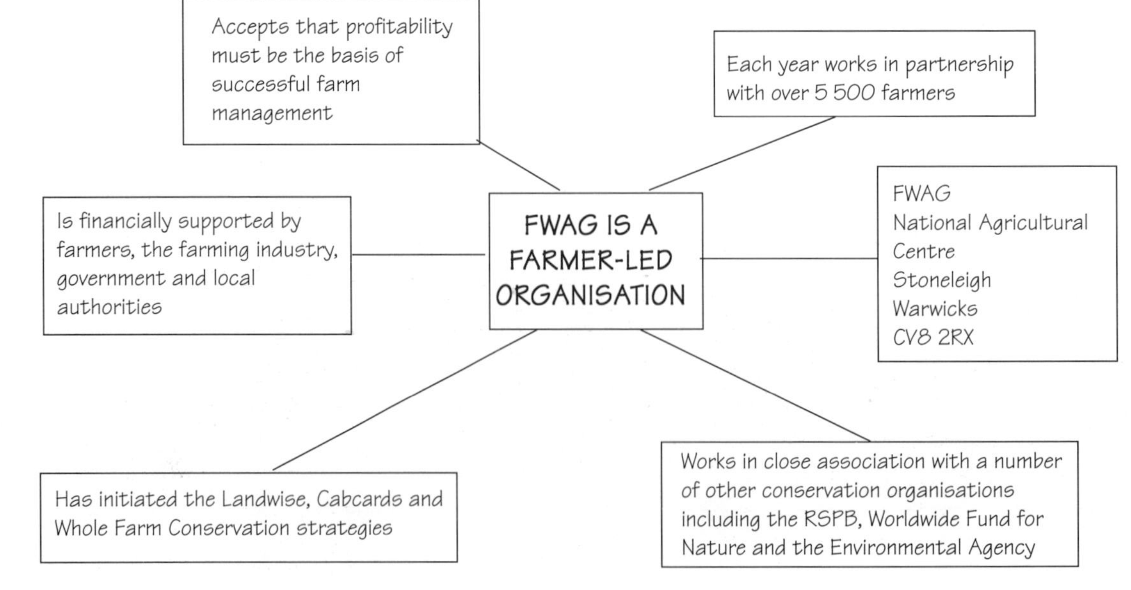

The following are extracts from the FWAG Annual Review of 1995, and emphasise the wide-ranging nature of their advisory activities.

Ecology and Habitat

During the year advice was given on a staggering 37,000 conservation items Some of the major headings for this are given in the figure below.

Advice relating to individual species remained high, occurring on 35% of our visits and dealing with anything from the rare (cirl bunting and corncrake) to the more "common" bank vole, frog and skylark. Without help those species perhaps even now erroneously termed "common" will continue to decline in numbers and distribution - another important reason for the whole farm approach

Shetland

In Shetland alone, FWAG's advice generated over £700,000 worth of earnings for crofters and farmers from environmental schemes. A further £130,000 was gained for capital works.

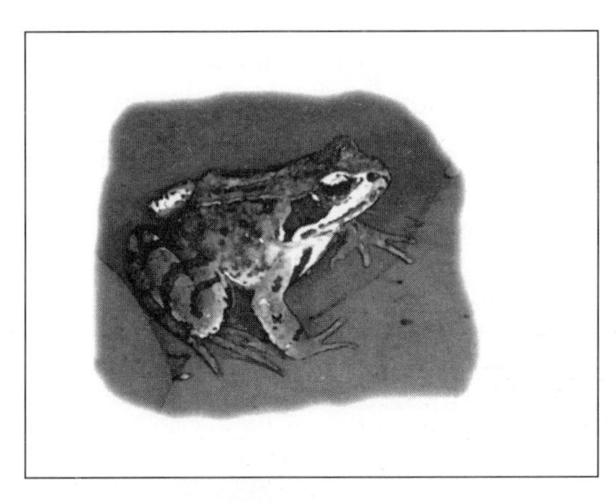

Across the whole spectrum...

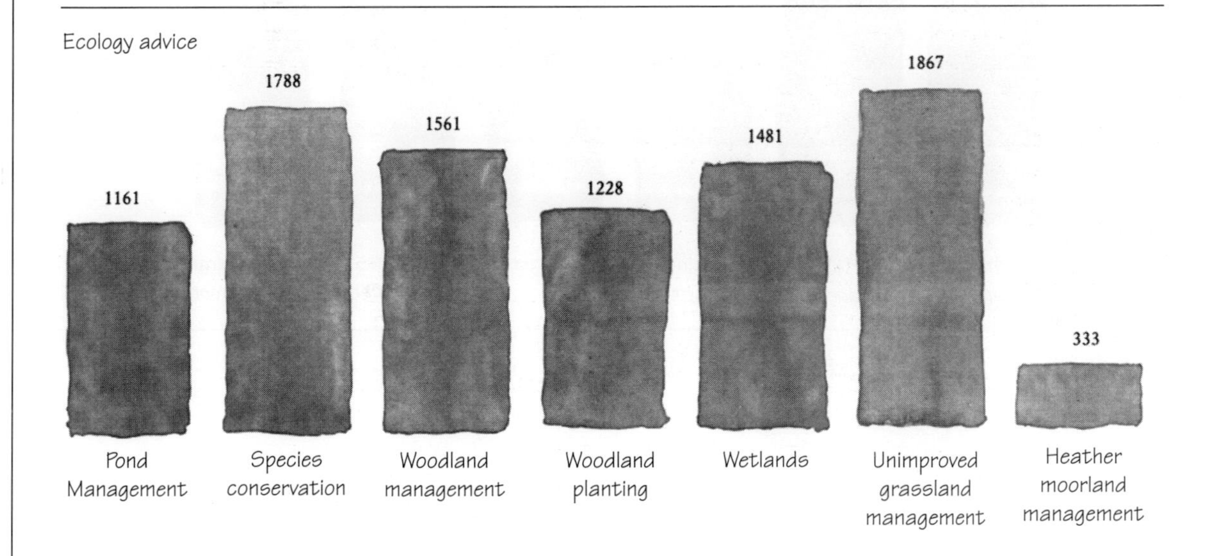

Lincolnshire

Lincolnshire FWAG prompted a substantial washland extension, creating a new flood water site capable of holding 80 million gallons of water, and incorporating significant river habitat improvements. This major project was a triumph of co-operation between FWAG, NRA, Countryside Commission, local Internal Drainage Board and of course local farmers without whom the scheme could not exist.

Cornwall

The Duchy of Cornwall teamed up with their local FWAG to put together a series of whole farm plans on the Manor of Duloc estate. Landlord and tenant farmer co-operation ensured the retention of natural habitats and the characteristic landscape across farm boundaries.

An integral part of whole farm advice is an explanation of the environmental impact of everyday operations on both productive and non-productive areas of the farm and its surroundings. The increasing amount of this advice is shown below.

Farm management advice

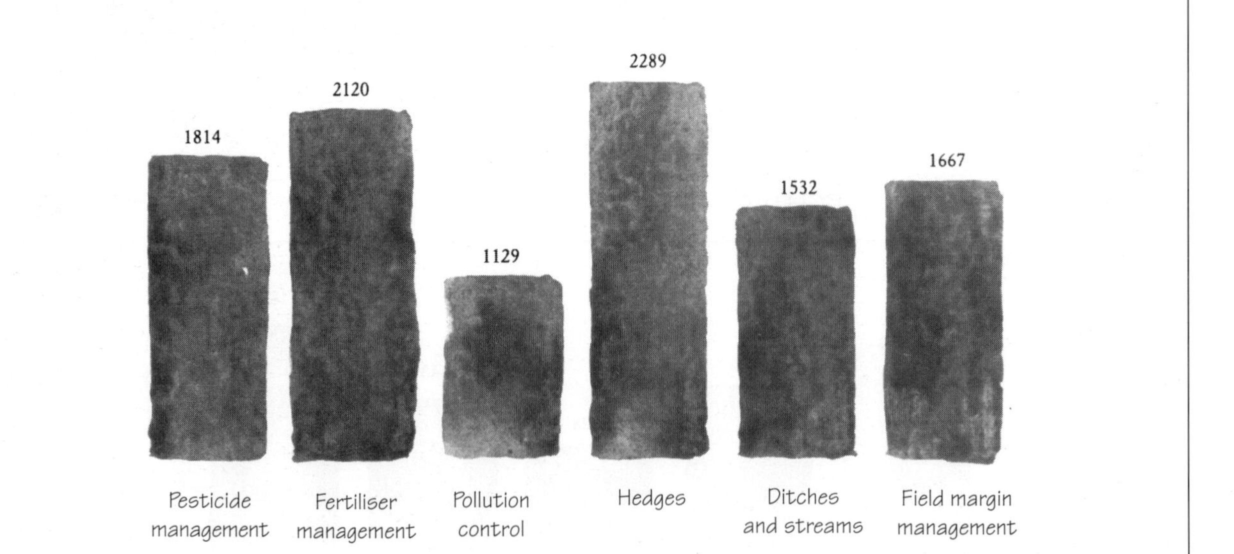

Conflicts in Forestry: Monoculture versus diversity

"The forests of Britain today are in most cases the result of human intervention on the landscape."

Famous landscape architects of past centuries created many of the estate and park woodlands, but after demands for timber from industrialisation and two world wars, Britain had only 5% of its land under trees. Then, as now, Britain imported a large proportion of its timber requirements (today, we import around 50% of our pulp and paper requirements, and 85% of other timber). Not only does this result in a large outgoing of the countries resources, but also imported timber often comes from countries who exploit their natural resources with little concern for sustainability. A national strategic reserve of timber would reduce reliance on other countries non-sustainable wood production. This may encourage countries to manage their resource with more regard to the environment. In developed countries such as Canada and Russia this is unlikely to cause many problems. However in developing nations, where timber exports are often relied upon as a source of foreign currency, assistance from richer nations may be required to achieve a painless transition to sustainable management.

"A conflict exists between economic yield and the maintenance of biodiversity"

The rapid establishment of a strategic reserve of timber is most effectively achieved by planting MONOCULTURES of high yielding tree species. Large areas of uniform ages and species are easier and cheaper to establish and harvest, hence the cost to the timber users is less. However, such monocultures may reduce species diversity where they are grown.

A conflict therefore exists between the desire to establish an industry based on a sustainable renewable resource, and the aim of maintaining and enhancing species diversity.

To reverse the trend of deforestation a programme of new planting was begun, spearheaded by the establishment of the Forestry Commission in 1919 and the provision of state aid to the private sector, to manage new and existing forests and woodlands, essentially to create a strategic reserve of timber. To achieve this aim, considerable research was required into the best techniques and species to plant. A large proportion of new planting was made with coniferous species originally from the West coast of North America, where the climate is similar to here in the UK. These species, when planted and tended correctly, could yield far higher quantities of timber than native species, and on far more hostile sites. The emphasis for new woodland creation tended to be on upland areas supporting only poor quality grazing, because this was where land was cheapest. The new coniferous species were well suited to such land, and tended to be planted in large blocks of uniform species groups.

The main species planted were
Sitka spruce (*Picea sitchensis*
Norway spruce (*Picea abies*),
native Scots pine (*Pinus sylvestris*),
Corsican pine (*Pinus nigra var. maritima*),
Lodgepole pine (*Pinus contorta*),
European Larch (*Larix decidua*),
Japanese larch (*Larix kaempferi*),
Hybrid larch (*Larix x eurolepis*),
Douglas Fir (*Pseudotsuga menziesii*) and
Western hemlock (*Thuja plicata*).

This process of afforestation was extremely successful in achieving the government's aim of building up a strategic reserve of timber. The Forestry Commission estate now comprises over 0.9 million hectares of woodland, which when coupled with a private sector of 1.4 million hectares provides a forest cover of 10% of the total UK land area (compared to 74% agriculture and 16% urban cover).

However, the drive for new planting introduced some conflicts with the ideals of biodiversity and conservation. Tax incentives for private owners tended to encourage planting on all available land in an area acquired for afforestation, as tax relief was given for all money spent on tree establishment. This resulted in trees being planted in straight lines following existing fence lines with little regard for the landscape. In both private and publicly owned woodlands, large uniform blocks with little species diversity or open space often resulted from the drive to establish trees. Close spaced even-aged monocultures tend to suppress most ground vegetation on the forest floor. The range of plant species may therefore be limited, as is subsequently the range of insect and bird life higher up the food chain. The Forestry Authority 'wing' of the Forestry Commission was responsible for the provision of grants and licences for planting schemes,

FORESTRY MANAGEMENT CAN BENEFIT WILDLIFE

STACKS OF 'BRASH' : the cuttings from commercial timber, or from roots extracted during forestry operations provide

- corridors for wildlife
- habitats for many insects
- calling/nesting sites for song birds
- windbreaks for the re-establishment of planted trees
- lying-up sites for nocturnal mammals

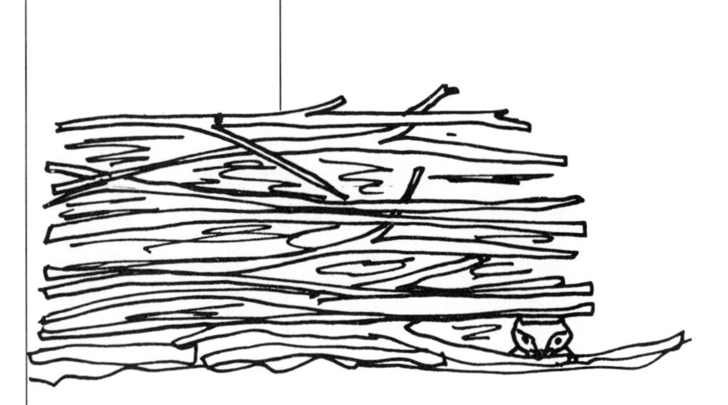

LEAF LITTER : the fallen leaves and fruits from broad leaved species decomposes more quickly and produces a less acidic environment than the litter of 'needles' from coniferous species. This permits the germination and growth of a wider range of herbaceous plants and fungi.

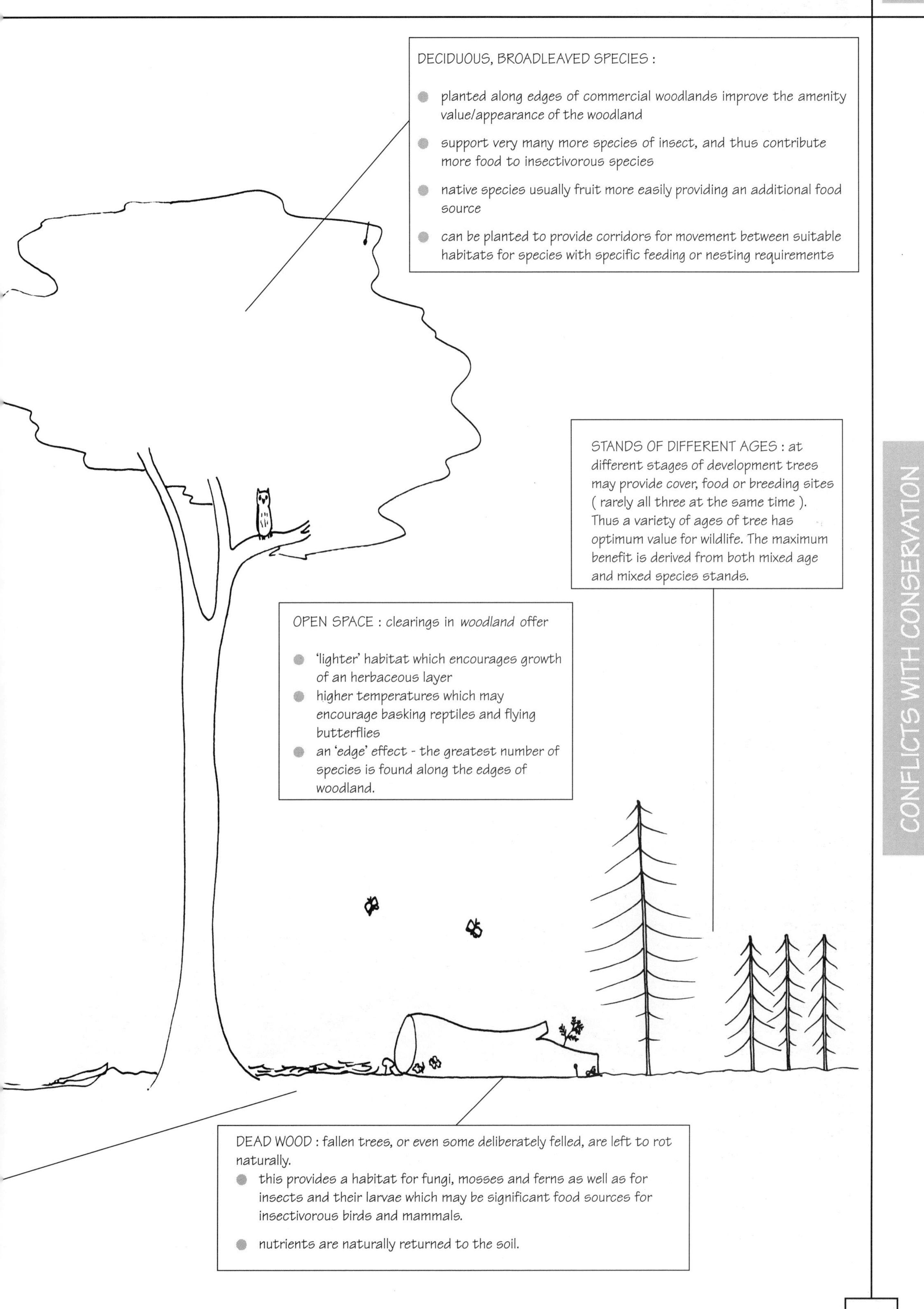
DECIDUOUS, BROADLEAVED SPECIES :
planted along edges of commercial woodlands improve the amenity value/appearance of the woodland
support very many more species of insect, and thus contribute more food to insectivorous species
native species usually fruit more easily providing an additional food source
can be planted to provide corridors for movement between suitable habitats for species with specific feeding or nesting requirements
STANDS OF DIFFERENT AGES : at different stages of development trees may provide cover, food or breeding sites (rarely all three at the same time). Thus a variety of ages of tree has optimum value for wildlife. The maximum benefit is derived from both mixed age and mixed species stands.
OPEN SPACE : clearings in woodland offer
'lighter' habitat which encourages growth of an herbaceous layer
higher temperatures which may encourage basking reptiles and flying butterflies
an 'edge' effect - the greatest number of species is found along the edges of woodland.
DEAD WOOD : fallen trees, or even some deliberately felled, are left to rot naturally.
this provides a habitat for fungi, mosses and ferns as well as for insects and their larvae which may be significant food sources for insectivorous birds and mammals.
nutrients are naturally returned to the soil.

and attracted increasing criticism for the major changes to Britain's landscape which it appeared to be funding.

In recent years a shift in emphasis towards the management of forests to achieve multi-purpose objectives has changed things considerably. Both public (Forestry Enterprise run) and privately owned woodlands, now follow guidelines set down by the Forestry Authority arm of the Forestry Commission, to help achieve this multi-purpose management. Generally speaking, ancient semi-natural broadleaved forest is recognised as having an immense wealth of plant and animal life. All those on Forestry Commission land are protected and managed to ensure their survival. However, more diverse coniferous or mixed coniferous and broadleaved forests, with a greater variety of tree ages and with more open space, can also be of great benefit. Current Forestry Commission policy is to manage existing forests to achieve such diversity. Even aged forests are being re-structured to form a mix of different aged blocks of trees. Some trees are felled earlier than normal, whilst others are retained to their biological maturity. A proportion of dead wood is also left in the forest to help support insect and fungal populations.

This process of re-structuring enables landscaping of forests to take place, to ensure they fit in with the existing landform. Different aged areas in the forest increases the diversity plant and animal life that can be supported. Up to 15% open space is left when stands of trees are felled or thinned, to encourage the establishment of ground flora. Along rides and watercourses trees immediately adjacent to the path or stream are removed, and shrubby species encouraged to create habitats for butterflies and birds. Ten percent of all new planting is with broadleaved species, such as oak *(Quercus spp.)* beech *(Fagus sylvatica),* and ash *(Fraxinus excelsior).* These species can take twice as long to mature as fast growing coniferous trees (120 as opposed to 60 years), so economic returns from them are marginal, even though the timber is generally of higher quality. They are also much more site- demanding, and may grow poorly on many upland sites. Broadleaves are however of great benefit for conservation, and are particularly valuable when used amongst conifers to break up uniform species blocks. In any one forest, up to 15% may be open ground, with a further 10% planted with broadleaved species. This will result in some reduction in income, although opportunities are taken to utilise naturally occurring open space and sites where timber producing species are not best suited in order to minimise losses in revenue. Nevertheless, private forestry concerns, being business organisations without the same pressure to fulfil government objectives as state forestry, are less willing to accept reduced income that will result from these policies, unless there is greater government compensation.

Within Forestry Commission forests, the policies to be followed to achieve the conversation aims as discussed, as well as the equally important objectives of recreation, rural employment, landscaping and timber production, are made implicit in **INDIVIDUAL FOREST DESIGN PLAN**. In the private sector these policies are encouraged through the structures of the **WOODLAND GRANT SCHEME**.

When management principles as described above are followed, forestry need not provide any conflict with the environment. Indeed by its very nature it has the potential to conserve and enhance conservation potential, as well as providing a sustainable natural resource for future generations.

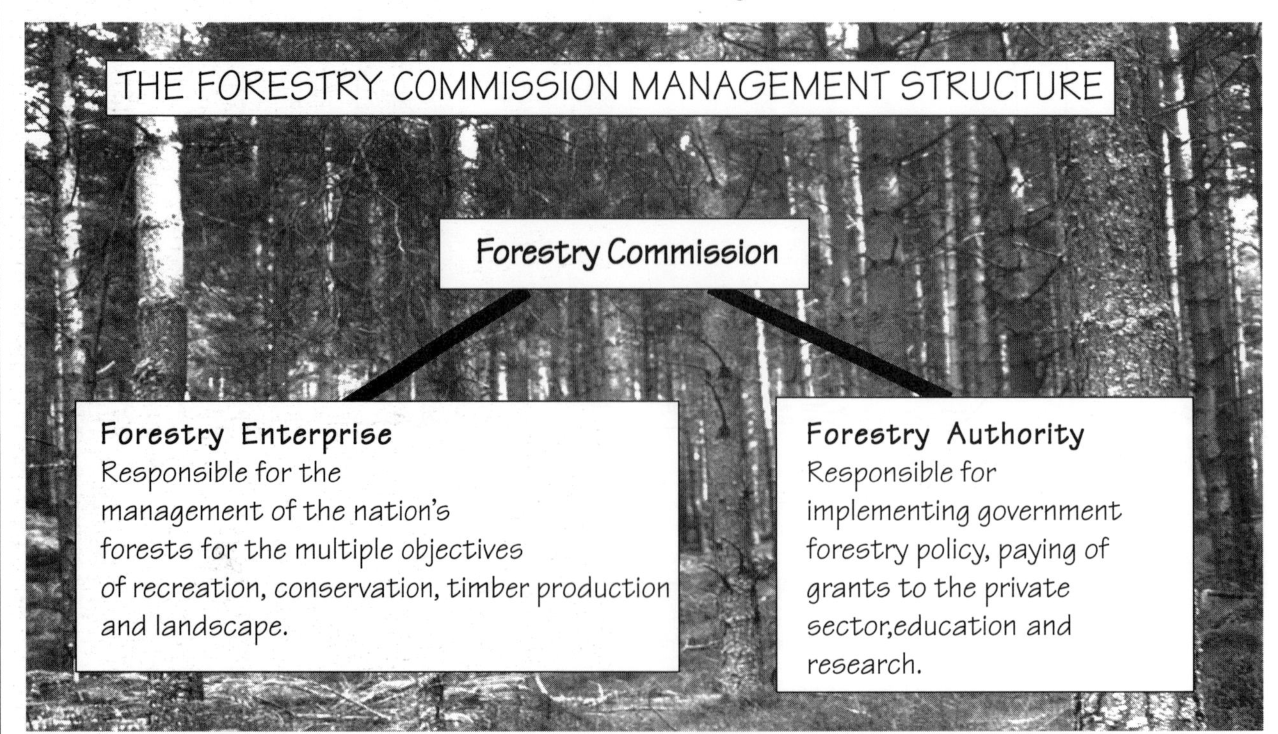

Urbanisation

Urbanisation presents a number of conservation problems:

- land may be consumed for building houses, shops and factories. This land may clearly represent a loss of habitat
- in order to service these buildings road networks may become more extensive. This not only consumes land directly, but fragments wildlife habitats so that individual units of the environment become too small to support viable populations of plants and animals
- both industrial and domestic consumers put greater demands on water supplies, so that management of water resources becomes tilted towards consumption and away from habitat conservation
- atmospheric and water pollution become concentrated in areas which are too small to cope with them naturally. Sewage systems must be developed - further loss of habitat and further 'non-conservation' water management
- energy demands create the need for power stations, which may in turn generate atmospheric and thermal pollution
- the need for building materials will increase the development of the extractive industries - loss of habitat, pollution and aesthetic damage. Ever-increasing demands for paper and wood promote the afforestation of uplands.

These are essentially *industrial* requirements, but there are also conservation problems caused by *recreational* interests.

- area of rough or marginal land may become sports grounds or parks
- increasing amounts of land will be taken up for gardening (which might actually increase the diversity of species) and for allotments (which may lead to direct conflict between humans and wildlife). Both of these support peat extraction which is devastating large areas of bogland with its unique flora and fauna.
- water sports (such as sailing, canoeing, water-skiing and wind surfing) lead to the disturbance of wildlife breeding and resting areas.

There are a number of particularly well-documented examples of these conflicts of interest.

THE ALDERSHOT HEATHLANDS

The earliest 'consumption' of heathlands was a result of the army's desire to set up specialised training areas. This resulted from several disastrous campaigns (including those in the Crimean war, when troops of 'gentlemen' brought up on foxhunting attacked fixed gun positions and were decimated) and began in earnest in the mid 19th century. At the time heaths were beginning to lose their economic importance as grazing land as the population became more urbanised so that there was little resistance to this change of use, but as military demands on these areas became less acute they were often sold off for building or industrial use. Between 1950 and 1984 there was a loss of 40% of all lowland heaths in this country.

THE HEATHLAND ECOSYSTEM

Heathland develops on poor soils in the lowlands. Rainfall washes nutrients out of porous (usually sandy) soils, leaving the surface layers impoverished and able to support only the heathland plants adapted to these conditions. Accumulation of dead plant material will, in time, enrich the soil and allow other plants to invade unless they are prevented by fires and grazing animals. True heathland plants can withstand these conditions.

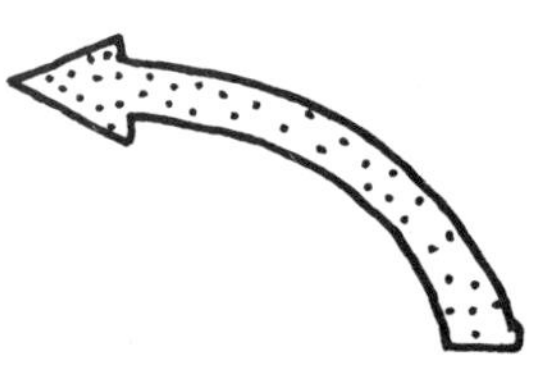

Periodic fires may result in ash and charcoal being carried away by the wind; a loss of materials from the system.

Sand lizards

CONSERVATION MANAGEMENT of heathland involves prevention of succession to woodland. This may involve clearance of scrub and trees by hand or by machine, occasional rotational burning and even use of 'flying squads' of sheep! Each of these measures creates one problem - there may be an increase in the nutrient content of the soil. This is the basic paradox of heathland conservation - in most other habitats management schemes are designed to increase biodiversity but the attraction of heathland is its reduced fertility and diversity. The plants and animals living on heathland are few in numbers of species but highly adapted to this environment and thus scarce elsewhere. Heathland conservation seeks to avoid new colonising species becoming established and avoid enrichment of the soil. There is considerable evidence that it is extremely difficult to return colonised heathland or reclaimed farmland to its original heathland form.

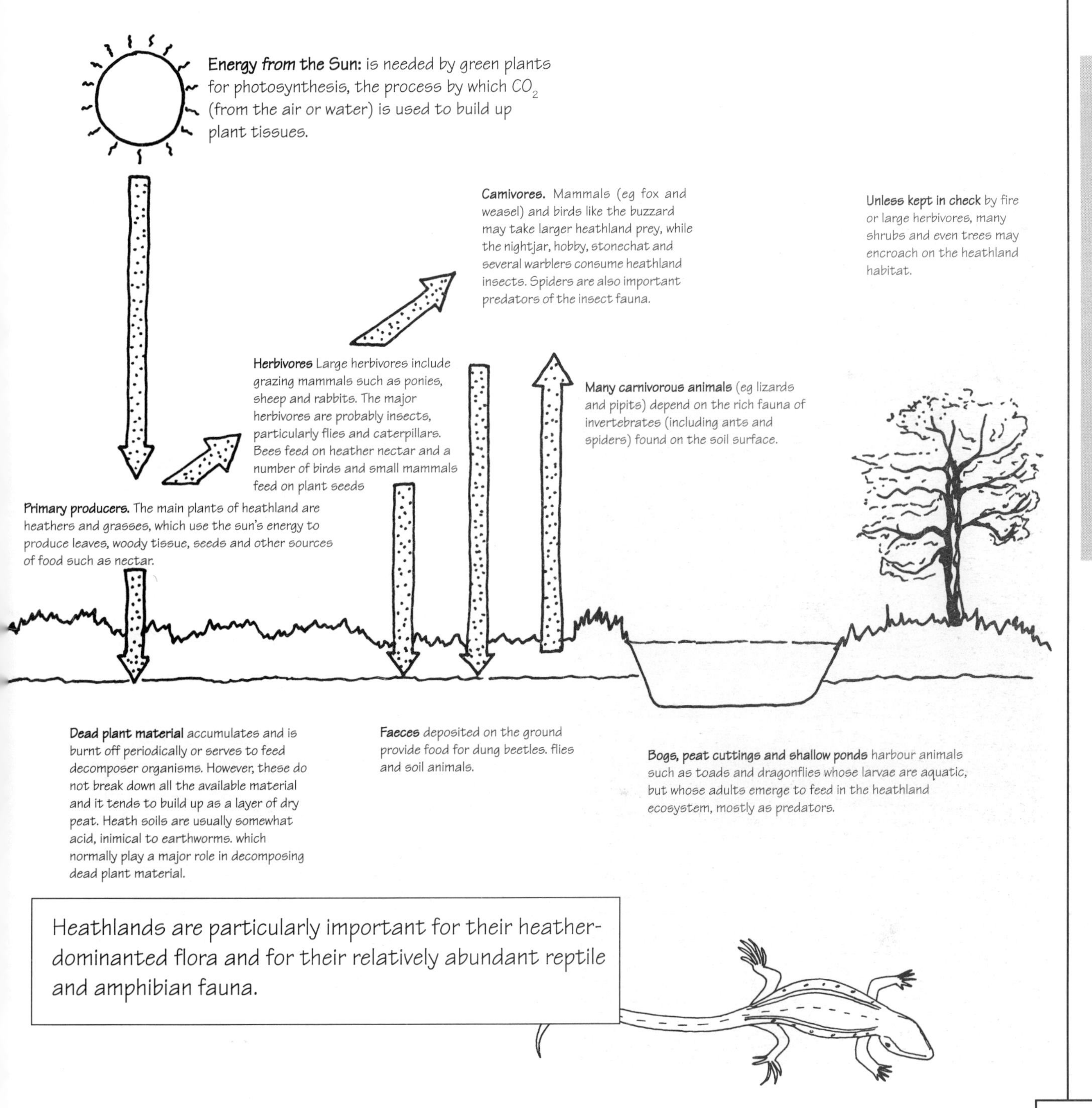

Heathlands are particularly important for their heather-dominanted flora and for their relatively abundant reptile and amphibian fauna.

2. Dartmoor

The use of granite as a building material, as railway ballast and as high-quality kerbstones has resulted in the development of large quarries. Deposits of China-clay have also resulted in large scale mining activities. Both of these extractive industries have high water demands, cause particulate pollution of air and water, make a lot of noise and leave behind enormous spoil heaps.

Soil erosion caused by the large numbers of walkers and pony-riders seeking "solitude and seclusion" is a serious problem. Recreational walkers and riders have disturbed some rare species of bird - the Merlin and Peregrine Falcon for example.

Conservationists on Dartmoor have attempted to balance the problems by concentrating industry and tourism into relatively confined areas - the major consideration seems to be the provision of car parks!

Dartmoor also suffers from over-grazing and from the "improvement" of land to generate produce which we have in excess anyway!

The 'Moor' includes the Dartmoor National Park adminstered by the National Park Authority, advised by English Nature (formerly the Nature Conservancy Council) and the Countryside Commission, funded by the Department of the Environment (75%) and Fee Income/Subscription (25%) and visited by 8 000 000 'units' per annum

TOURISM : generates cash and enthusiasm, which may promote the use of political influence in determination of local policy,
but
may create litter, noise, atmospheric and water pollution and conflicts over access to sensitive areas

so park management can compromise by confining visitors to restricted areas and providing carparks, snackbar and toilet facilities and well-defined pathways

MINISTRY OF DEFENCE : may have a negative influence - danger from live ammunition stock may be moved during war games disturbance to feeding/nesting birds deaths caused by bird strikes erosion, particularly by tracked vehicles
but
large areas of land may be kept undeveloped and inaccessible for training purposes, thus protecting many species

FARMING : overstocking with sheep and cattle, which maintain a sub-climax grassland

too many ponies of poor quality, many of which are sold as petfood or as meat to French markets

the overstocking has been supported by subsidies

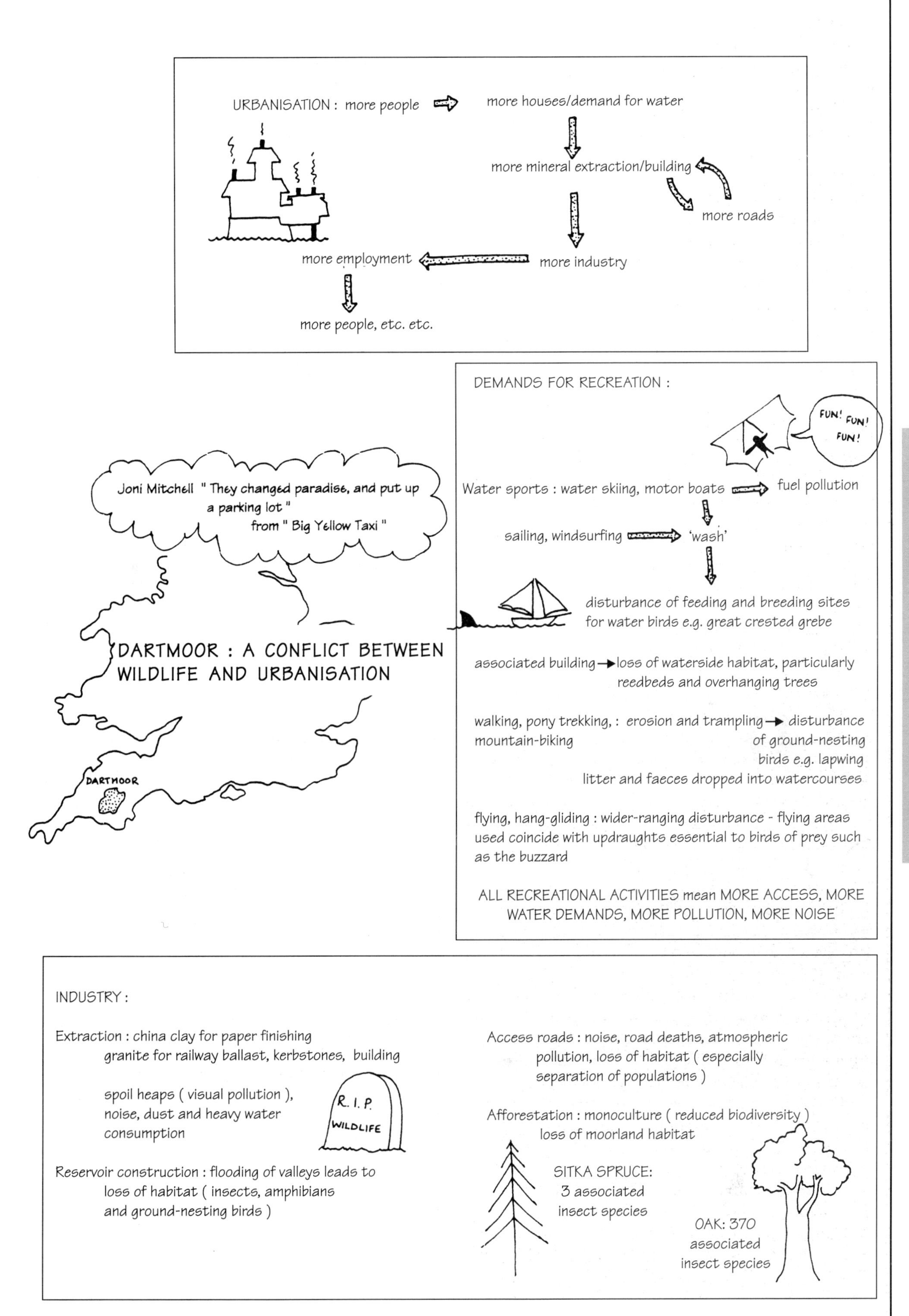
URBANISATION : more people
more houses/demand for water
more mineral extraction/building
more roads
more industry
more employment
more people, etc. etc.
DEMANDS FOR RECREATION :
FUN! FUN! FUN!
Water sports : water skiing, motor boats
fuel pollution
sailing, windsurfing
'wash'
disturbance of feeding and breeding sites for water birds e.g. great crested grebe
associated building → loss of waterside habitat, particularly reedbeds and overhanging trees
walking, pony trekking, mountain-biking : erosion and trampling → disturbance of ground-nesting birds e.g. lapwing
litter and faeces dropped into watercourses
flying, hang-gliding : wider-ranging disturbance - flying areas used coincide with updraughts essential to birds of prey such as the buzzard
ALL RECREATIONAL ACTIVITIES mean MORE ACCESS, MORE WATER DEMANDS, MORE POLLUTION, MORE NOISE
Joni Mitchell " They changed paradise, and put up a parking lot "
from " Big Yellow Taxi "
DARTMOOR : A CONFLICT BETWEEN WILDLIFE AND URBANISATION
DARTMOOR
INDUSTRY :
Extraction : china clay for paper finishing
granite for railway ballast, kerbstones, building
spoil heaps (visual pollution), noise, dust and heavy water consumption
R. I. P.
WILDLIFE
Reservoir construction : flooding of valleys leads to loss of habitat (insects, amphibians and ground-nesting birds)
Access roads : noise, road deaths, atmospheric pollution, loss of habitat (especially separation of populations)
Afforestation : monoculture (reduced biodiversity) loss of moorland habitat
SITKA SPRUCE:
3 associated insect species
OAK: 370
associated insect species

3 British Coasts

Many estuaries important for wintering wading birds and other wildlife are under threat from development. Schemes include yacht marinas, luxury housing and holiday accommodation (e.g. Cardiff Bay, the Hayle Estuary), industrial development (e.g. chemical works at Teesmouth) and barrages for hydro-electric schemes (e.g. the Severn Estuary). All of these areas include SSSIs, in particular there are areas of international importance for wading birds - species such as knot (*Calidris canutus*), sanderling (*Calidris alba*), turnstone (*Arenaria interpres*), bar-tailed godwit (*Umosa laponica*)and grey plover (*Pluvalis squaterola*) may either winter in Great Britain or use these estuarine mudflats as stopover sites on their migration flights between northern breeding grounds and southern wintering areas. Birds other than waders may also be affected - the Brent Goose (*Banta bernicla*) overwinter in very large numbers on the Maplin Sands, a site threatened by the possible development of an airport, wildfowl overwintering on the Shannon estuary are threatened by the development of a coal-fired power station and an alumina smelter, and winter populations of both peregrine falcon and merlin are very dependent on the availablity of prey species at estuarine sites. The Royal Society for the Protection of Birds has investigated the effects of urban and commercial development of estuarine sites on bird populations .

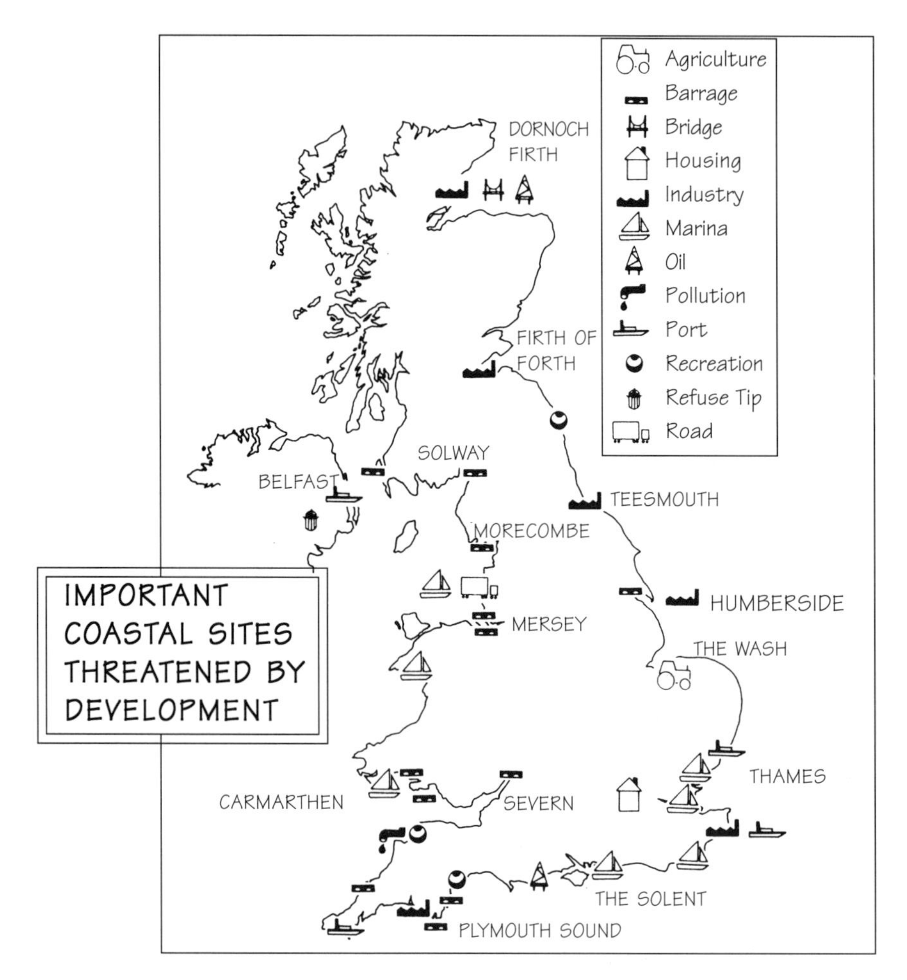

The scale of habitat loss in estuaries can be enormous. In the 1930's the intertidal mudflats at Teesmouth occupied about 2 500 ha but the industrial development, particularly associated with the chemical industry, had reduced this to about 150 ha by 1975. This loss, of more than 90% of possible wildlife habitat, is devastating but may be upstaged by the losses threatened as tidal power generation becomes a real possibility. If a tidal barrier is constructed across an estuary major habitat changes are inevitable. Inside the barrage tidal amplitude is reduced so that the exposure of mudflats is limited, there is less 'washing out' of pollutants and there is increased disturbance through recreational activity. In 1988 the government approved plans for a £450 million barrage across the Mersey estuary - this would create about 5 000 temporary jobs in an economically-depressed area and would generate about 0.5% of the national energy demand, but would wipe out the Ince and Stanlow marshes which are the most important winter habitat for Pintail (*Anas acuta*).

Roadbuilding and habitat loss

In 1989 a government White Paper, 'Roads to Prosperity', was published. It listed some 450 roadbuilding schemes which the Department of Transport planned to implement but gave little justification for them. The D.o.T. attempted to soften the blow to environmentalists by promising to concentrate on widening existing motorways and trunk roads rather than on ploughing up even more wildlife habitat, and attempted to justify both the enormous expenditure and environmental impact by suggesting that the construction programme aims "to meet the needs of industry and other road users for a modern strategic road network which also helps to reduce accidents and improve the environment".

It has now been suggested, however, that the transport costs are only a very low proportion (probably as low as 3.5%) of total production costs and the present Government is soft-pedalling by proposing a reduction in these roadbuilding schedules.

Roadbuilding and mineral extraction clearly has a direct environmental impact - wildlife habitats are lost and replaced by hard surface. These effects are relatively short term, but there are some more long-lasting effects

- roadside sites become highly desirable for shopping centres, service areas and hotels, all of which consume more wildlife habitat
- roads kill - many animal populations are severely diminished by road deaths. Some of those most at risk are animals following established feeding or breeding routes. Thus many badgers, hedgehogs and toads die every year.
- road lighting can be disorientating, and may affect feeding behaviour in birds and bats
- roads fragment habitats - if an animal cannot cross a road then populations may become isolated from one another .

The unceasing demand for roadbuilding materials may have severe aesthetic effects, as well as affecting wildlife populations. There are reclamation techniques by which areas used for mineral extraction may be returned to valuable wildlife habitat. Some of these points are illustrated in the diagram overleaf.

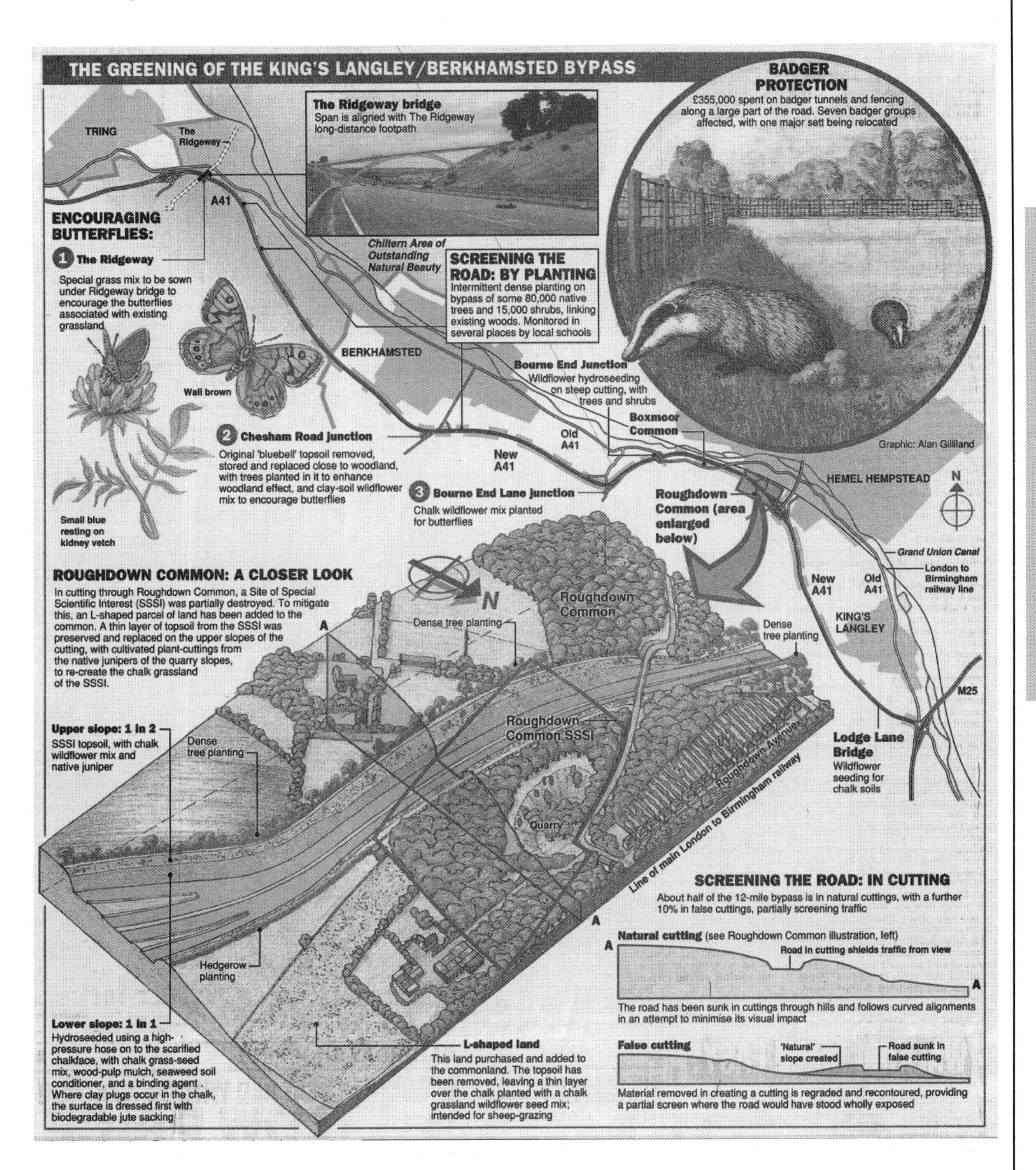

QUARRYING IS A RESULT OF URBANISATION

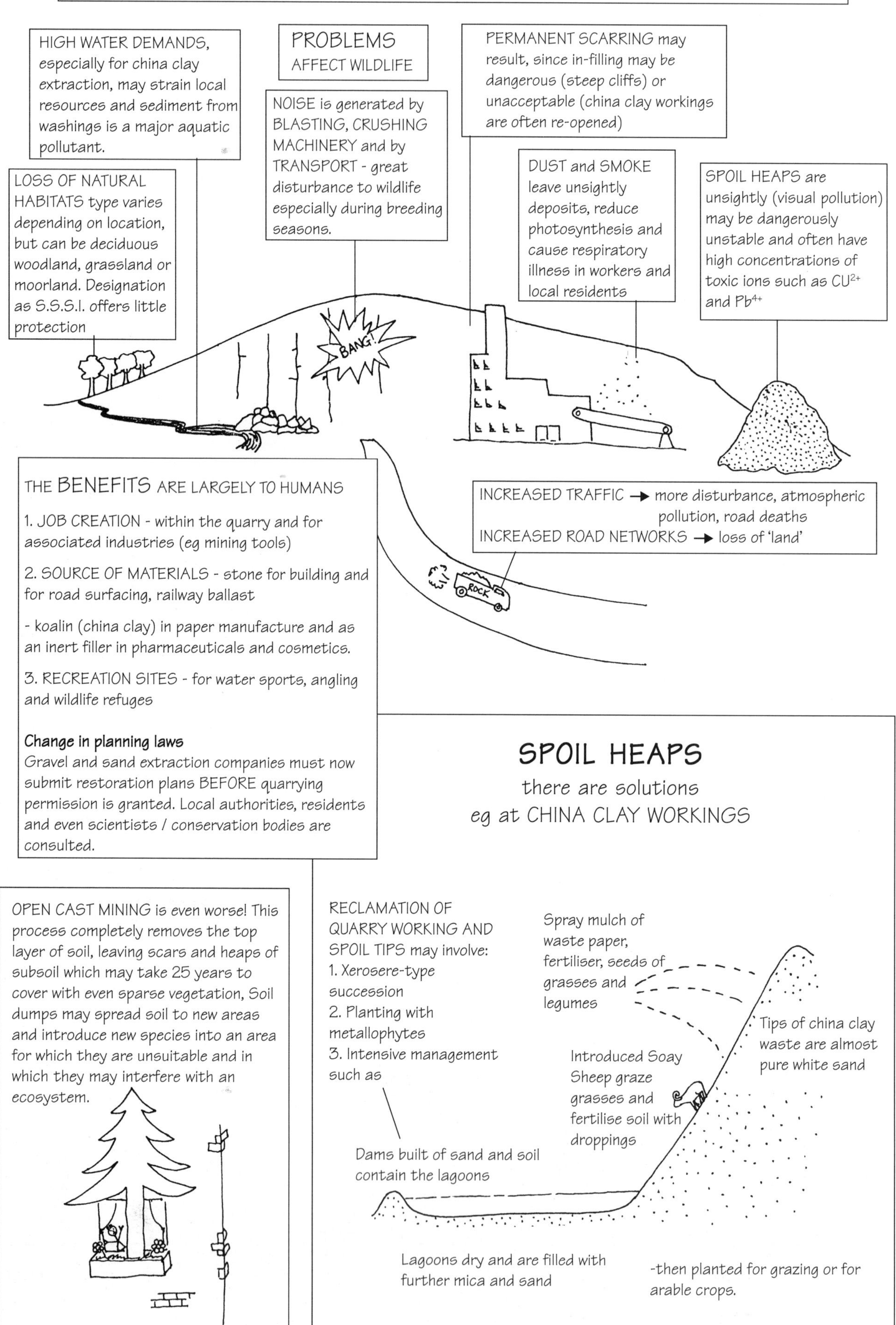

Guardians of the Land: Conservation and the Ministry of Defence

The Ministry of Defence (M.O.D.) is one of the most significant landholders in Great Britain - these land holdings are managed by the Defence Estate Organisation. one part of which is the Ministry of Defence Conservation Office. The land has been acquired for the training of military personnel and the development of weapons, and makes the M.O.D. the second largest landholder in Great Britain (only the Forestry Commission is larger).

The earliest training exercises were probably organised by Roman legions, and would have been conducted close to their large camps. The M.O.D. estate has developed over the last 150 years as military requirements have changed - up until the end of the eighteenth century training of British forces typically took place locally in the village archery butts or close to garrison towns. Increases in the range and the lethality of weapons, and in the manoeuvrability of vehicles, meant that such local training was neither practical nor safe so that specialised training areas had to be purchased. These tended to be either

low grade agricultural land, such as heathland and moorland, since such areas were relatively inexpensive

or coastal, since weapons could be trained out to sea and greater use could thus be made of limited areas

The current estate consists of an area of almost 250 000 hectares involving some 3 200 separate sites. These range in size from the 38 000 hectare expanse of Salisbury Plain to individual buildings and communication masts.

The Defence Estate Organisation has established priorities in its management of this land:

1. The Service Facility i.e. the suitability and availability of the estate for military activity. Closely allied to this is the maintenance of safe conditions for the public.
2. The use of the estate for agriculture and conservation.
3. Access to the estate for recreation and amenity.

It should be obvious that the service facility **must** have the first priority on the lands in the Defence Estate - in fact the service use is less of a conflict with the conservation programme than is the use for recreation and amenity. The heathland communities of southern Britain may well suffer more from motor-rallying, orienteering and mountain biking than from military exercises!

In 1973 the Nugent Report (Report of the Defence Lands Committee) was published, and for the first time a full-time Conservation Officer was appointed. The Department over which this officer holds brief has gradually expanded as there has been an increasing awareness of the legal and moral responsibilities which the M.o.D. has for the lands under its management, and now includes scientific advisers and administrators. The Conservation Office has

several main areas of responsibility, which include:

- coordination of the recording of natural history and archaeology, mainly through the activities of local military conservation groups
- coordination of integrated conservation management plans
- education of military and civilian staff, and increasing public awareness of the M.O.D's conservation effort
- liaison with other Government Departments, statutory bodies (e.g. English Nature) and non-Governmental organisations (e.g. R.S.P.B.)
- advising M.O.D. Ministers on conservation policy.

The widespread deployment of the three Services across the country means that the estate now includes examples of the main indigenous habitats, from raised bogs to limestone pavements and chalk grassland, and with it an immensely wide diversity of species, many of which are rare or endangered . Due to the nature of military training and weapon development many of these areas have escaped intensive farming, agrochemical sprays and major development. The Conservation Officer has a watching brief over all of them!

RELATIONSHIPS WITH OTHER CONSERVATION BODIES

The M.O.D. has no separate budget for conservation, but instead conservation is regarded as an integral part of good estate management. It is not in the interests of the M.O.D. to over-use land for military purposes - the needs of the military and of wildlife are carefully balanced.

Establishing an appropriate balance is achieved through local conservation groups, which contain both military and civilian personnel. The Commanding Officer of the site is usually the Chairman, and the civilian members include representatives of statutory bodies and experts in natural history and conservation matters. These experts are all volunteers, and their field of expertise will be appropriate to the conservation value of the site. These conservation groups are like any other in that they:

1. survey the site
2. identify and record the flora and fauna of the site
3. assist in the preparation of management plans
4. carry out practical conservation work
5. monitor the effects of the management plan.

The M.O.D. has also signed " Declarations of Intent " with English Nature, Scottish Natural Heritage and the Countryside Council for Wales. These declarations formally recognise the M.O.D's difference from other landowners in that the primary role for its land must be for the preparation of our defence forces. The M.O.D. also maintains contact and liaison with many other national and international wildlife and countryside organisations, the most prominent including the Royal Society for the Protection of Birds, The County Wildlife Trusts and the Herpetological Conservation Trust.

SALISBURY PLAIN - THE JEWEL IN THE CROWN

Nowhere is the M.O.D's importance as a landholder seen more clearly than on the Salisbury Plain Training Area (SPTA). In November 1993 the Secretary of State for the Environment announced the designation of 20 000 hectares of SPTA as a special protection area (SPA) under the 1979 EC Birds Directive. This followed the notification earlier in the year of the Site of Special Scientific Interest (SSSI) covering the same area and gives the training area formal recognition as a site of national and international importance for its wildlife.

Chalk grassland has been created and maintained by clearance of the original woodland and centuries of grazing by domestic animals. The constant defoliation combined with a soil low in nutrients has led to a short turf with a very rich diversity of plants and insects adapted to this management and provides a habitat for several rare species of birds.

The downland once covered vast areas of southern England and supported huge numbers of sheep, but during this century there has been a gradual loss to intensive farming so that only a small fraction of this type of grassland now remains. Most of the sites are small, fragmented and on steep slopes which have avoided the plough.

Parts of Salisbury Plain have been used by the military since the end of the last century and land has been steadily acquired to make this the largest military training area in the United Kingdom, covering almost 40 000 hectares. The military presence has prevented the encroachment of intensive farming over the greater part of the area, with most of the arable land restricted to the periphery while the rest is in grassland or under forestry.

Although much of this grassland was ploughed in Roman times, grasslands which have developed over hundreds of years without the use of fertilisers and herbicide sprays are rich in flowers; there is a core of about 20 000 hectares of this old herb-rich grassland with the biggest extent on the danger zones of Larkhill and Imber. This is the largest area of chalk downland in north-west Europe, and constitutes about 40% of this declining habitat in Britain. It is the extent of the habitat on Salisbury Plain which enables it to support such important populations of birds, insects and plants.

Much of the rich grassland is dominated by Upright Brome (*Bromopsis erecta*) which in the absence of grazing forms a tall tussocky grassland in which many herbs will survive

THE SALISBURY PLAIN TRAINING AREA

combines limited public access with informed management to provide many habitats for wildlife

Dormouse (*Muscardinus avellanarius*) requires coppiced woodland, which provides hazelnuts for food and honeysuckle bark for building their ground-level nests. Coppicing is very much diminished in Britain, but the DEO's forestry division has re-established a coppicing cycle and dormice have recolonised the area.

Stone Curlew (*Burhinus oedicnemus*) needs bare or sparsely-vegetated ground on which to nest. The bare chalk and random stones revealed by military activity has created ideal nest sites, and the unimproved grassland provides food - about 10% of the British population lives on the SPTA.

A Solitary Bee (*Melitta dimidiata*) is widespread on the Plain - it feeds entirely on Sainfoin (*Onobrychis sativa*) a herb which is abundant on SPTA but uncommon elsewhere.

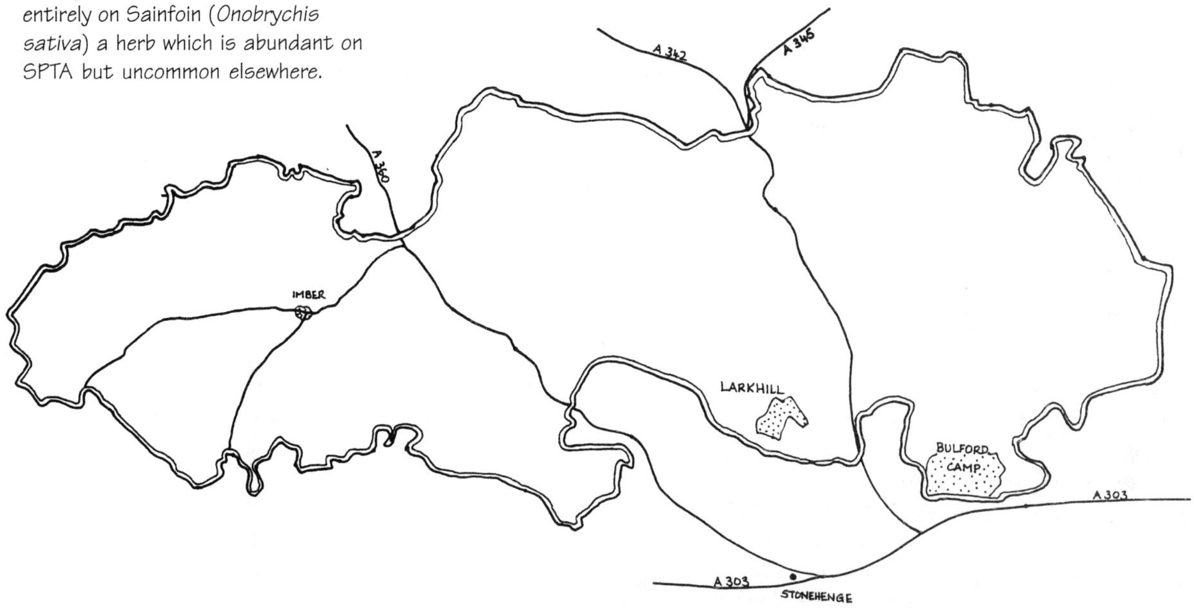

Hobby (*Falco subbuteo*) is found throughout SPTA. The herb-rich flora supports a large insect population which in turn provides a food source for this falcon and for some of its major prey species, the swallows and martins. SPTA also provides suitable nesting habitat in the numerous small blocks of woodland.

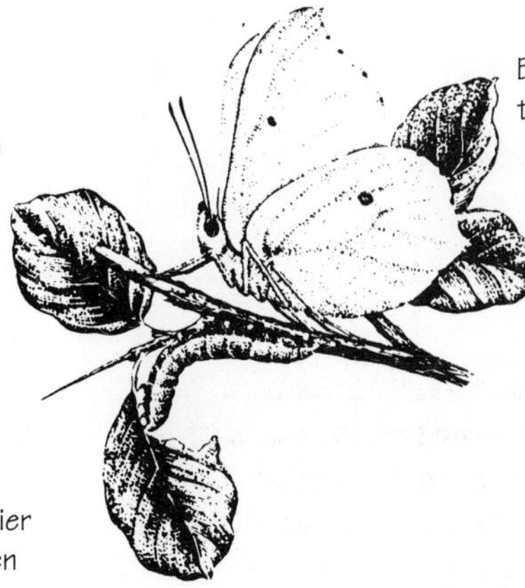

British butterflies have good populations on the Plain. The Green Hairstreak (*Callophrys rubi*) benefits from the scrubby areas and the Adonis Blue (*Lysandra bellargus*) from the steep, undisturbed south-facing slopes. Lesser Butterfly Orchid (*Platanthera bifolia*) benefits from the grazing/low fertiliser application regime.

Merlin (*Falco columbarius*) and Hen Harrier (*Circus cyaneus*) occur in winter. The Hen Harriers, feeding on the abundant small mammals and birds, have traditional roosts maintained in the long grass areas on the live firing ranges at Larkhill. The Merlin hunts in low, fast flight by ambushing small birds feeding on the widespread, open grassland.

The Quail (*Coturnix coturnix*) is abundant on SPTA - 20% of the British population is found here - where it benefits from the low intensity farming, particularly from the relaxed grass cutting regime.

even after many years. The re-introduction of grazing will then quickly restore a rich turf. Land ploughed during the 1939 - 45 war and now back to grassland is dominated by False Oat Grass (*Arrhenatherum elatius*) and, although it is less rich than the older grassland, it is gradually gaining in number of species. There has recently been a decline in herb-rich grassland on the SPTA caused mainly by the use of fertiliser but also by the conversion to forestry and arable usage. Direct losses due to military activity have been very small and much of what might have been perceived as damage, such as the creation of bare ground through tank movements and shell impact has in fact led to the creation of a wonderful mosaic of vegetation. Indeed, the Fairy Shrimp (*Chirocephalus diaphanus*), a nationally rare crustacean, depends on the temporary pools formed in tank tracks for its survival, as it is unable to live in permanent ponds - the eggs of the shrimp are actually dispersed on the tracks of the vehicles!

There is no reason why the wildlife of the Plain should not continue to flourish alongside the military as it has for the past 100 years, and the MOD are determined to preserve the outstanding flora and fauna. This determination is demonstrated by the signing of the Declaration of Intent which pledges English Nature and the MOD to work together to maintain and enhance the nature conservation interest of Salisbury Plain - English Nature and the Defence Estate Organisation have jointly produced a management plan which will integrate the needs of nature conservation with those of military training. Implementation of this plan will require the co-operation of all the users of the SPTA, in particular the farmers whose stock are the most important factor in the maintenance of the grasslands, and of course the military as the primary users of the area. The use of fertiliser on herb-rich grassland will be halted and grazing reintroduced to areas of rank grass. There are huge areas, in particular in the impact area, where there has been no grazing for many years and long term aims will be to restore grazing to some of these where possible. Areas reverting back to grassland after being in arable can be enhanced by a good grazing regime without the use of fertilisers - eventually these will become herb-rich and an ideal habitat for butterflies.

With the MOD's acceptance of Salisbury Plain as a Special Protection Area, and the implementation of the joint English Nature - MOD Conservation Office management plan, the future of this site will hopefully be assured. Its value cannot be overstated in a countryside where natural and semi-natural habitats are becoming increasingly fragmented.

MINISTRY OF DEFENCE AREAS

- cover almost 600,000 acres
- occupy 3,200 separate sites
- range in size from less than 1 to more than 90,000 acres
- include
  - Sites of Specific Scientific Interest
  - Areas of Outstanding Natural Beauty
  - RAMSAR (Wetlands of International Importance)
  - National Nature Reserves
  - Special Protection Areas
  - Special Areas of Conservation

MINISTRY OF DEFENCE CONSERVATION POLICY

takes account of national and international legislation, including:

- Wildlife and Countryside Act (1981-amended)
- EC Birds Directive
- EC Habitats and Species Directive and is determined after consultation with
- Statutory bodies such as English Nature and Conservation bodies such as RSPB

M.o.D. CONSERVATION OFFICER

- oversees a team of scientists, administrators and liaison officers
- coordinates conservation work on all M.o.D. sites
- publishes 'Sanctuary', an annual review of the M.o.D.'s work in conservation.
- can be contacted at:
  M.o.D. Conservation Office
  Room B2/3
  Government Buildings
  Leatherhead Road
  Chessington
  Surrey KT9 2LU

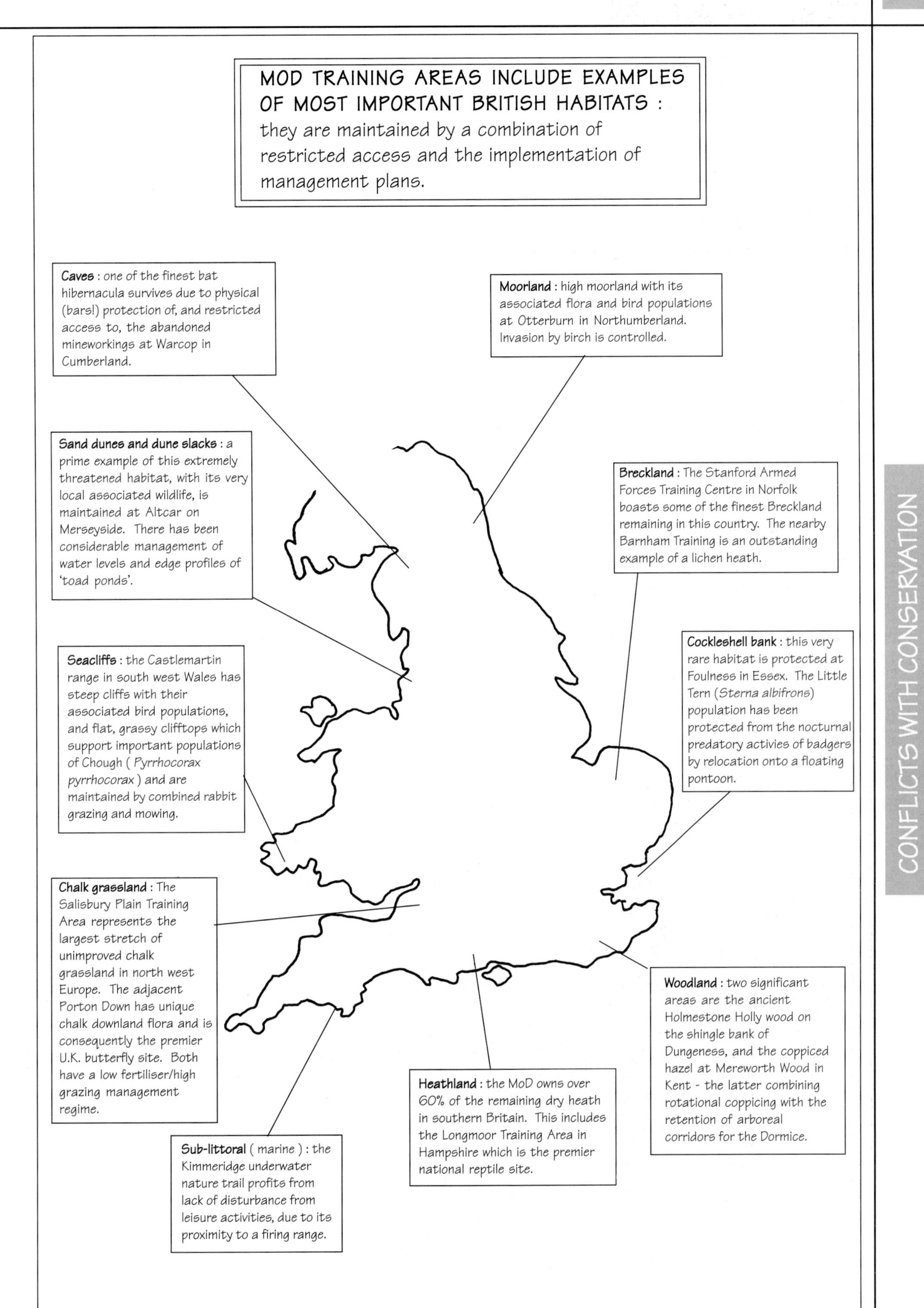
MOD TRAINING AREAS INCLUDE EXAMPLES OF MOST IMPORTANT BRITISH HABITATS : they are maintained by a combination of restricted access and the implementation of management plans.
Caves : one of the finest bat hibernacula survives due to physical (bars!) protection of, and restricted access to, the abandoned mineworkings at Warcop in Cumberland.
Moorland : high moorland with its associated flora and bird populations at Otterburn in Northumberland. Invasion by birch is controlled.
Sand dunes and dune slacks : a prime example of this extremely threatened habitat, with its very local associated wildlife, is maintained at Altcar on Merseyside. There has been considerable management of water levels and edge profiles of 'toad ponds'.
Breckland : The Stanford Armed Forces Training Centre in Norfolk boasts some of the finest Breckland remaining in this country. The nearby Barnham Training is an outstanding example of a lichen heath.
Cockleshell bank : this very rare habitat is protected at Foulness in Essex. The Little Tern (Sterna albifrons) population has been protected from the nocturnal predatory activies of badgers by relocation onto a floating pontoon.
Seacliffs : the Castlemartin range in south west Wales has steep cliffs with their associated bird populations, and flat, grassy clifftops which support important populations of Chough (Pyrrhocorax pyrrhocorax) and are maintained by combined rabbit grazing and mowing.
Chalk grassland : The Salisbury Plain Training Area represents the largest stretch of unimproved chalk grassland in north west Europe. The adjacent Porton Down has unique chalk downland flora and is consequently the premier U.K. butterfly site. Both have a low fertiliser/high grazing management regime.
Woodland : two significant areas are the ancient Holmestone Holly wood on the shingle bank of Dungeness, and the coppiced hazel at Mereworth Wood in Kent - the latter combining rotational coppicing with the retention of arboreal corridors for the Dormice.
Heathland : the MoD owns over 60% of the remaining dry heath in southern Britain. This includes the Longmoor Training Area in Hampshire which is the premier national reptile site.
Sub-littoral (marine) : the Kimmeridge underwater nature trail profits from lack of disturbance from leisure activities, due to its proximity to a firing range.

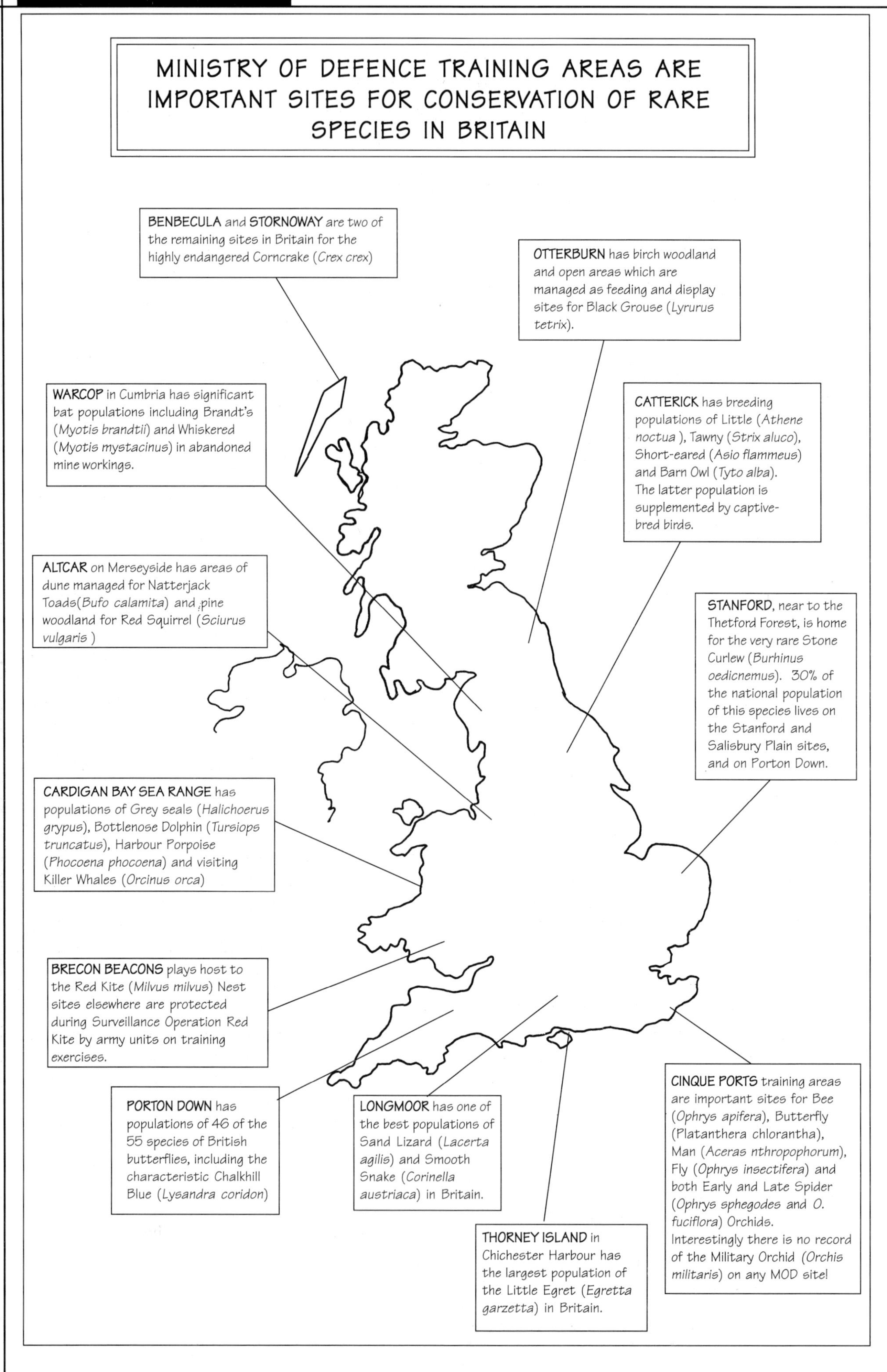
MINISTRY OF DEFENCE TRAINING AREAS ARE IMPORTANT SITES FOR CONSERVATION OF RARE SPECIES IN BRITAIN
BENBECULA and STORNOWAY are two of the remaining sites in Britain for the highly endangered Corncrake (Crex crex)
OTTERBURN has birch woodland and open areas which are managed as feeding and display sites for Black Grouse (Lyrurus tetrix).
WARCOP in Cumbria has significant bat populations including Brandt's (Myotis brandtii) and Whiskered (Myotis mystacinus) in abandoned mine workings.
CATTERICK has breeding populations of Little (Athene noctua), Tawny (Strix aluco), Short-eared (Asio flammeus) and Barn Owl (Tyto alba). The latter population is supplemented by captive-bred birds.
ALTCAR on Merseyside has areas of dune managed for Natterjack Toads(Bufo calamita) and pine woodland for Red Squirrel (Sciurus vulgaris)
STANFORD, near to the Thetford Forest, is home for the very rare Stone Curlew (Burhinus oedicnemus). 30% of the national population of this species lives on the Stanford and Salisbury Plain sites, and on Porton Down.
CARDIGAN BAY SEA RANGE has populations of Grey seals (Halichoerus grypus), Bottlenose Dolphin (Tursiops truncatus), Harbour Porpoise (Phocoena phocoena) and visiting Killer Whales (Orcinus orca)
BRECON BEACONS plays host to the Red Kite (Milvus milvus) Nest sites elsewhere are protected during Surveillance Operation Red Kite by army units on training exercises.
PORTON DOWN has populations of 46 of the 55 species of British butterflies, including the characteristic Chalkhill Blue (Lysandra coridon)
LONGMOOR has one of the best populations of Sand Lizard (Lacerta agilis) and Smooth Snake (Corinella austriaca) in Britain.
CINQUE PORTS training areas are important sites for Bee (Ophrys apifera), Butterfly (Platanthera chlorantha), Man (Aceras nthropophorum), Fly (Ophrys insectifera) and both Early and Late Spider (Ophrys sphegodes and O. fuciflora) Orchids. Interestingly there is no record of the Military Orchid (Orchis militaris) on any MOD site!
THORNEY ISLAND in Chichester Harbour has the largest population of the Little Egret (Egretta garzetta) in Britain.

The Role of Legislation

Management of the countryside is of prime importance for the conservation of wildlife. Farmers play a major part in the management of land in Britain, and have opportunities to help wildlife into the next century. The farming community is greatly affected by legislation.

> "For the past twenty years farming has been dominated by Europe's Common Agricultural Policy (CAP)."

To make their living, farmers have been forced by the CAP to adopt intensive methods : larger fields, bigger harvests, greater input of fertilisers and more sophisticated farm machinery consuming more fossil fuels and run by fewer staff. The costs to the environment of the CAP were probably never intended and, in the view of many conservation bodies, have never been recognised. The RSPB has produced data which emphasises many of the points made earlier in this book:

- over half of our grazing marshes lost since the Second World War
- 95% of herb-rich meadows lost since the Second World War
- 120 000 km of hedgerow lost between 1984 and 1990
- over 500 SSSI's damaged between 1990 and 1992

and with habitat loss has come the well-documented decline of once-common birds

- nesting Lapwings numbers dropped by half in the last thirty years
- half of the Barn Owl population gone since the 1930's
- Corncrakes driven from most of Britain
- Corn buntings declining in England, largely extinct from Wales and increasingly rare in Scotland and Northern Ireland

Farmers responded so successfully to the calls for increased farm outputs that they outgrew the more-is-better philosophy underlying the CAP. The CAP guaranteed prices to farmers for their produce, so they had every reason to grow more. The result was wine lakes and beef, butter and grain mountains; food that wasn't needed and yet was produced at the expense of Britain's wildlife habitats.

> "In May, 1992, the European Commission (now the EU) announced major reforms to the Common Agricultural Policy. It wasn't working for farmers, let alone for wildlife."

The aim of these reforms was to cut the cost of farm subsidies, reduce surplus production and boost rural life. It was hoped that these reforms would limit damage to the environment and might prove beneficial to wildlife.

The new CAP aimed to

- change subsidies to make some crops less profitable and so do away with the food mountains
- take some land out of cultivation (set-aside) and pay livestock farmers who stock their cattle at low densities
- pay farmers to adopt 'environmentally-friendly' farming methods

POSSIBLE EFFECTS ON WILDLIFE

> "The level of subsidies available is a major consideration for any farmer choosing what to grow"

SUBSIDIES : Corn Buntings do well in barley fields, but not in fields of wheat. A change in grain subsidies could help the return of Corn Buntings without any more direct conservation measure being taken. Yellow Wagtails eat insects kicked up by cattle. They do not fare well in close-cropped overgrazed sheep fields and moors. EU directives to make cattle more profitable would make Yellow Wagtails a more common sight.

> "To limit the surplus of production over consumption, farmers will be encouraged to 'set-aside' 15% of their land each year."

SET-ASIDE : Part of the CAP reforms reduced the subsidies on grain production (by up to 35% over the first three years of the reforms). Farmers would naturally suffer a drop in income with this reduction in subsidy, but would be compensated *only if they took some land out of production.* This 'set-aside' land could be determined as **rotational** i.e. a different 15% each year for five years, or **non-rotational** i.e. the same 15% for a fixed period, typically of five years. One year set-asides could result in weedy stubble fields being left over winter. These could provide food for finches and buntings that are in decline. The five year set-asides could provide important rough hunting grounds for species such as the barn owl (hunting habitat is a major factor in their decline - see p16). Longer term set-aside, if introduced, could encourage farmers to create wetlands, heaths and other habitats without affecting Britain's ability to produce food *or* the farmers' income.

IS THE SET-ASIDE SYSTEM REALLY WORKING?

YES	and	NO
approximately 15% of once arable land is not being used to grow crops, and might thus be available for wildlife conservation		15% of land out of production does not mean 15% less food is being produced - some farmers use the set-aside payments to farm the remaining 85% more intensively
advice is available from FWAG on the optimum management of set-aside		close Government restrictions on the use of set-aside - no harvestable product may be sown - can mean that possible wildlife food sources are destroyed by enforced application of weedkillers, or land which might become a grazing meadow cannot be so used since the grazing cattle might qualify as a 'harvestable product'.

Obviously farmers seeking to illegally exploit the set-aside regulations must be discouraged, but at the same time the Government should seek the advice of conservation bodies - particularly FWAG - in adopting a more flexible approach to the permitted uses of set-aside land.

"Most farmers enjoy wildlife and would welcome a role as true stewards of the countryside, in addition to growing food."

Unfortunately, many of the traditional methods of farming that are so good for wildlife don't make farmers any money. They produce less food and may need more farm workers. On the other hand, they often require less machinery and fewer chemical inputs. It is clear that if farmers are going to return to these methods they will have to be financially compensated for the benefits which they bring to wildlife and rural employment. Hay meadows, for example, are cut later in the summer than grass for silage. This allows wild flowers to set their seeds and ground-nesting birds to rear their young before the grass is cut. The Corncrake is now virtually restricted to those areas in the North and West of the UK where tradtional hay-making is still practised - financial compensation is made available to farmers who adopt these wildlife-friendly traditional methods.

Statutory Conservation Bodies

Although the voluntary movement is powerful in Britain there are also many statutory bodies with a concern for the environment and its conservation. These are government and state funded.

1. **English Nature** (Formally The Nature Conservancy Council) has a number of roles:

- It has the power to at least nominally safeguard **Sites of Special Scientific Interest (SSSIs)** by regulating the activities of local authorities. Note that, despite this protection, a number of SSSIs are under threat (e.g. the Cardiff Barrage scheme) and that powerful vested interests make the protection of SSSIs a difficult task.
- It is responsible for the running of **National Nature Reserves (NNRs**), which tend to be larger and of a higher conservation status than most wildlife sanctuaries. Many are on private land and have limited public access.
- It has established a series of **Industry and Conservation Associations** (**INCAs**) in an attempt to foster closer liaison between industry and its local environment.

NATIONAL NATURE RESERVES (NNR's)
In January 1994 there were 268 NNR's in England, Scotland and Wales, identified specifically as important in protection of biological diversity. NNR's have four functions in addition to conservation:

- research
- advice and information
- education
- amenity and access

SITES OF SPECIAL SCIENTIFIC INTEREST (SSSI 's)

- are defined as " an area of land which is of special interest by reason of its flora, fauna, geological or physiographic features ".
- there are about 6,000 SSSI's in England, Scotland and Wales
- should be protected from development since any activity likely to damage them must be notified to local planning authorities - in practice as many as 5% of SSSI's are damaged each year

2. The **Countryside Commission** is responsible for the wider countryside. It is an advisory and promotional body but does not own land or property. It can designate **Areas of Outstanding Natural Beauty (AONBs),** it can define heritage coasts and it may establish long distance footpaths

It has a management role in the running of the country's National Parks. Each National Park is administered by a **National Park Authority** with funding (about 75%) from the **Department of the Environment.**

Because they cover so much of Britain's land area, National Parks are of great importance. However, they do not *directly* conserve natural habitats because human activity continues within their boundaries. As a result farming, quarrying and forestry continue to affect them (see Dartmoor p. 100) and there is an increasing effect of recreational activities.

In addition to their work with National Parks, the Countryside Commission advises local and regional planning authorities on countryside matters, taking a particular interest in urban fringe areas.

It has encouraged the setting up of Country Parks whose recreational and educational emphasis has relieved pressure on the more sensitive and scientifically important sites managed by English Nature.

NATIONAL PARKS

defined in 1945 as " an extensive area of beautiful and relatively wild country in which, for the nation's benefit and by appropriate national decision and action

- the characteristic landscape beauty is strictly preserved
- access and facilities for public open-air enjoyment are amply provided
- wildlife, buildings and places of architectural interest are suitably protected
- established farming use is effectively maintained

The first National Park to be set up was the Peak District in 1949 as a result of the passing of the National Parks and Access to the Countryside Act. There are now ten of them, with two equivalent areas of the Broads and the New Forest, occupying about 8% of the land area of England and Wales

3. **The National Environment Research Council** is the government body with the greatest concern for wildlife conservation. This body is widely involved with all aspects of wildlife conservation and environmental protection, and co-ordinates with those also doing research in the universities and polytechnics.

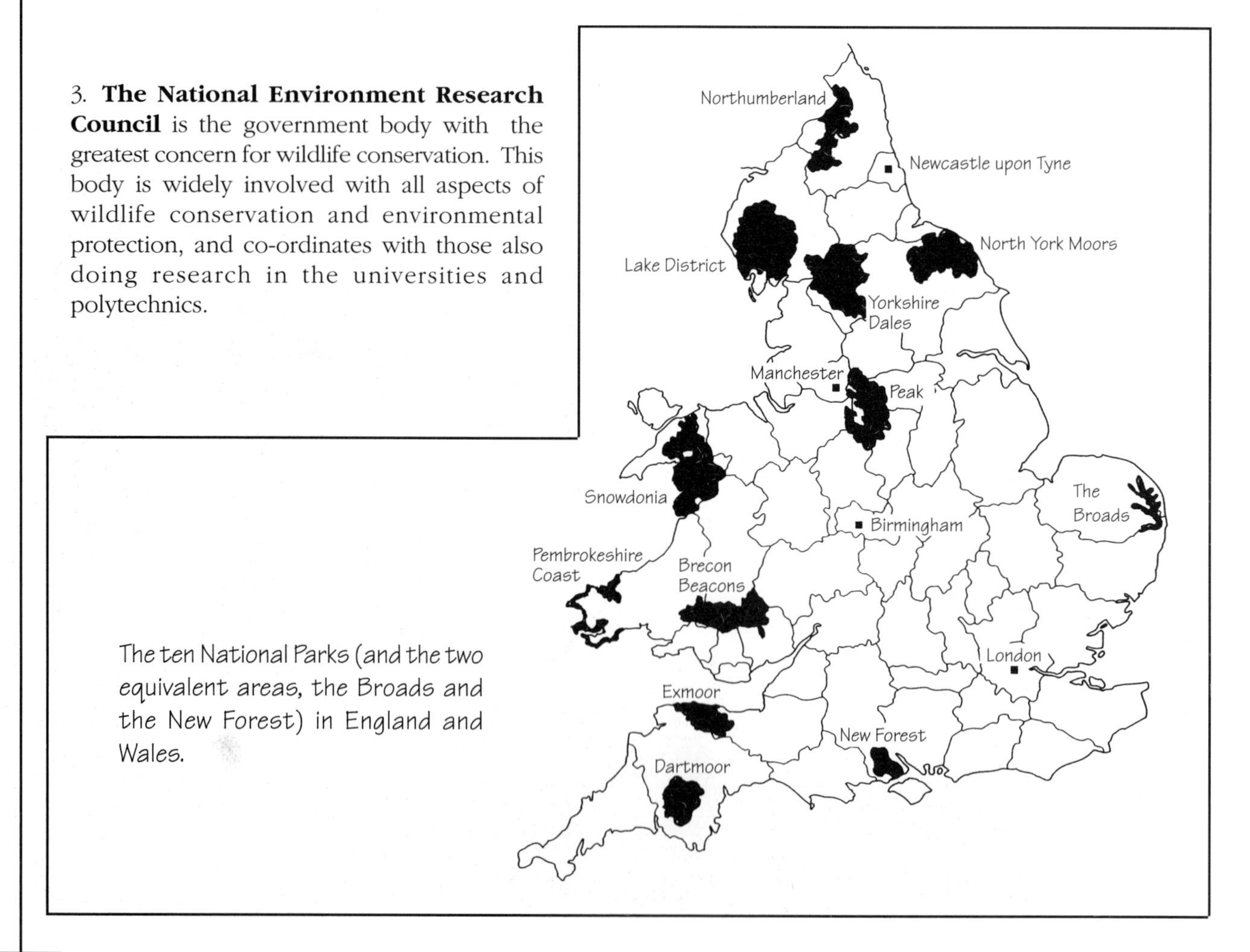

The ten National Parks (and the two equivalent areas, the Broads and the New Forest) in England and Wales.

4. The **Ministry of Agriculture** has the power to determine **Environmentally Sensitive Areas (ESA's)**.

These must satisfy the following criteria Environmentally-sensitive areas in the UK

" Areas of national environmental significance whose conservation depends on the adoption, maintenance or extension of a particular form of farming practice; in which there have occurred, or there is likelihood of, changes in farming practices which pose a major threat to the environment; which represent a discrete and coherent unit of environmental interest; and which would permit the economicadministration of appropriate conservation aids"

Important habitats conserved in ESA's include

- chalk downland with its varied flora water meadows and
- mature deciduous woodland

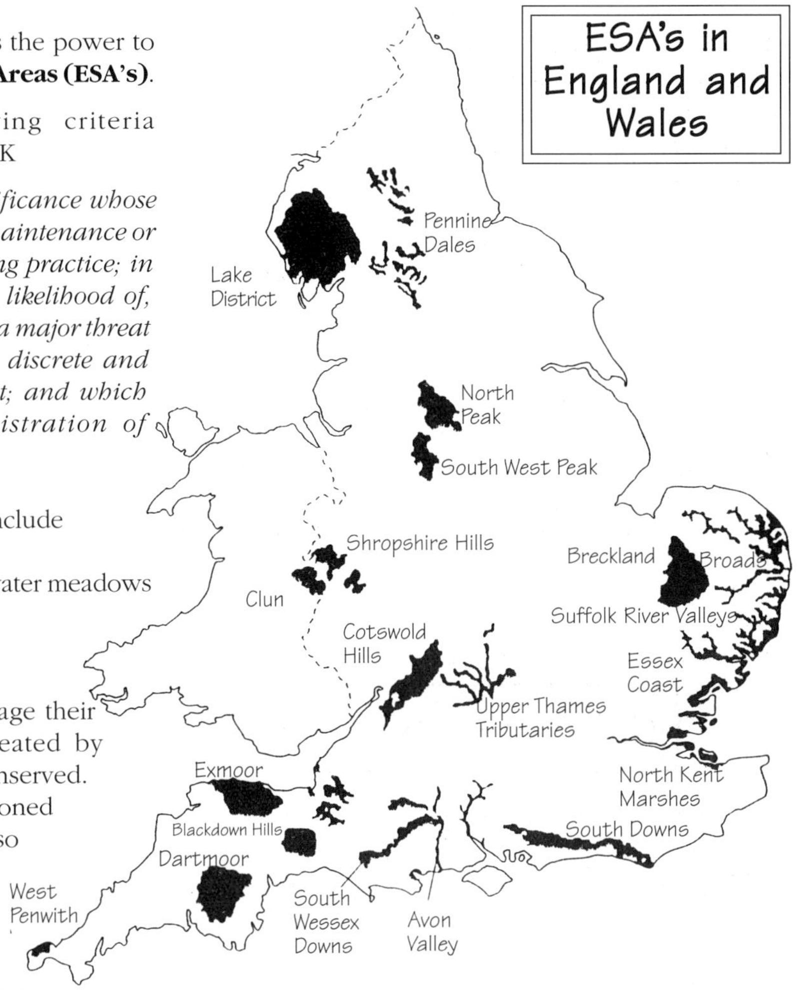

In these areas farmers are paid to manage their land in such a way that features created by traditional land-use management are conserved. For example, the chalk downland mentioned above is favoured by sheep grazing, so farmers might receive financial incentives to keep sheep when this would otherwise be unprofitable for them. The Farming and Wildlife Advisory Group (p. 89) is an important advisor in appropriate management.

ESA's in England and Wales

Lake District
Pennine Dales
North Peak
South West Peak
Shropshire Hills
Clun
Breckland
Broads
Suffolk River Valleys
Cotswold Hills
Essex Coast
Upper Thames Tributaries
North Kent Marshes
Exmoor
Blackdown Hills
Dartmoor
West Penwith
South Wessex Downs
Avon Valley
South Downs

Two highly significant pieces of legislation which greatly influence conservation in Britain are the **Set-aside scheme** and the **Wildlife and Countryside Act**

Set-Aside Scheme

Wildlife and Countryside Act (1981 amended)

THE ROYAL SOCIETY FOR THE PROTECTION OF BIRDS is primarily concerned with national issues (eg preservation of Caledonian pine forest in Scotland) but plays a large part in international conservation by e.g.

a Monitoring trade in birds
b Advising on the management of overseas nature reserves

GREENPEACE runs a series of non-violent, direct action campaigns such as PROTECTION OF MARINE MAMMALS and the REGULATION OF THE DISPOSAL OF TOXIC WASTE.

COUNCIL FOR THE PROTECTION OF RURAL ENGLAND (C.P.R.E.) is a national body which has particular concerns for local issues e.g. the planning of roads through sensitive areas such as ancient woodlands

INTERNATIONAL + NATIONAL +

FLORA AND FAUNA PRESERVATION SOCIETY concentrates on funding research into the preservation of INDIVIDUAL SPECIES (e.g. Ploughshare tortoise in Madagascar)

WORLDWIDE FUND FOR NATURE (WWF) attempts to maintain HABITATS and thus the species of animal and plant they contain. May utilise individual FLAGSHIP SPECIES to draw attention to and raise funding for the need to conserve habitats

ENGLISH NATURE (there are equivalent bodies in Scotland and Wales) nominates SITES OF SPECIFIC SCIENTIFIC INTEREST (SSSI's), runs the NATIONAL NATURE RESERVES (NNR's) and had established liaison organisations called INDUSTRY AND CONSERVATION ASSOCIATIONS (INCA's)

CONVENTION ON INTERNATIONAL TRADE IN ENDANGERED SPECIES (C.I.T.E.S.) monitors trade in wildlife and wildlife products and tries to impose controls where necessary

THE COUNTRYSIDE COMMISSION is an advisory and promotional body which does not own land or property but can designate AREAS OF OUTSTANDING BEAUTY (AONB's), helps to manage NATIONAL PARKS and has encouraged the setting up of COUNTRY PARKS which have recreational and educational emphasis which relieves pressure on the more sensitive sites run by English Nature

INTERNATIONAL UNION FOR THE CONSERVATION OF NATURE AND NATURAL RESOURCES (I.U.C.N.) tries to co-ordinate action and monitor success on species survival. The I.U.C.N. publishes the RED DATA BOOKS which list in detail the animal and plant species threatened with extinction

CONSERVATION OPERATES FROM INTERNATIONAL TO LOCAL LEVEL...

CONTRIBUTE INCOME via DONATIONS AND MEMBERSHIP FEES
(eg WWF membership doubled between 1989-92)

OUTSTANDING SCIENTIFIC AND POLITICAL CONTRIBUTIONS
eg Diane Fossey : Gorillas
Jane Goodall: Chimpanzees
Gerald Durrell: Captive breeding of Golden Lion Tamarin
John Aspinall: Tigers

LOCAL + INDIVIDUALS

COUNTY NATURALISTS' TRUSTS will often liaise with landowners and local authorities over the management of local nature reserves. Organise voluntary wardening of nature reserves.

NATIONAL ENVIRONMENT RESEARCH COUNCIL (NERC) is widely concerned with all aspects of wildlife conservation and environmental protection. It also co-ordinates the research into associated problems being carried out by universities.

SPECIFIC LOCAL ORGANISATIONS
eg OTTER TRUST (NORFOLK) which hopes to re-introduce otters to the wild
STOUR VALLEY PRESERVATION SOCIETY (KENT) lobbies MP's and applies pressure to control development of the Stour Valley

...and INDIVIDUALS CAN OFFER FINANCE, EXPERTISE AND PHYSICAL LABOUR!

English Nature was set up by the Environmental Protection Act 1990. It is a statutory body funded by the Department of the Environment. Its purpose is to promote the conservation of England's wildlife and natural features. The work of this organisation includes:

English Nature's total budget for 1995/96 was £41,749 million. This was made up of £40,419 million grant in aid from the Department of the Environment and £1,330 milion receipts.

- provision of information and advice to Government and other organisations
- identification and sustainable management of Sites of Special Scientific Interest
- supporting academic research relevant to conservation of nature
- establishment of National Nature Reserves and Marine Nature Reserves
- implementation of international conventions and EU directives on nature conservation
- implementation of the Biodiversity Action Plan and the practical application of sustainable development
- offering grants to help others carry out nature conservation

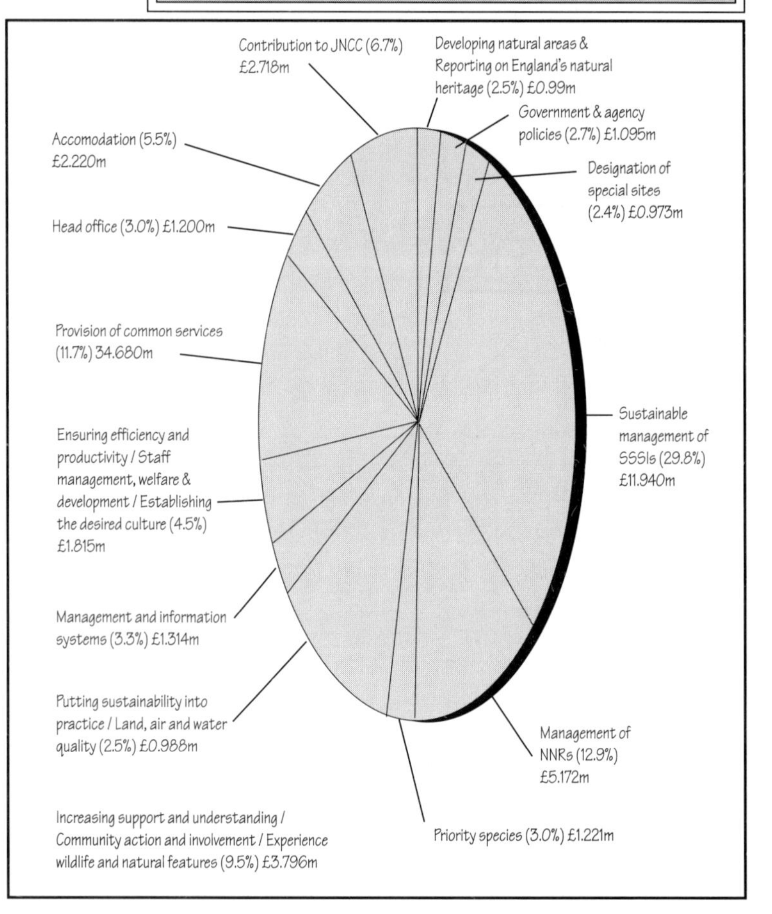

The main duties of English Nature have been granted by the following Acts of Parliament

- National Parks and Access to the Countryside Act 1949
- Countryside Act 1969
- Nature Conservancy Council Act 1973
- Wildlife and Countryside Act 1981 as amended
- Environmental Protection Act 1990

English Nature is principally funded by the Department of the Environment, i.e. by the taxpayer.

True to its stated belief that nature conservation can only be achieved with the willing co-operation and active involvement of many organisations and individuals English Nature maintains strong contacts with

- Government and statutory agencies
- SSSI landowners and managers
- voluntary nature conservation organisations
- local planning authorities
- members of the public seeking licences or grants, or information about nature conservation
- research institutions

DESIGNATED SITES IN ENGLAND

NNRs and MNRs

National Nature Reserves are sites which have been declared by English Nature or its predecessors under Section 19 of the National Parks and Access to the Countryside Act 1949 or Section 35 of the Wildlife and Countryside Act 1981. They are either owned or controlled by English Nature or held by approved bodies such as wildlife trusts.

Marine Nature Reserves in England are declared by the Secretary of State for the Environment. At present there is one MNR, Lundy in Devon.

Tenure	*Hectares As at 30.9.95*
Owned by English Nature	16,147
Leased by English Nature	30,222
Nature Reserve Agreement with English Nature	14,170
Held by an approved body	5,280
Total area	65,819
Total number of NNRs	168

SSSIs

Sites of Special Scientific Interest are notified by English Nature because of their plants, animals, or geological or physiographical features. Most SSSIs are privately owned or managed. About 40% are owned or managed by public bodies, such as the Forestry Commission, Ministry of Defence and The Crown Estate, or by the voluntary conservation movement.

	Number	Hectares
As at 30.9.95	3,840	897,2441

SSSIs cover approximately **6.8010** of England's total area. English Nature liaises with about 23,000 owners and occupiers on these sites.

SPAs / Ramsar sites

Ramsar sites

The UK Government signed the Convention on Wetlands of International Importance Especially as Waterfowl Habitat (the Ramsar convention) in 1973. Under the Convention the Government is committed to designate 'Wetlands of International Importance' (Ramsar sites) and to use the wetlands within its territory wisely.

Special Protection Areas (SPAs)

The Government is bound by the European Communities Council Directive of April 1979 on the Conservation of Wild Birds. Under this Directive the Government has to designate Special Protection Areas to conserve the habitat of certain rare or vulnerable birds (listed under the directive) and regularly occurring migratory birds. It has to avoid any significant pollution or disturbance to or deterioration of these designated sites.

All designated SPAs and Ramsar sites are Sites of Special Scientific Interest. Some sites qualify for both Ramsar and SPA designations. English Nature's particular involvement is the identification of these sites, their notification as SSSIs and carrying out consultations on the proposed designations with owners, occupiers, local authorities and other interested parties.

	Ramsar sites	*SPAs*
Number of sites designated (in whole or part) as at 30.9.95	58*	56*
Total area designated as at 30.9.95 (hectares)	265,875	297,187

* Of these sites 43 were designated as both Ramsar sites and SPAs.

Local Nature Reserves

All LNRs are owned or controlled by local authorities and some, but not all, are SSSIs. Local authorities consult English Nature on all new proposals for LNRs in England.

	Number	Hectares
As at 30.9.95	464	18,068

Looking after Britain

The new Environment Agency for England and Wales is a most powerful regulator of our use and abuse of the environment. It provides an extremely comprehensive approach to the protection and management of the environment by combining the regulation of aquatic, terrestrial and aerial environments. The agency was set up to merge the activities of the National Rivers Authority, Her Majesty's Inspectorate of Pollution, the Waste Regulation Authorities and several smaller units from the Department of the Environment.

On its inception the Chief Executive of the Environmental Agency wrote:

> " The Agency must make a real difference to the environment that will last through the next generations. We must therefore carry public opinion with us and be as effective and efficient as the industries we seek to regulate in order to have credibility for this major task."

The Agency's stated aim of protecting and enhancing the whole environment contributes to the world-wide environmental goal of **Sustainable Development**, which has been defined as " Development that meets the needs of the present without compromising the ability of future generations to meet their own needs".

The Agency aims

- to integrate environmental protection and enhancement without imposing disproportionate costs on industry or society as a whole
- to set high professional standards using best sources of information and analytical techniques
- to establish a close and responsive relationship with the public and other environmental organisations.

Although it has a wider brief than any of the organisations from which it was formed the Agency will endeavour to maintain the standards set by those organisations. In the illustrative example which follows the work of the former NRA is described. In the absence of any other name, the term NRA (National Rivers Authority) is retained in this section.

The National Rivers Authority - NRA

CONSERVATION OF THE AQUATIC ENVIRONMENT

When we think of the water environment, most of us might envisage an unspoilt river in its natural state, meandering across open countryside, its banks rich with flora and fauna, its waters teeming with aquatic life. In fact, very little of our water environment remains unaffected by human activity.

Alterations to rivers probably started with forest clearances about 3 000 BC. The subsequent development of water-milling, navigation, drainage and irrigation systems caused major and lasting changes to the shape of rivers and associated habitats and vegetation. Channelization, water pollution, drainage of wetlands and over abstraction of water have all significantly reduced the wildlife interest of many rivers.

The National Rivers Authority has accepted a duty to further conservation, to rehabilitate degraded sites and to promote the re-creation of habitats previously damaged by environmentally-insensitive practices.

The NRA was formed as a result of the Water Act 1989. Those aspects of this Act which concerned the NRA were later consolidated into the Water Resources Act 1991. Effectively this legislation, and certain elements of EC directives, require that the NRA should

> " act to maintain and, where necessary, improve the water environment "

The NRA has crystallised the conservation aspects of these requirements in the NRA Conservation Strategy. This document includes a statement of the NRA's 'mission'

"We will protect and improve the water environment by the effective management of water resources and by substantial reductions in pollution. We will aim to provide effective defence for people and property against flooding from rivers and the sea. In discharging our duties we will operate openly and balance the interests of all who benefit from and use rivers, groundwaters, estuaries, and coastal waters. We will be businesslike, efficient and caring towards our employees".

Note those important elements which effective and realistic conservation requires - "effective management" and " balance the interests". Of course we have already noted two other significant features of a successful conservation strategy - there must be effective **monitoring and assessment** of the system, and any management plan can only be implemented if there is **adequate finance** available

ASSESSING THE RESOURCE

To date there has been no systematic attempt to assess the value to wildlife of habitat features of the waterways in England and Wales, or to introduce a classification scheme for assessing their conservation interest. The NRA needs to evaluate the conservation value of inland and coastal waters, and to achieve this will:

1. identify and develop standard methodologies for **assessing the conservation interest** of waterways
2. develop systems for **classifying the habitat features** of rivers which affect their wildlife value
3. establish a national database system for storage and retrieval of conservation data
4. make data available to external bodies as required by EC directives

FINANCING THE STRATEGY

The NRA is funded largely by a combination of Government grant-in-aid (GIA) and self-generated income from NRA charging schemes. At the moment most of the direct conservation funding is dependent upon GIA, but approximately 80% of the NRA's total conservation expenditure is related to normal operational expenditure - for example, flood control measures may contribute to enhancement of NRA controlled areas as wildlife habitats.

AN INTEGRATED APPROACH

The NRA believes that the best way of arriving at sustainable solutions is to take an integrated approach to river management. This treats a river, together with the land, tributaries and underground water connected with it, as a discrete unit or catchment. The NRA's approach is called **catchment management planning**. Under this system, the major uses within a catchment - such as abstraction, recreation, navigation, conservation and flood control - are investigated and a **catchment management plan** is devised in consultation with interested parties and the public.

THE WATER ENVIRONMENT - A FINITE RESOURCE UNDER PRESSURE

The demands which we make on the water environment include:

WATER ABSTRACTION for public and private water supply, industry, agriculture and navigation

EFFLUENT DISCHARGE from sewage treatment works, industrial processes and farms

RECREATION in the form of bathing, boating and fishing

COMMERCIAL HARVESTING of fish and shellfish

All of these are legitimate and necessary for the continuance of our way of life - **the human population imposes pressures on its environment.**

THE PRESENT STATUS OF THE WATER ENVIRONMENT - there is a rich variety of landscapes, habitats and wildlife features associated with the streams, rivers, ponds, lakes, wetlands, estuaries and coastal waters of England and Wales. This reflects a network of inland watercourses which totals more than 250 000 km in length and a coastline exceeding 4000 km.

Subtle effects of CLIMATE CHANGE that may have a direct or indirect impact on the conservation interest of rivers and coastal areas.

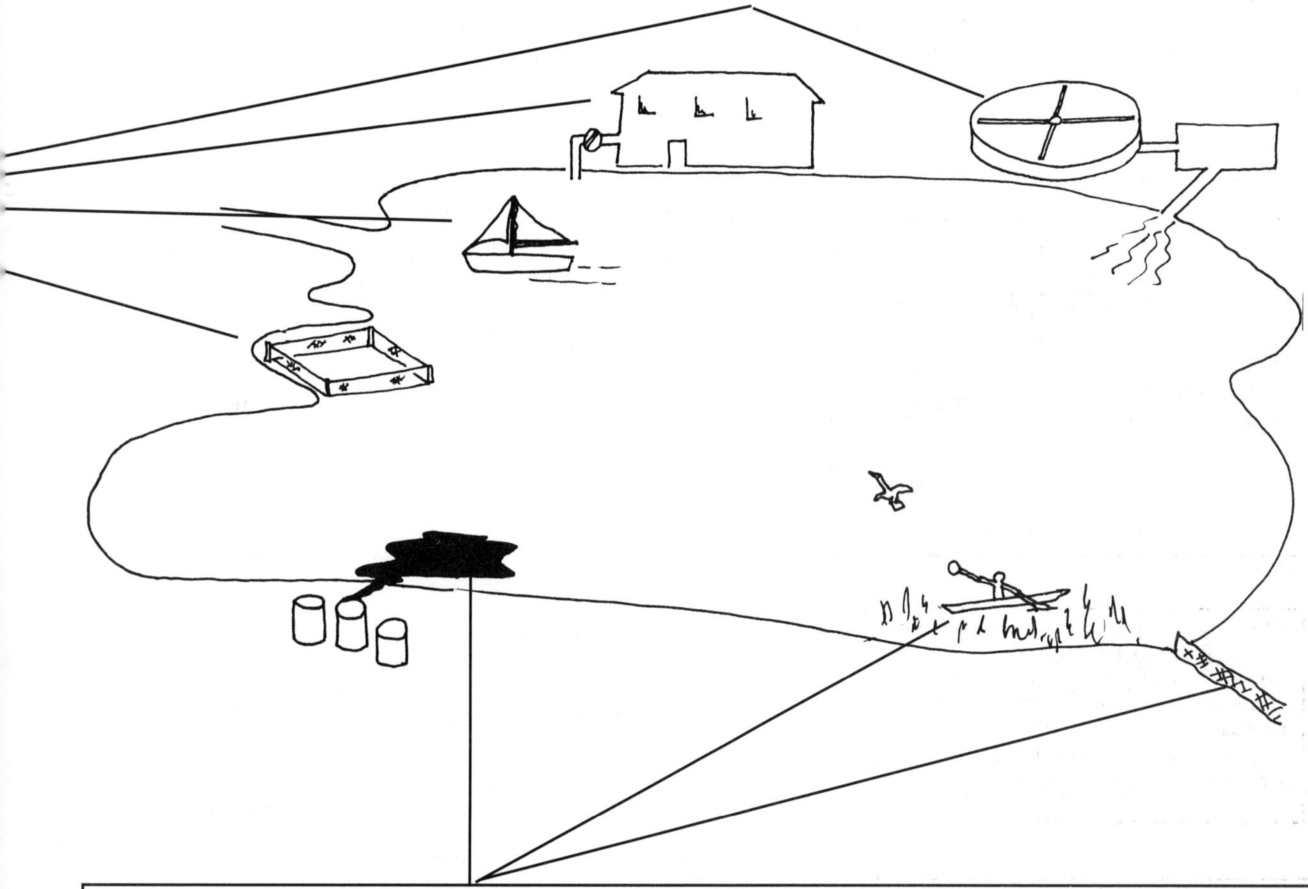

The pressures on the water environment include:

OVER ABSTRACTION OF WATER which can produce low river and groundwater levels, exacerbated during drought conditions. In extreme cases, wetlands and parts of rivers may dry out.

WATER POLLUTION, in particular the impact of nutrient enrichment (eutrophication) and noxious chemical substances. WATER ACIDIFICATION also has serious consequences for aquatic plant and animal life in some upland streams and rivers.

HABITAT IMPOVERISHMENT, which can be caused by environmentally insensitive flood and sea defence works.

RECREATIONAL DISTURBANCE, which may adversely affect sensitive plant and animal species.

INTENSIVE AGRICULTURAL AND URBAN USE of land adjacent to rivers, which impoverishes wildlife value and fragments the river corridor.

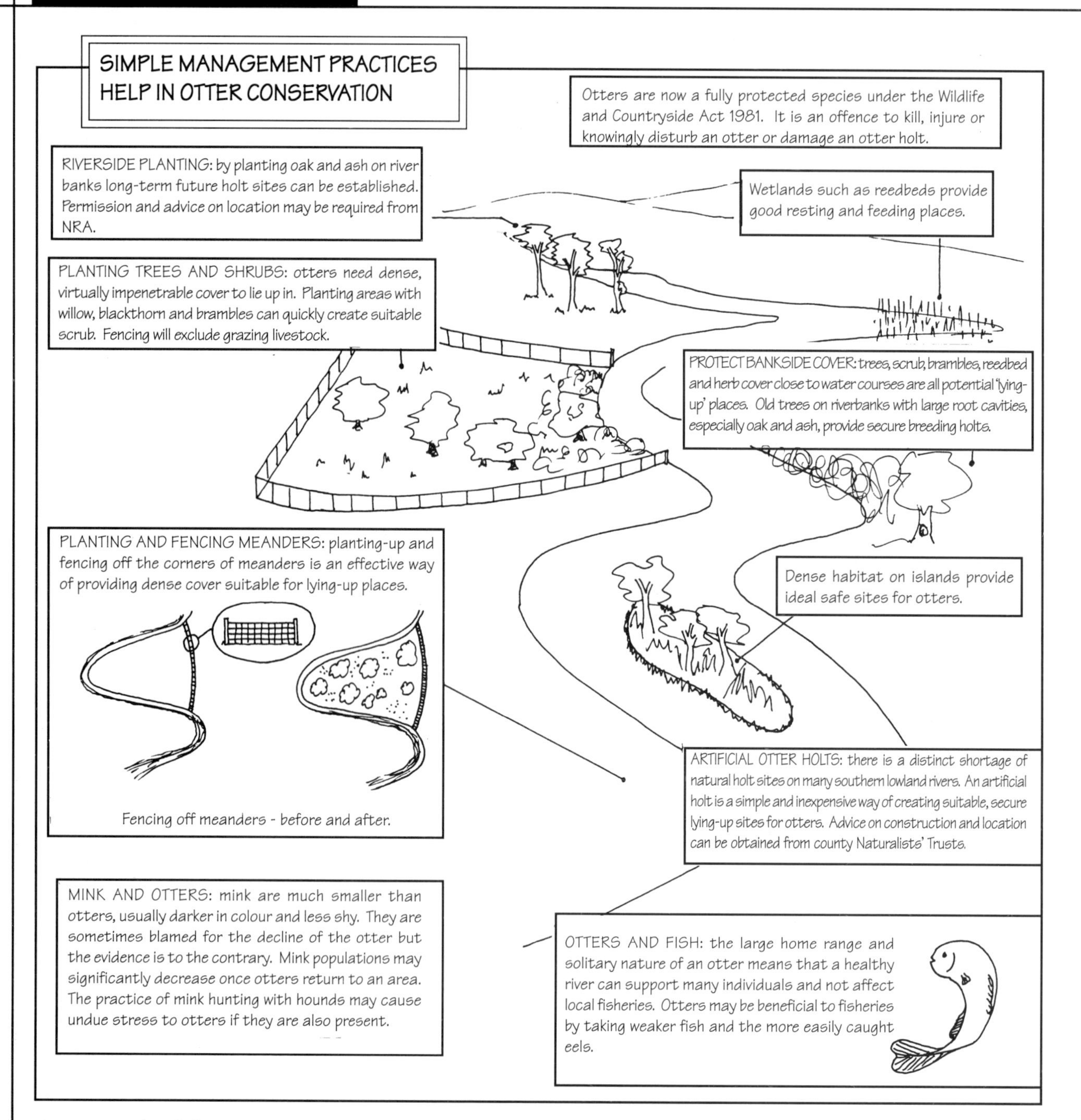

One example of the support given to the management of a particular species is the work which the NRA is carrying out, in conjunction with local Wildlife Trusts, on conservation of the Otter (*Lutra lutra*). This animal is under threat for a number of reasons, including

1. **pollution** by polychlorinated biphenyls (PCBs) and heavy metals which accumulate in the aquatic food chain is particularly damaging to 'top carnivores' (see page 70) such as the otter
2. **habitat loss**, which has usually been the result of unsympathetic river management, has reduced the number of secure lying-up sites for otters
3. **disturbance** caused by recreational use of waterways, walking dogs and hunting for mink, and
4. **drowning** in fyfe nets set for eels.

The NRA has acted in an advisory role to a number of sympathetic landowners and interested conservation bodies on means of river management to encourage otter populations. As a result there have been significant increases in otter numbers in the Severn-Trent, Southern and Welsh regions of the NRA's jurisdiction.

Thus the NRA Conservation Strategy meets the requirements identified earlier (p. 12) :

1. assessment
2. management planning
3. finance
4. reappraisal of implemented projects

The following pages investigate the demands on the aquatic environment, the ways in which the NRA works in conjunction with other conservation bodies to balance these demands with wildlife conservation, and some specific examples of the work of the NRA.

CONSERVATION DESIGNATIONS WHICH AFFECT THE WORK OF THE NRA include

Ramsar Sites (wetlands of international importance)

Special Protection Areas (SPAs)

Sites of Special Scientific Interest (SSSIs)

Environmentally Sensitive Areas (ESAs)

National, Local and Marine Nature Reserves (NNRs, LNRs and MNRs)

Areas of Outstanding Natural Beauty (AONBs)

Rare plants and animals associated with the water environment are also specifically protected under the Wildlife and Countryside Act 1981, as amended.

The NRA is not responsible for site or species protection *per se*, which is a function of English Nature and the Countryside Council for Wales. However, through management of rivers, the Authority plays a fundamental role in maintaining or creating habitat and water quality conditions suitable for aquatic and wetland plants and animals.

RIVER REHABILITATION

A number of rivers in England and Wales have been so heavily polluted that very few living organisms have been able to survive in them. These rivers usually face pressure from other areas, such as new developments in industry, housing and agriculture. Parts of many such rivers have usually been straightened to act as flood channels making even less attractive to wildlife. The NRA has, since 1989, made great efforts to improve the water quality in these rivers, so that many of them can now support populations of fish and other wildlife. In addition the NRA has begun a number of restoration or rehabilitation projects which serve the dual purpose of improving wildlife habitats and educating the public in the use of our water resources. The following serves as an example of such a rehabilitation project.

RIVER ROTHER ENVIRONMENTAL IMPACT SCHEME

The River Rother is in South Yorkshire, and had a reputation as the dirtiest river in Europe. Water quality was very poor and there was little habitat for wildlife. During the period from 1978 to 1981 the river was straightened and diverted, leaving very few natural habitat features.

Recently industrial pollution of the river has declined so that water quality has recovered. The NRA has worked on a section of the river in the reclaimed industrial land of the Rother Valley Country Park - improvements here could benefit a large section of the local community. Work included

1. creation of bay areas to provide off-channel fish refuges - these are areas where the fish can go if the river is running very very high or there has been a pollution incident. To support the recovering fish population the NRA released 2500 roach (*Rutilus rutilus*) and 2500 chub (*Leuciscus cephalus*) into the river.

2. construction of a lumpstone weir which increases the oxygenation of the water and makes the river run more quickly. This has helped to remove layers of built-up sediment, leaving gravel beds which will provide spawning areas for fish.

3. creation of a backwater area which was separated from the river by an island. This area offered undisturbed water for fish to spawn in and for young fish to develop, and improved nesting and feeding opportunities for waterbirds.

4. in conjunction with the Yorkshire Wildlife Trust the NRA is introducing meanders to the river channel and improving wetland habitats by adjustment of water levels.

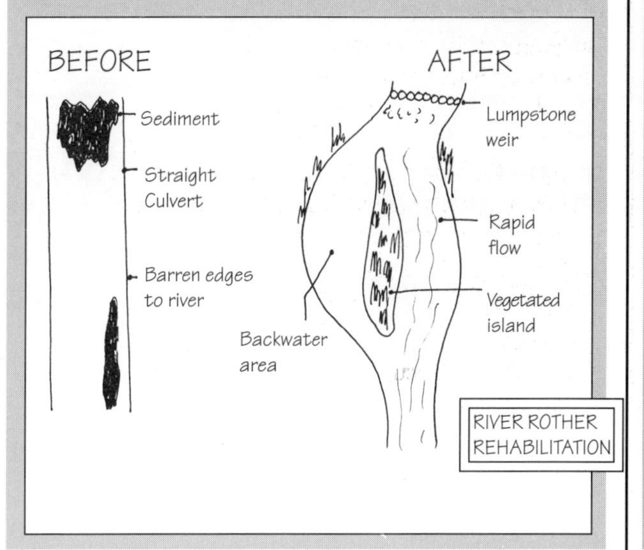

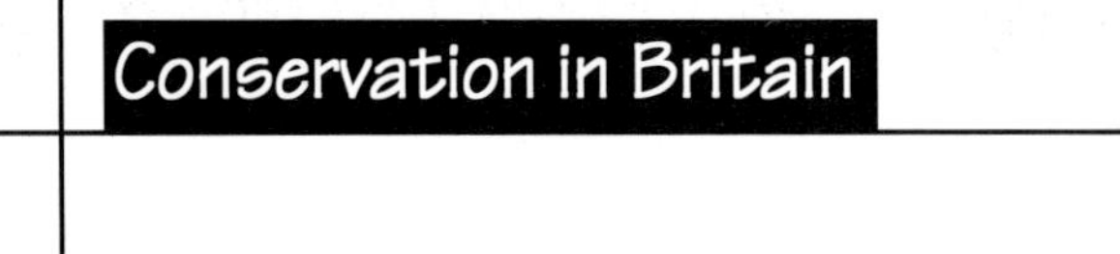

The RSPB works for the conservation of wild birds and the wider environment on which they depend. We believe that the beauty of birds and nature enriches the lives of many people, and that nature conservation is fundamental to a healthy environment on which the survival of the human race depends.

The R.S.P.B.

(Royal Society for the Protection of Birds) is the largest voluntary conservation organisation in Europe. It has recently joined with bird and habitat conservation organisations worldwide to form a global partnership called Birdlife International.

The Royal Society for the Protection of Birds is *the* charity that takes action for wild birds and the environment. The threats are real - pollution, destruction of heathlands, moorlands, hedgerows and estuaries, and illegal shooting, trapping and poisoning of wildlife. The RSPB is fighting these threats, but your support is vital. Do you enjoy and care about the countryside enough to support us?

The Royal Society for the Protection of Birds, The Lodge, Sandy, Bedfordshire SG19 2DL. Tel: 01767 680551

1. Aims

To conserve wild birds and their environment, maintaining the richness of our heritage of birds and increasing it where possible.

Conserving **habitats** is regarded as most important

a. by acquiring and managing land
b. by influencing what happens in the rest of the countryside, so that land use practices and government policies are directed in a way that benefits wildlife

This can only succeed in a favourable climate of opinion, so **education** and **communication** are seen as important, to make people aware of the beauty of birds and nature in general, and the need for conservation.

2. Membership

The Society, now just over 100 years old, has 650 000 adult members and 300 000 members of the junior branch (the Y.O.C.) Nearly one million visits are made to its reserves each year. Its large membership

a. demonstrates the strength of popular support - important in politics
b. provides it with a sound financial basis.

3. Reserves

In 1989 the Society had 114 reserves, covering 170 000 acres (All reserves, belonging to all national and voluntary conservation bodies, cover 1.3% of Britain, but 10% of land is regarded as having high conservation value, so there is still a need for more)

RSPB NATURE RESERVES
EXTEND OVER MUCH OF BRITAIN

Examples of RSPB reserves' importance

Minsmere and **Havergate** in Suffolk allowed the establishment and consolidation of a British Avocet population.

Loch Garten on Speyside : site of the first recolonising pair of Ospreys. Breeding has continued there, while the Scottish population has risen to about 90 pairs. About 100 000 people visit Loch Garten annually.

Loch of Strathbeg holds up to a quarter of the worlds' Pink-footed Geese in winter.

Grassholm, off the Pembrokeshire coast, holds 60 000 Gannets, the worlds' second largest colony.

Dungeness, near Lydd — see p. 36-37

The Society also gives protection outside its reserves. For example, Montague's Harrier (only about 10 British pairs) and Stone Curlew are based on farmland near Martin Down in Dorset and at other sites in southern England.
The Society a) maintains guards on the breeding sites in summer, and b) buys areas of crops in which they breed, to protect them from spraying, rolling and harvesting operations.

Principles of Reserve Management (refer to Dungeness study)

a. Identify the right areas (understanding the birds' needs) and buy them.

b. Make detailed investigations of what is there - both flora and fauna - and plan reserve management.

c. Put stage (b) into practice, and monitor the results.

4. Lobbying in Parliament and elsewhere.

Influences Wildlife and Countryside Acts, agricultural matters etc. so that wildlife interests are protected. Increasingly important in opposing Private Members Bills which are being introduced as a means of avoiding normal planning procedures for large developments e.g. the Cardiff Bay Barrage Bill, which would destroy a SSSI (Site of Special Scientific Interest), holding up to 10 000 wintering waders.

Also increasingly important internationally, particularly in the E.U., as Europe's largest voluntary wildlife conservation organisation. Laws, policies, decisions made in Brussels and Strasbourg are very important because

a. they directly affect Britain

b. our bird populations migrate through Europe (pressure brought to bear on the murderous instincts of the Maltese and the Italians)

RSPB is consulted even more widely - for example, North America took RSPB advice on survival strategies for the Peregrine Falcon, Brazil seeks guidance on maintenance of parrot populations, and RSPB attempts to regulate trade in wild birds from West Africa, particularly Senegal.

BIODIVERSITY STARTS AT HOME

As well as preventing the loss of any regular UK species due to human activities, the RSPB seeks an increase in numbers, ranges and productivity of 11 species, chosen as barometers for bird conservation in the UK.

Using these they can:

- measure progress in conserving species that are threatened worldwide: the corncrake, red kite and white-tailed eagle
- keep in touch with birds of high conservation priority such as the bittern, capercaillie, grey partridge, stone-curlew and ciri bunting
- target habitat conservation work for special species - reedbeds (bittern), native pine (capercaillie), estuaries, saltmarshes and wet meadows (redshank) and coastal heath (chough)
- see how well we influence land use policies in agriculture (for grey partridge, corncrake and cirl bunting); forestry (capercaillie); and moorland management and persecution (hen harrier).

The RSPB believes that UK bird conservation should aim to maintain the numbers and range of bird species and to increase these where it is of benefit to conservation. This is a demanding, challenging objective. With limited resources they must focus their activities on priority species and habitats. While the 11 chosen species help judge the effectiveness of bird conservation in the UK, they have prepared more than 60 action plans for particular species, habitats and issues. These assess the current situation, identify the threats, determine actions to be taken and outline the means to monitor their success.

International Conservations concerns

Conservation issues need to be tackled across national boundaries. We have already referred to the work of the RSPB on overseas projects, and within Britain there are branches of international organisations concerned with conservation.

The Flora and Fauna Preservation Society funds much species-specific conservation research and protection.

The Worldwide Fund for Nature (formerly the World Wildlife Fund, WWF) raises very large sums of money for both research into and purchases of endangered environments.

The International Union for the Conservation of Nature and Natural Resources (IUCN) is a wider network of those concerned with conservation. In particular it co-ordinates action and monitors success on species survival all over the world. Endangered species are descibed in the Red Data Books, which list in detail all animals and plants on the verge of extinction.
In addition, British expertise and (to a diminishing extent) political and commercial power can influence conservation management on the world stage.

Saving a species is not just a biological problem

Traditionally, scientists considered the extinction of plants and animals as a biological problem, with smaller and smaller populations confined within shrinking fragments of natural habitat. Consequently support for endangered species has largely been biological - field studies, captive breeding programmes, techniques for *in vitro* fertilisation and the establishment of 'banks' for genes, seeds and embryos (including the so-called "frozen zoos"). However, many scientists now feel that this approach will not be enough - *" We can't study the trees, monkeys and elephants and expect to save tropical rain forest; it is a social, political and economic problem"* said Jeffrey McNeely, the chief conservation officer of the IUCN. Experts disagree on how to solve these broader issues, but they do agree on the need for wider international co-operation, both in the sharing of data and in the implementation of conservation strategies. Several significant points have arisen from this call for co-operation:

1. **Documentation of disappearing species** : the most reliable data widely available has been provided by the World Conservation Monitoring Centre in Cambridge. The WCMC document 'Global Biodiversity: Status of the Earth's Living Resources' lists 311 scientifically described species which have perished since 1600 - the list includes

96 invertebrates
24 fish
20 reptiles
117 birds and
54 mammals

and 13 species, the American black-footed ferret, the bison-like wisent, the dromedary, the Arabian oryx, Przewalski's horse, Pere David's deer and seven species of Polynesian tree snails which have been exterminated in the wild and survive only in captivity.

The WCMC data also show that islands are the most important sites of extinction (more than 180 of the listed extinctions have taken place on islands) and that island bird species are particularly at risk (90% of recorded bird extinctions have been on islands). As a result of these data scientists now appreciate that particular efforts need to be made for the conservation of island species, especially birds.

The Biological Conservation Strategy Programme is an international co-ordinating group involving more than 30 organisations (including the Smithsonian Institution, the Ramsar Conservation Secretariat and the WCSC) with the stated aim of

" outlining concrete steps to achieve global goals while meeting local needs - give assistance to individuals and institutions as they fight to defend, understand and use biodiversity widely "

Jeffrey McNeely observes that political scientists can assess the way decisions about scientific recommendations are made, anthropologists can learn how people use local species and economists can demonstrate the financial benefits of biodiversity .

3. The **Convention on Trade in Endangered Species in Wild Flora and Fauna** (CITES)was set up in 1972 by the UN Conference on the Human Environment in response to the threat posed by the illegal trade in wildlife and their products. By August 1990 the convention had 109 signatories, each of which contributes financially to the convention. CITES does not seek to stop trade in wildlife completely, but rather *to encourage it in a sustainable way* - this can help to generate vital income for the developing countries which are typically the major suppliers to the wildlife trade.
CITES lists three appendices (overleaf) indicating the status of species in relation to trade.

Appendix I: Species threatened with extinction which are or may be affected by trade
No commercial trade of these species is permitted, but certificates of exemption and export permits may be issued under restricted circumstances, such as for specimens bred in captivity or artificially propagated, or for scientific research. Among those species listed are:

all apes	Asian elephant	some parrots
all lemurs	African elephant	some crocodiles
Giant panda	Cheetah	Coelacanth
Great whales	Leopard	some shells
all rhinos	Tiger	some orchids and cacti

Appendix II: Species which may become threatened with extinction unless trade in specimens is subject to strict regulation
Commercial trade is closely controlled by the issue of export permits and some restrictions may operate such as marking of products and imposition of export quotas. Among those species listed are:

all primates*	some antelopes	some corals
all cetaceans*	all crocodiles*	medicinal leech
all hummingbirds	all owls	all cacti*
all pythons*	all sea turtles*	all orchids*

* except species already listed in appendix I

Appendix III: Species requiring protection in certain states only
Export from listed countries requires a permit whereas export from other countries needs a certificate of origin.
Among those species listed are:
Common hippopotamus (Ghana)
Cuvier's gazelle (Tunisia)
Royal cobra (India)

Each of the member states is required to operate the convention through two bodies -

a. a Management Authority which controls licences and permits and
b. a Scientific Authority which advises the Management Authority on the status of the national flora and fauna.

and to provide trade records which are then incorporated into the data bases at the WCMC in Cambridge.

CITES has certainly helped to monitor and regulate trade in endangered species, but there remain many areas of difficulty in implementation of the three appendices. One of the most contentious areas has been the source of funding for CITES activities - it has been pointed out that financial donations from traders involved with wildlife products might suggest that vested interests might influence decision making. There are a number of well-documented examples to illustrate the problems which CITES faces:

a. **Should there be a ban on ivory trading to save the elephant?**

Several countries from the north of Africa, including Kenya, Tanzania and the Gambia have been seeking a complete ban on the international trade in ivory, arguing that the trade is responsible for the deaths of up to 100 000 elephants each year. Some countries in Southern Africa, including Zimbabwe, Botswana and South Africa, oppose the ban claiming that southern populations of elephant are increasing because of excellent management and that they now need to be "culled". One major difficulty is that, because of migrations caused by adverse weather conditions, some of the 'southern' populations are actually 'northern' elephants which have migrated south - populations being protected in one area may be subject to "culling" in another.
Demand by consumer countries inspires intensive poaching. Even in 'protected' areas such as Zimbabwe whole populations of elephant have been wiped out by insurgent poachers from nearby Mozambique. However the supply of ivory might be valueless without the infrastructure of dealers to arrange its sale and distribution, and thus current attempts to save the elephant have been aimed at breaking up this network of dealers. The first step in doing so would be

to withdraw all CITES 'licences under appendix 2', i.e. to prevent even the "legal" trade in ivory, since conservationists believe that Hong Kong distributors launder poached ivory through the legal CITES system. It is believed that these Hong Kong businessmen are financially backing South Africa in its attempts to retain the ivory trade.

As ever with conservation, the problem is not a simple one

i. Zimbabwe and Botswana are poor countries - the income they would enjoy from a legal ivory trade might help to convince the native population that wildlife is a valuable resource, and might help to finance long term conservation programmes. The Zimbabwe Wildlife Department has estimated that the "culling" of a single animal could generate up to £3 500 (including £1 500 as a trophy fee), and has advocated the transfer of game ownership from the state to private hands. They also point out that the transfer of the Black Rhino to full appendix 1 status has done nothing to protect it, and that populations have continued to decline.

ii. Once Tanzania proposed an international ban, and the EEC and USA responded by banning ivory imports, prices being paid for ivory within Tanzania and its neighbours have plummeted. Dealers and middlemen are moving out, and supporters of the ban suggest that the fall in the value of ivory to poachers would make the risks involved in obtaining it less acceptable. As long as there is any legal trade it might remain worthwhile for poachers from neighbouring countries to gradually reduce herds in those states imposing a complete ban.

The arguments will continue to rage - **conservation will inevitably be a compromise!**

b. **Can the killing of whales ever be justified?**

Modern whaling is often said to have begun in 1864, with the development of the bow-mounted harpoon gun, and accelerated even more rapidly once it became possible to inflate the dead whale with air so that the carcass would float. The use of floating processing vessels, improved navigational aids and greater knowledge of the habits of whales meant that their pursuit for meat, oil and whalebone became ever more profitable and ever more successful. In the late 1930's catches exceeded 30 000 whales per annum, but had begun to fall so that in 1945 the International Council for the Exploration of the Sea at last began to look to the future. Delegates to this conference agreed

1. young and immature whales were to be protected
2. humpback whales were considered to be at risk of total extinction
3. factory ship activities should be limited
4. the south Pacific should become a whale sanctuary
5. catching seasons should be reduced
6. a whaling inspector should be appointed

In 1946 the International Whaling Commission (IWC) was established with the aim of *"achieving maximum sustainable utilisation of whale stocks, and, by definition, protection of the future of these stocks as a resource"*

Unfortunately it was very difficult to implement these proposals, largely because some countries refused to accept them and the IWC was given no powers of enforcement whatsoever, so that as catching technology improved still further the catches began to rise again. Between 1956 and 1965 403 490 whalebone whales and 228 328 sperm whales were killed - humpbacks, blues, fin and sei whales had become commercially extinct. Since that time conservation efforts have swung between a total ban on whaling and a return to whaling advocated by some countries with high investment in whaling fleets. A 'calendar' of some of the key events is shown below.

1975	IWC devised a New Management Policy that divided whales into several stocks with the ultimate objective of using computers and mathematical models derived from fish population studies to give the data required to determine a maximum sustainable yield
1979	moratorium on factory ship whaling
1980	IUCN and WWF produce World Conservation Strategy calling for total ban on commercial whaling
1986	Full moratorium proposed by IWC in 1986 comes into effect - Japan, Norway and USSR object.
1987	Norway, Japan, Iceland and South Korea stop'commercial'whaling but instead continue with 'scientific' whaling.
1990	Rejection by IWC of proposal by Norway, Japan and Iceland to resume Minke whaling

The full moratorium on whale hunting was declared because not enough was known about whale populations to allow the IWC to determine sustainable yields. The populations shown in Table below are, at best, estimates since the physical vastness of the oceans makes gathering such data very difficult. This is the basis of the 'scientific' whaling carried out by Japan, Iceland and Norway, but it is noteworthy that each of these countries has a high investment in whaling and a large market for whale products. It is ironical that these nations are attempting to camouflage commercial exploitation with scientific investigation! Once again, conservation is likely to involve a compromise between biologists, accountants and politicians.

ESTIMATES OF TOTAL POPULATION SIZES

SPECIES	AREA	ORIGINAL[a]	PRESENT
Sperm	Southern Hemisphere	1 250 000	950 000
	Northern Hemisphere	1 150 000	1 000 000
Blue	Southern Hemisphere	220 000	11 000
	Northern Hemisphere	8 000	3 000
Fin	Southern Hemiphere	490 000	100 000
	Northern Hemisphere	58 000	20 000
Sei	Southern Hemisphere	190 000	37 000
	Northern Hemisphere	66 000	17 000
Bryde's	Southern Hemisphere	30 000	30 000
	Northern Hemisphere	60 000	60 000
Minke	Southern Hemisphere	436 000	380 000
	Northern Hemisphere	140000	125 000
Grey	Southern Hemisphere	-	-
	Northern Hemisphere	20 000+	18 000
Right	Southern Hemisphere	100 000	3 000
	Northern Hemisphere	-	1 000
Bowhead	Southern Hemisphere	-	-
	Northern Hemisphere	30 000	7 200
Humpback	Southern Hemisphere	100 000	3 000
	Northern Hemisphere	15 000	7 000

(a) ,Original' means the best estimate of the population before intense exploitation began.
Note: Calculation of the numbers of whales around the world have been made by members of the IWC Scientific Committee for many years. Recently however, doubts have been expressed by some scientists on the precise values and accuracy of these estimates, because of the nature of the data used and their analysis. The following figures are, therefore, given as indications of the orders of magnitude of the stock sizes, based on recent published estimates.

At the most recent (June, 1996) meeting of the IWC the whaling countries, particularly Norway and Japan, again called for the moratorium to be lifted, citing scientific evidence that stocks were within the safe limits of 54 - 72% of their pre-exploitation levels. Members of the IWC had hoped that during the moratorium the whaling industry would collapse, but the pro-whaling countries seem poised to aim for full commercial exploitation again. The British government has stated what many anti-whalers feel

> " whaling meets no pressing nutritional, economic or social needs and, as the global demand to watch whales in the wild demonstrates, it is possible for local communities to derive substantial benefits from whales without the need to kill them".

In other words, Britain is going beyond the IWC's convention that any anti-whaling regulations should be based on scientific evidence alone. The fear of many anti-whaling nations is that the whalers may choose to follow the scientific evidence, ignore the moral pressure and resume unrestricted commercial whaling.

Other examples of endangered species requiring international co-operation to ensure their conservation are listed below

Britons care about whales - from BBC Wildlife magazine

Species	*Reason for exploitation*	*Countries involved in conservation and trade*
North American Black Bear	Gall bladder preparations used in traditional Eastern medicine	Japan wishes to give black bear appendix 2 status to prevent 'laundering' of gall bladder
Coelacanth (*Latimeria chalumnae*)	Museum collection. Also private collection by Japan because of rumoured medicinal properties of notocord	Comoro Islands are the only legal traders in the fish. West Germany proposes appendix 1 status for the fish. Japan proposes free access for "research collecting"
Fruit bats (*Pteropus*)	Capture for eating. Loss of forest habitat	Guam and western Pacific islands seek to continue capture. Sweden and USA propose appendix 1 status to protect pollinating species
Snowdrops (*Galanthus*)	Collection for horticulture	Turkey is the main source, USA proposes appendix 1 status but is opposed by horticultural business in Netherlands
Asian lady's slipper orchid (*Pahpiopedilum*)	Collection for horticulture	Thailand is the main source, USA the main importer. WWF is suggesting appendix 1 status.

Since 1990 CITES has made available lists of countries which violate the convention, but has been hindered by the governments or management agencies of Egypt (which simply refuses to reply to requests for information about trade in wildlife) and Equador, Italy, Senegal, Spain and Thailand (which "rarely" reply). Much of the illegal trade in birds and animal skins has been going through Spain. Forged documents are becoming increasingly common. CITES comments that

> "there are still cases where an infraction is deliberate and is due to domestic policy, economic reasons or even corruption".

Britain has great skills in the formulation and implementation of conservation management plans. The figure which follows overleaf summarises the conservation battleground in one area particularly under threat - the remaining rainforest of Madagascar- and points out some of the contributions made by Britain

- directly, in the captive breeding programme for the Ploughshare Tortoise
- indirectly as a member of the World Bank, which can use financial 'muscle' to control some of the development plans for this country.

MADAGASCAR : CONFLICTS IN CONSERVATION

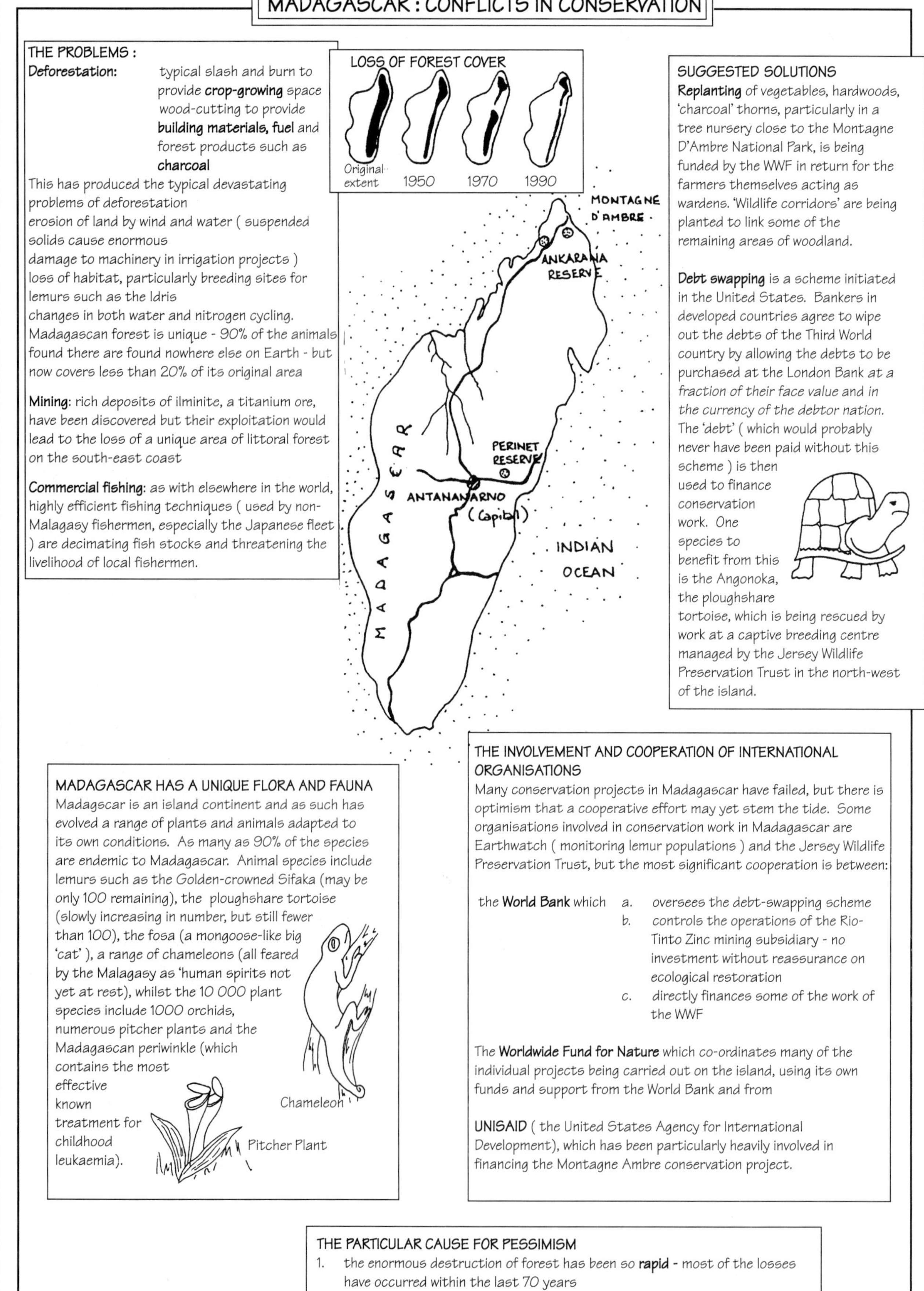

THE PROBLEMS :

Deforestation: typical slash and burn to provide **crop-growing** space wood-cutting to provide **building materials, fuel** and forest products such as **charcoal**

This has produced the typical devastating problems of deforestation
erosion of land by wind and water (suspended solids cause enormous
damage to machinery in irrigation projects)
loss of habitat, particularly breeding sites for lemurs such as the Idris
changes in both water and nitrogen cycling.
Madagascan forest is unique - 90% of the animals found there are found nowhere else on Earth - but now covers less than 20% of its original area

Mining: rich deposits of ilminite, a titanium ore, have been discovered but their exploitation would lead to the loss of a unique area of littoral forest on the south-east coast

Commercial fishing: as with elsewhere in the world, highly efficient fishing techniques (used by non-Malagasy fishermen, especially the Japanese fleet) are decimating fish stocks and threatening the livelihood of local fishermen.

SUGGESTED SOLUTIONS

Replanting of vegetables, hardwoods, 'charcoal' thorns, particularly in a tree nursery close to the Montagne D'Ambre National Park, is being funded by the WWF in return for the farmers themselves acting as wardens. 'Wildlife corridors' are being planted to link some of the remaining areas of woodland.

Debt swapping is a scheme initiated in the United States. Bankers in developed countries agree to wipe out the debts of the Third World country by allowing the debts to be purchased at the London Bank *at a fraction of their face value and in the currency of the debtor nation.* The 'debt' (which would probably never have been paid without this scheme) is then used to finance conservation work. One species to benefit from this is the Angonoka, the ploughshare tortoise, which is being rescued by work at a captive breeding centre managed by the Jersey Wildlife Preservation Trust in the north-west of the island.

MADAGASCAR HAS A UNIQUE FLORA AND FAUNA

Madagscar is an island continent and as such has evolved a range of plants and animals adapted to its own conditions. As many as 90% of the species are endemic to Madagascar. Animal species include lemurs such as the *Golden-crowned Sifaka* (may be only 100 remaining), the ploughshare tortoise (slowly increasing in number, but still fewer than 100), the fosa (a mongoose-like big 'cat'), a range of chameleons (all feared by the Malagasy as 'human spirits not yet at rest), whilst the 10 000 plant species include 1000 orchids, numerous pitcher plants and the Madagascan periwinkle (which contains the most effective known treatment for childhood leukaemia).

THE INVOLVEMENT AND COOPERATION OF INTERNATIONAL ORGANISATIONS

Many conservation projects in Madagascar have failed, but there is optimism that a cooperative effort may yet stem the tide. Some organisations involved in conservation work in Madagascar are Earthwatch (monitoring lemur populations) and the Jersey Wildlife Preservation Trust, but the most significant cooperation is between:

the **World Bank** which
a. oversees the debt-swapping scheme
b. controls the operations of the Rio-Tinto Zinc mining subsidiary - no investment without reassurance on ecological restoration
c. directly finances some of the work of the WWF

The **Worldwide Fund for Nature** which co-ordinates many of the individual projects being carried out on the island, using its own funds and support from the World Bank and from

UNISAID (the United States Agency for International Development), which has been particularly heavily involved in financing the Montagne Ambre conservation project.

THE PARTICULAR CAUSE FOR PESSIMISM

1. the enormous destruction of forest has been so **rapid** - most of the losses have occurred within the last 70 years
2. the local people are the major cause of the destruction - they believe that the spirits of their ancestors will help to save them

Madagscar is seen as a conservation 'flagship'. If an area of such outstanding beauty and wildlife significance cannot be saved, there may be little hope for less spectacular parts of the world.

Protection measures for species: The role of Zoos

Zoos, or zoological gardens, are areas of confinement keeping samples of species alive under varying degrees of captivity. Many 'zoos' or animal collections in Britain have closed down, and many have tried to change the public perception of their activities by changing their titles to, for example, 'Wild Animal Parks', but the fact remains that they have been accused of **animal exploitation** on the grounds that

- animals are exhibited on the basis of their 'crowd-pulling' power, rather than on their endangered status
- animals are kept under inappropriate conditions, both in terms of their physical environment (poor substrates in cages, for example) and their mental and social well-being (limited feeding stimuli, or atypical social grouping)
- capture of animals for exhibition may seriously deplete wild populations
- re-introduction of species to the wild cannot be successful

Some of the arguments for and against the maintenance of animal collections in 'zoos' are summarised overpage. The problem of captive breeding and re-introduction is worth particular consideration. On a worldwide scale it is thought that 800 species of mammal, 800 species of bird, 400 species of reptiles and amphibians and as many as 80% of all Lake Malawi cichlid species could disappear if there were no captive breeding. Breeding successes in captivity have increased in range and frequency, partly because of

- environmental enrichment improving animals' physical and mental well-being, and their readiness to breed (e.g. the social grouping of lowland gorillas in the John Aspinall wild animal parks in Kent has made them the most successful breeding colony in the world)
- increased understanding of reproductive physiology (e.g. an appreciation of oestrus cycles in rhinocerous has improved breeding success of both black and white rhinos at Whipsnade Park)
- the International Species Inventory System, set up at Minnesota Zoo and designed to reduce the genetic dangers of inbreeding (e.g. Arabian Oryx at Whipsnade and Golden Lion Tamarin at Jersey Zoo have benefited from contrived matings with distantly-related animals
- the 'frozen zoo' concept - the maintenance of banks of sperm, ova and even embryos until such time as finance or habitat availability makes breeding a reasonable proposition
- embryo transfer and surrogacy - involves obtaining ova from a captive female treated with reproductive hormones, fertilising these ova *in vitro* and implanting the resulting embryos into a surrogate mother of a closely-related but more common species

There are those who believe that breeding animals *in* captivity often results in breeding them *for* captivity, and that reintroduction to the wild is rarely successful. The Ne-Ne, or Hawaiian Goose (*Branta sandvicensis*) is often quoted as an example of the success of captive breeding techniques, since a wild population which may have been as low as 12 breeding pairs has been supplemented by more than 3 000 captive bred individuals. The credit for this outstanding breeding programme is largely due to the Wildfowl Trust in Slimbridge who developed techniques in incubation, hatching and rearing of goose eggs, and who ensured the introduction of 'wild genes' from geese still living in Hawaii. Unfortunately, however, the reintroduction of Ne-Ne to Hawaii and the neighbouring island has not yet been a complete success (captive bred animals are less successful at feeding themselves, and at avoiding predators) but at least its status as a species has been ensured by the captive breeding programme. The skills of British biologists working in British institutions has been critical in many such successful captive breeding programmes.

The case of the Ne-Ne does emphasise a most important point - reintroduction is unlikely to prove successful if the conditions which caused the animal to *become* endangered have remained unchanged. Once again, the importance of conserving a **habitat** as well as preserving a **species** is illustrated.

Much of the work on species preservation carried out in Britain is co-ordinated by The Federation of Zoological Gardens of Great Britain and Ireland, with its headquarters at Regent's Park in London. In addition to the work described in their promotional literature, members of the federation are closely involved in conservation projects on British species including moths, shrimps, spiders, crickets, the Sand Lizard, the Natterjack Toad, the Chough, the Barn Owl, the Red Kite, the Otter, the Red Squirrel, the Dormouse, the Polecat and the Pine Marten.

ATTRACTION TO VISITORS
-generates REVENUE which

1. can be used to keep animals under optimum conditions
2. can provide funding for academic research, particularly into reproductive physiology and nutritional biology
3. might be used to pay for fieldwork and reserve management

and may stimulate INTEREST and CONCERN

a. in conservation issues
b. in the "world of wildlife" (> 50% of zoo visitors are children)

ACADEMIC RESEARCH is carried out by many zoo-based organisations, e.g. the Royal Zoological Society of London (RZL).

e.g. reproductive physiology of the Asian rhinoceros

gene-pool make-up of the Arabian Oryx

nutritional demands of the Giant Panda

TAKE A ZOO PICTURE

WIN A CAMERA

Incentives to attract young conservationists

STUD BOOKS AND GENE BANKS

the family history of all captive animals can be compared so that matings between close relatives can be discouraged

frozen sperm and/or embryos may be kept at - 197°C for long periods until breeding techniques are improved

ZOOS AND CONSERVATION
- how can zoos be justified?

WHAT ABOUT THE ANIMALS?

they are usually well-fed and receive veterinary care so are longer-lived than wild relatives

they may suffer inappropriate social grouping and limited sensory stimulation

Thus much current research centres on
BEHAVIOURAL ENRICHMENT

SECURITY : appropriate den/nestbox to act as a **retreat**

SPECIES-SPECIFIC BEHAVIOUR :
mud-baths for wallowing(rhinos)
deep litter for foraging (gorillas)

FORAGING : hiding food, or presenting it in a challenging form e.g. termite sticks, marmoset gum-trees

LOCOMOTORY CHALLENGE : climbing animals such as Tamarins and monkeys require "**challenges**" rather than "safe" substrates

SOCIAL STIMULI : "calls" for Gibbons and Tamarins help them to develop **social and hierarchical** skills
and some researchers also recommend

SELECTIVE CHALLENGES
e.g. predators, severe climatic changes

CAPTIVE BREEDING PROGRAMMES
form a part of the work of even the smallest zoo

e.g. Lowland Gorilla at Howlett's Sumatran Rhino at Port Lympne Cheetah at Whipsnade Golden Lion Tamarin at Jersey
and, eventually, should lead to
REINTRODUCTION TO THE WILD.

The Willmot Pertwee Conservation Trust

Much of the Trust's purpose is inspired by the foundation of innovative work in English conservation laid down by Willmot Pertwee Limited, the major independent U.K. agricultural and agronomical company and other members of the Agriculture and Conservation Partnership.

This partnership has been recognised for pioneering work in developing techniques to reconcile the potential conflicts between farming, scientific research and care of the environment. Notable projects have included the development of natural wildflower margins, the creation of habitats for some butterfly species, the breeding and release of Barn Owls, and research into both hoverfly and small mammal populations.

Major projects

The trustees have decided to promote two major initiatives - a national competition for schools which will relate to projects based upon 'A' level courses in Biology, and the production of this textbook.

The Trust aims to raise the awareness in schools of conservation issues which apply particularly to the United Kingdom, and to offer the opportunity to the conservationists of tomorrow to involve themselves in original and genuine research. Other projects will be developed from time to time - these will be geared to the changing circumstances and developments in the agricultural industry and the environment.

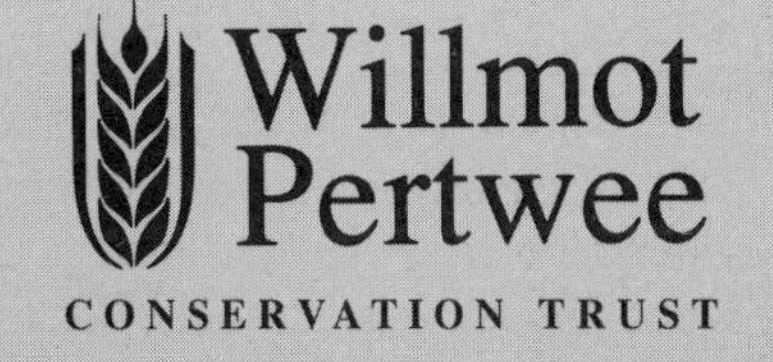

MAIN OBJECTIVES

To promote the education of the public in the management of land so as to improve the environment

To promote the training of individuals in and research into methods of land management and conservation.

The trust will pursue these objectives primarily by way of:

- the publishing of journals and other documents containing information on land management and the environment
- promoting or establishing endowments for scholarships, bursaries, prizes and fellowships connected with educating the public in land management and conservation
- providing books, equipment or other research materials

Address
Lodge Lane
Langitam, Colchester
Essex. CO4 5NE

THE WILLMOT PERTWEE CONSERVATION TRUST
(Registered Charity number 1042365)

The goldfinch in my garden: whose responsibility?

Any stroll around a country or suburban area will illustrate that the majority of British homes have some sort of garden - if the stroll is taken on a summer evening or at the weekend it will also be obvious that the majority of home-owners accept responsibility for their 'patch' and put some effort into maintaining it. It has become increasingly common for garden owners to direct their efforts at achieving a balance between regimented flower borders and benefit to wildlife. A most significant feature of the wildlife value of gardens is that gardens support an enormous *variety* of animal and plant life. Much of this variety is due to the activities of the gardener, who grows as many different species of plants as possible - some for eating, some for decorative effect, some as boundaries and for privacy and some for shade. Each plant species will provide food for a variety of herbivores which in turn are preyed on by a variety of carnivores. In addition, the gardener will provide other habitats as buildings are erected, ponds are dug out, fences are built and some form of rubbish heap develops. As the need to grow *food* in private gardens has declined the opportunities for *recreation* , including provision for wildlife, have increased. Some possibilities for wildlife management in a small garden are outlined opposite.

" There are an estimated 14.5 million home gardens in Britain with a total garden area of about 300 000 ha "

Individuals rightly take a pride in their gardening efforts, and can become quite proprietorial about its occupants. Garden bird feeders will be supplied with ever more tempting contents to attract and keep species in 'our' garden. One species which represents a particular prize to the bird gardener is the Goldfinch (*Carduelis carduelis*) - this bird is a native of forest edges, nesting high in trees. It is an unlikely breeder in a typical small garden, but can readily be attracted in autumn since it enjoys the seeding heads of thistles, teasels and burdock which grow easily in 'rough' areas of gardens. In the absence of garden food sources the goldfinch will forage around unkempt areas of farmland, field margins or woodland edges or indeed may spend the colder months on continental Europe. So, if you don't see 'your' goldfinch in 'your' garden you might ask

- am I cultivating may garden in a way which might provide an attractive food source
- are the local farmers adopting farming strategies which are sympathetic to this species
- is 'your' goldfinch enjoying a safe trip to and from Europe, and does it enjoy any protection during its winter feeding period?

What begins as a simple interest in wildlife in 'your' garden might provoke a feeling of greater responsibility. What can you do, if you feel that wildlife is under unacceptable pressures? You could

- join a local, national and international conservation agency - such bodies can call upon scientific expertise but depend on your financial and political support
- write to your M.P. - much of Britain is owned by the Government or is under direct Government 'control'. If you can offer reasoned arguments you are more likely to be listened to
- seek advice - if you are managing an area which might be of potential benefit to wildlife ask the experts (FWAG or the RSPB, for example) for guidance on the best use of the resources which you have.

Remember, the goldfinch in your garden is one of a population of goldfinches in the neighbourhood, and is part of the community of living organisms, plants and animals, in Great Britain. The goldfinch in your garden and the community of living things - they are **YOUR RESPONSIBILITY.**

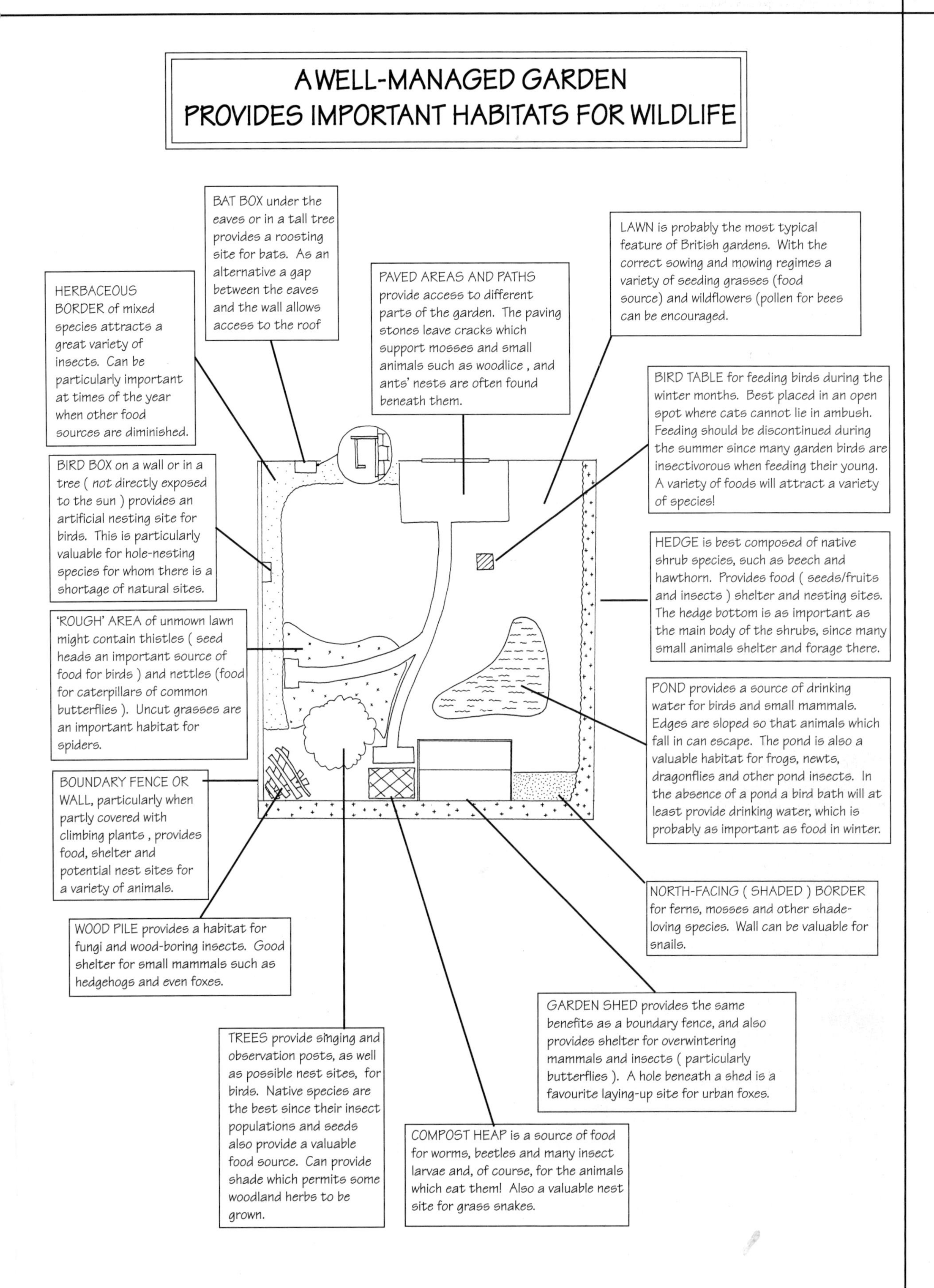
A WELL-MANAGED GARDEN
PROVIDES IMPORTANT HABITATS FOR WILDLIFE
BAT BOX under the eaves or in a tall tree provides a roosting site for bats. As an alternative a gap between the eaves and the wall allows access to the roof
HERBACEOUS BORDER of mixed species attracts a great variety of insects. Can be particularly important at times of the year when other food sources are diminished.
PAVED AREAS AND PATHS provide access to different parts of the garden. The paving stones leave cracks which support mosses and small animals such as woodlice , and ants' nests are often found beneath them.
LAWN is probably the most typical feature of British gardens. With the correct sowing and mowing regimes a variety of seeding grasses (food source) and wildflowers (pollen for bees can be encouraged.
BIRD TABLE for feeding birds during the winter months. Best placed in an open spot where cats cannot lie in ambush. Feeding should be discontinued during the summer since many garden birds are insectivorous when feeding their young. A variety of foods will attract a variety of species!
BIRD BOX on a wall or in a tree (not directly exposed to the sun) provides an artificial nesting site for birds. This is particularly valuable for hole-nesting species for whom there is a shortage of natural sites.
HEDGE is best composed of native shrub species, such as beech and hawthorn. Provides food (seeds/fruits and insects) shelter and nesting sites. The hedge bottom is as important as the main body of the shrubs, since many small animals shelter and forage there.
'ROUGH' AREA of unmown lawn might contain thistles (seed heads an important source of food for birds) and nettles (food for caterpillars of common butterflies). Uncut grasses are an important habitat for spiders.
POND provides a source of drinking water for birds and small mammals. Edges are sloped so that animals which fall in can escape. The pond is also a valuable habitat for frogs, newts, dragonflies and other pond insects. In the absence of a pond a bird bath will at least provide drinking water, which is probably as important as food in winter.
BOUNDARY FENCE OR WALL, particularly when partly covered with climbing plants , provides food, shelter and potential nest sites for a variety of animals.
NORTH-FACING (SHADED) BORDER for ferns, mosses and other shade-loving species. Wall can be valuable for snails.
WOOD PILE provides a habitat for fungi and wood-boring insects. Good shelter for small mammals such as hedgehogs and even foxes.
GARDEN SHED provides the same benefits as a boundary fence, and also provides shelter for overwintering mammals and insects (particularly butterflies). A hole beneath a shed is a favourite laying-up site for urban foxes.
TREES provide singing and observation posts, as well as possible nest sites, for birds. Native species are the best since their insect populations and seeds also provide a valuable food source. Can provide shade which permits some woodland herbs to be grown.
COMPOST HEAP is a source of food for worms, beetles and many insect larvae and, of course, for the animals which eat them! Also a valuable nest site for grass snakes.

Resources : Useful addresses

British Association For Nature Conservationists (BANC)
Rectory Farm
Stanton St. John
Oxford OX9 1 HF

British Ecological Society
Burlington House
Piccadilly
London W1V 0LQ

British Trust for Conservation Volunteers
36 St. Mary's Street
Wallingford
Oxon OX10 0EU

British Trust for Ornithology
The Nunnery
Nunnery Place
Thetford
Norfolk IP24 2BR

CITES
(Convention on International Trade in Endangered Species)
6 Rue Maupas
Case Postale 78
CH-1000
Lausanne 9
Switzerland

Countryside Commission
John Dower House
Crescent Place
Cheltenham
Gloucestershire GL50 3RA

Countryside Commission for Scotland
Battleby
Redgorton
Perth PH1 3EW

English Nature
Northminster House
Peterborough PE1 1UA

Environment Agency
Rivers House
Waterside Drive
Aztec West
Almondsbury
Bristol BS12 4UD

Fauna and Fauna Preservation Society (FFPS)
79 - 83 North Street
Brighton
East Sussex BN1 1ZA

Friends of the Earth
26 - 28 Underwood Street
London N1 7JQ

Greenpeace (UK)
30 - 31 Islington Green
London NW1 8XE

Farming and Wildlife Advisory Group (FWAG)
National Agricultural Centre
Stoneleigh
Warwicks CV8 2RX

Federation of Zoological Gardens of Great Britain and Ireland
Zoological Gardens
Regent's Park
London NW1 4RY

Field Studies Council
Preston Montford
Montford Bridge
Shrewsbury SY4 1HW

Forestry Commission
231 Corstophine Road
Edinburgh EH12 7AT

Game Conservancy Trust
Mrs C Duggins
Fordingbridge
Hampshire SP6 1EF

Institute of Terrestrial Ecology
Monks Wood
Abbots Ripton
Huntingdon
Cambs PE17 2LS

International union for the Conservation of Nature and Natural Resources (IUCN)
Avenue du Mont-Blanc
CH-1196 Gland
Switzerland

Jersey Wildlife Preservation Trust
Les Augres Manor
Trinity
Jersey
Channel Islands

Ministry of Defence Conservation Group
Room B2/3
Government Buildings
Leatherhead Road
Chessington
Surrey KT9 2LU

Royal Society for Nature Conservation (RSNC)
The Green
Witham Park
Waterside South
Lincoln LN5 7JR

Royal Society for the Protection of Birds (RSPB)
The Lodge
Sandy
Bedfordshire SG19 2DL

Scottish Wildlife Trust
25 Johnstone Terrace
Edinburgh EH1 2NH

Wildfowl and Wetlands Trust
Slimbridge
Gloucestershire GL2 7BX

Willmot Pertwee Conservation Group
Lodge Lane
Langham
Colchester
Essex CO4 5NE

World Wide Fund for Nature (UK)
Panda House
Weyside Park
Catteshall Lane
Godalming
Surrey GU17 1XR